The Massey Legacy

Volume Two

The Massey Legacy

Volume Two

A Product and Company Review
of Massey, Harris, Massey-Harris,
Ferguson and Massey Ferguson

John Farnworth

Farming Press

ISBN 0 85236 404 0

A catalogue record for this book is available
from the British Library

Published by Farming Press
Miller Freeman U.K. Ltd
Wharfedale Road
Ipswich IP1 4LG
U.K.

Front cover photographs: MF 40 combine harvester;
MF 244 tracked loader shovel; Sunshine harvester
Back cover illustrations: M-H No. 9 cream separator;
MF 83 mower conditioner; Sundex farm engine

Distributed in North America by
Diamond Farm Enterprises
Box 537, Alexandria Bay, NY 13607, U.S.A.

Designed by Andrew Thistlethwaite
Page layout by Hannah Berridge
Edited by Claire Newbery
Typeset by Winsor Clarke
Printed and bound in Great Britain
by Jarrold Book Printing,
Thetford, U.K.

CONTENTS

FOREWORD — by Peter M. Ledwith   VI

PREFACE   VII

ACKNOWLEDGEMENTS   IX

INTRODUCTION   XI

CHAPTER ONE — General Farm Equipment   1

CHAPTER TWO — Harvesting Equipment   51

CHAPTER THREE — Industrial Equipment   131

CHAPTER FOUR — Massey-Harris in Wartime   169

CHAPTER FIVE — Household, Farmyard and other Equipment   179

CHAPTER SIX — Landscape, Garden and Forestry Equipment   195

CHAPTER SEVEN — Stationary Engines   211

CHAPTER EIGHT — Memorabilia   225

CHAPTER NINE — Trends, Innovations and the Present Status

                 of Massey Ferguson   243

APPENDIX ONE — Sales and Production   261

APPENDIX TWO — Product Lists   291

APPENDIX THREE — Model, Serial Number and Engine Data   303

FURTHER READING AND USEFUL ORGANISATIONS   363

INDEX   365

FOREWORD

by Peter M. Ledwith

When Daniel Massey first opened the doors of his new foundry in Grafton, Ontario in 1847, he could not possibly have predicted the impact his company would ultimately have on agriculture around the world. Within fifty years it could be said, as of the British Empire, that 'The sun never sets on Massey-Harris implements.' This remains true of today's Massey Ferguson products, the quality and technical excellence of which are recognised around the world. Vintage Massey-Harris and Massey Ferguson equipment also has widespread popularity among growing legions of antique farm machinery enthusiasts.

Yet despite the size, scope and breadth of the company, no single source has been available which clearly identifies and describes the incredible array of machinery made by this important organisation over the years. John Farnworth has filled this gap with a monumental work which will prove to be an indispensable reference tool for Massey-Harris and Massey Ferguson fans around the world.

Massey Ferguson donated its corporate archives to the Ontario Agricultural Museum in 1987. Since that time, this incredible resource has been accessed and appreciated by hundreds of historians and collectors of Massey-related machinery and memorabilia. No one, however, has delved as deeply into it as John. It was a great pleasure for us to make this material available to him, and to see this impressive collection so appropriately utilised.

How fitting it is that this historical review is published in 1997 — one hundred and fifty years after Daniel Massey began what was to become an incredible corporate journey. Congratulations are due to John Farnworth for recognising this anniversary with a reference work which, like the company whose rich history it documents, will clearly stand the test of time.

Former Curator, The Farm Museum, Ontario.

PREFACE

This book, the second in a two-volume set prepared in the 150th anniversary year of Massey Ferguson, is an endeavour to both recall some of the history of the company, and to present a representative, but fairly comprehensive selection of the range of products which MF and its predecessor companies have marketed internationally since Daniel Massey founded his first agricultural machinery business in 1847. The objective has been a representative selection rather than an absolute record because the enormous range of products marketed over this long period merits an encyclopaedia rather than a text of a mere two volumes!

As I did my research, the extensive equipment range within the Massey Ferguson companies was brought firmly home to me. For example, a 1922 Massey-Harris catalogue listed 56 ploughs and 96 wagons, the 1975-76 MF World Wide Catalogue weighs almost 6 kg and has over 600 pages, and the MF-Landini link alone is currently producing over 50 tractor models for the MF stable. With odd exceptions I have not covered any equipment which was not badged or officially sold by MF or its predecessor companies.

I have endeavoured to capture the international flavour of the company's development which has been so important from early days, and the diversity of products marketed. MF is now a multinational company marketing in most countries of the world and manufacturing or assembling in several.

There have been many powerful personalities involved in the history of MF. As with other aspects of the company's history, these too merit a volume to themselves. I have chosen to give some biographical detail of a select few who, in my judgement, have played a major creative role in company development. In taking this approach I have not included many of the senior figures, and no underestimation of their efforts is implied.

I have deliberately not attempted to address commercial aspects of the company's development. This has been covered in three other major texts and any interested reader might consult *Harvest Triumphant, Massey at the Brink* and *A Global Corporation,* details of which are given in the further reading section.

It is clearly impossible to present specification data for all the equipment referred to. I have taken a selective approach to this with some bias towards that which is presently of most interest to vintage enthusiasts. The reader should be aware that individual machine specifications are not definitive, but rather ones which I have come across in the literature I have consulted - models tended to be continuously refined and updated and hence deviations from the data presented here will occur. For much of the equipment I have relied on photographic coverage with what I hope are adequate captions. I have particularly relied on intensive photographic rather than text coverage for the cultivation, planting and harvesting equipment as this is so extensive in terms of the numbers of models which have been produced. It has been my aim to achieve a varied balance of text and photographs which takes into account both the material and space available, the need to give an adequate coverage to all types of subject material, and, hopefully, to produce a text which will enthuse the very broad spectrum of people interested in the history of MF and its products.

As for dates presented in the text, I hope that these are in the main reasonably accurate but inevitably I have come across variations, of up to three years, in different sources of material. Where confusion exists I have tended to use the earlier one. Dates presented with photos usually refer to the date of the photograph, and not necessarily to the year of first manufacture of the equipment.

The appendix in volume one contains a series of price lists from throughout the history of the company, and some sales data. This data provides extra, very concise, product and specification details which supplement the main text. Volume two has a large appendix of serial number data together with some production statistics, engine and model data.

American spellings have been retained when referring to American tradenames for machinery, as, for example, in a large number of tables of machinery data; English spelling is used elsewhere. The only exception is the spelling of the word 'draft' for which American spelling has been retained as this spelling has been universally adopted in MF literature.

During the course of the publication of this book the MF companies have seen much change which may not be recognised in some of the text. Virtually all the MF companies have been taken over by AGCO and MF is now used as a worldwide brand of the AGCO Corporation.

The information in this text has been presented in good faith, and every attempt has been made to ensure accurate reproduction of data from the original sources. However, neither the publisher nor I can accept responsibility for its absolute accuracy.

ACKNOWLEDGEMENTS

Many people and organisations have contributed help and material for this book, but the bulk of the material has been sourced from MF and the Ontario Agricultural Museum recently renamed the Farm Museum, Ontario.

The majority of photographs and illustrations are reproduced by kind permission of the Ontario Agricultural Museum and MF.

Thanks go to Lynn Campbell, my researcher in Ontario, Sue Bennett (Librarian) and Peter Ledwith (Curator) at the Ontario Agricultural Museum who, besides facilitating a most professional research visit to their archives, hosted me with great kindness.

Massey Ferguson in North America, the U.K. and France have been especially helpful and thanks go to Aaron Jones, John Briscoe, Peter Brown, Glenn Christians, Jeanne Douce, Ted Everett, Ivor Clarke, John Kirkham, Terry Healey, Marion Kendrel, Nathalie Peslerbe, John Walker; also to Khayyam Cannon of AGCO Australia Ltd.

Thanks are also due to the following people and organisations:

Dr Andrea Bedosti of Landini S.A. in Italy; Tony Edwards of Landini in the U.K; Richard Ghent and John Sheehan at FERMEC in Trafford Park; Kristen M. Bihary of Lucas Varity; Diana Probert at Varity Perkins U.K; Jack R. Nowling of Varity, New York; Barbara Arkuszewska of URSUS Trading in Poland; Trevor Follard of E.V. Twose Ltd; Taner Degirmenci of UZEL in Turkey, Tony Woodhall of Woodhall Communications and David Fletcher at the Tank Museum, Dorset, U.K.

The following individuals helped with queries or loans of archive material and photographs from their private collections:

Mike Adamson, Tony Allen, Colin Booth, John Burge, John Caldwell, Geoffrey Davies, Rory Day, Delbert Gentner, Herman Granger, Derek Hacket, Tilahun Hailu, A.H. Hattingh, Selwyn Houghton, Richard Jackson, David Lory, Henry Mackintosh, John Moffitt, John Melloy, Wilfrid Mole, Kent Nicholls, Keith Oltrogge, William Ostapchuk, Austin O'Sullivan, Alfredo Pompili, Theo Roberts, Malcolm Robinson, Jim Russell, Martin Schmidt, Ed Thompson and Charles Voss.

Permission to use the following is also acknowledged: tables of data on sales and production, in the appendix in volume two from the book *A Global Corporation* by E. P. Neufield (University of Toronto Press); in the memorabilia chapter in volume two – £20 bank note from the Northern Bank in Belfast, and the Canadian stamps showing farm and frontier vehicles, from the Canadian Post Corporation. In chapter one, volume one — Key People in Company Development — the section on Harry Ferguson is adapted from 'The Ferguson Legacy', an article I wrote for the *Royal Agricultural Society of England Journal*. 156 (1996) pp 45-57. Material from the book *The Grain Harvesters* by G.R. Quick and W.F. Buchele (ASAE, 1978) was used in the chart on p55, volume one. The two photos on p74, volume one are used by kind permission of

Michael Williams, from his book *Massey-Ferguson Tractors* (Farming Press, 1987).

When preparing the Chronology for volume one I referred to three very informative books: *Harvest Triumphant, A Global Corporation* and *Massey at the Brink;* I also made use of a number of Massey annual reports. Full details of the books can be found in the further reading section at the end of both volumes.

Mike Schram of Shoot Photographic, Campbelville, Milton, Ontario took over 700 photographs from archive material in the Ontario Agricultural Museum; Roystons Photographic in Bangor, Gwynedd have reproduced many shots from similar archive material which I had gathered together.

I also thank the Farming Press team for their extremely professional publishing services, without whom this text could not have been completed within a one-year period.

Finally, thanks go to my wife for typing and editing services and copious cups of tea and coffee, to my son for his ideas and memory in tracing material from my own archive material, and my daughter who has put up with a house in chaos for a year.

We have made every effort to contact the copyright holders of the material reproduced in this book, but owing to the age of some of the information, have been unable to find the original source of the material in a few instances.

INTRODUCTION

The Massey Ferguson story is a classic example of how the stoicism of seventeenth and eighteenth century British emigrants to Canada led to the development of a worldwide trading and manufacturing organisation. The company undoubtedly initially benefited from Canada's colonial status. From early days key figures in the company's development recognised the value of international trade. From that time onwards an international approach to product development and acquisition has always been taken. For example, the company has consistently sought to circumvent trade barriers of many different types by making a diverse range of manufacturing and marketing agreements.

Often throughout the history of the company, good products or ideas have been identified and taken on board by strategic acquisition of companies, licensed production and marketing arrangements. This pattern of company development has continued almost to the present day, although most of the Massey Ferguson companies have been amalgamated into larger organisations. MF (agricultural equipment) is now one of a group of agricultural machinery companies held by a parent company — AGCO. MF Industrials, having been bought by FERMEC some years ago, has recently been purchased by the Case Company, which dropped the MF badge from its products in early 1997.

The pattern of acquisitions was perhaps initially set by the founder of the company, Daniel Massey, when he bought out his partner R.F.Vaughan only six months after the foundation of his original farm workshop!

The development of MF took a somewhat parallel course on both sides of the Atlantic, as well as across the Pacific in Australia. M-H was a Canadian company which initially spread its main manufacturing activities into the U.S.A., then to Europe and Australia and down into South America. Complimenting this, Ferguson, originating in Northern Ireland, established manufacturing plants in the U.K. and the U.S.A., and also marketed internationally. In Australia the original M-H link with H.V. McKay subsequently led to the development of what at one time was MF's second largest factory.

CHAPTER ONE

General Farm Equipment

BARN MACHINERY

Straw cutters, cake crushers, pulpers, maize shellers, grinders and mills have been well represented in company sales through the years. They started with hand-driven machines, progressed to stationary engine drive, sometimes through a horse-engine phase to electric and, finally, to large tractor-drive units.

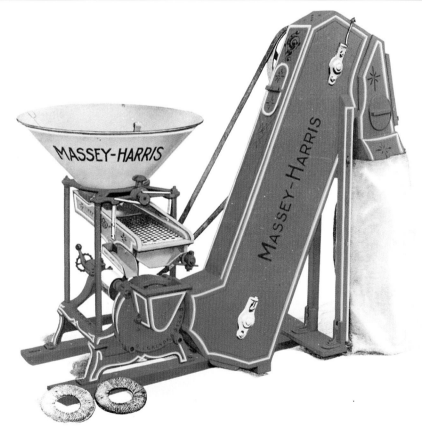

Massey-Harris Grinder—Three Styles—Seven Sizes

▲ Selection of M-H barn machinery at the Farm Museum, Ontario.
Note the winnower to the extreme right.

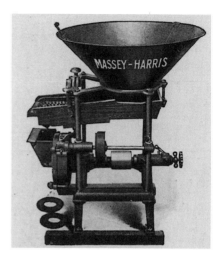

▲ M-H No. 1 grinder without
bagger attachment, c.1917.

▲ M-H No. 2 grinder with bagger attachment.

▲ M-H speed jack for increasing
speed of grinders, c. 1917.

▲ M-H No. 2 grinder, c. 1917.

Specifications of Some early M-H Grinders

No.	Size in.	Diameter of grind plates in.	Weight without bagger lb	Pulley diameter/ width in.	Speed rpm	Floor space ft	Machine height ft	hp
1	6.5	6.5	195	4 × 5	2000–2500	3 × 2.5	3.25	2–3
1	8	8	208	4 × 5	2000–2500	3 × 2.5	3.25	3–6
1	9	9	236	4 × 5	2300–2500	3 × 2.5	3.33	4–6
2	9.25	9.25	380	5.5 × 6.5	2600–3000	3.5 × 2.75	3.33	6–8
2	110.5	10.5	400	5.5 × 6.5	2600–3000	3.5 × 2.75	3.33	6–10
3	13	13	1204	7 × 8	3300–3500	5 × 4	4.5	15–25
3	15	15	1427	8 × 9	3300–3500	5.5 × 4.41	5	25–40

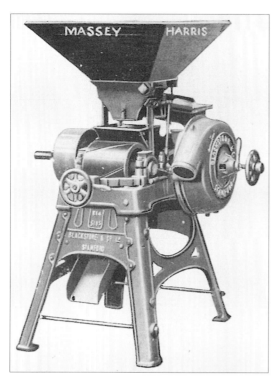

▲ An M-H Blackstone-made roller mill for crushing, grinding and kibbling grains, U.K., 1930s.

▲ An M-H No. 12 electric model plate mill. It could be fitted with 1.5, 2 or 3 hp motors to give outputs of 150-500 lb/hr, 1950.

▲ An M-H No. 15 electric model Tornado feed mill, 1950.

▲ The Sunshine Sunfeed No. 1 grinding mill marketed by H. V. McKay Massey-Harris in Australia. The power requirement was 2-4 hp and output from 5-10 cwt/hr depending on grain type.

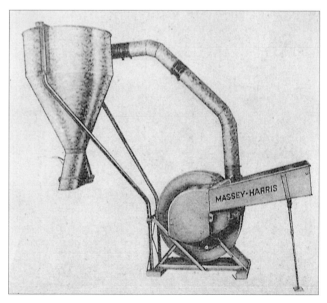

▲ British-made M-H No. 725 Tornado feed mill designed to run at 2000-2200 rpm by belt pulley. A minimum of 20 hp was required to drive the mill. It was designed for use with grain or roughage and screens were available from $^1/_{32}$-1 in., 1951.

The Massey-Harris No. 721A was one of the most popular mills to be sold in the U.K. and was usually driven by tractor-belt pulley. It was typical of many of this type which were marketed by M-H.

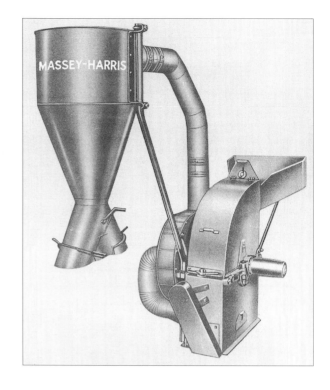

The M-H 721A hammer mill. ▶

Specifications of the M-H 721A Hammer Mill

Power required hp	20 upwards
Standard pulley in.	5 × 8.75, 6, 7, 8 and 10 optional
Mill speed rpm	2000–2100 loaded
Screen hole diameters in.	0.003–1.25 range available
Screen dimensions in.	10 × 43.5
Hammers in.	24–10.25 × 2 × 0.375
Blower diameter in.	23.375 with 6 blades
Floor space with collector in.	64 × 92
Capacity lb/hr	1500–5000 according to material and screens

M-H also marketed the 'Rowell Mastiff' hammer-type feed mills which could mill grains and a range of materials such as alfalfa, sheaf oats, corn stalks and bones. It was offered in three sizes.

The M-H Rowell No. 3 hammer-type feed mill which required 25-40 hp. ▶

◀ **M-H Rowell No. 10 hammer-type feed mill, 1933.** ▼

Specifications of M-H Rowell Mastiff Hammer-type Feed Mills

	Model No. 1	Model No. 2	Model No. 3
Capacity lb/hr	200–2000	600–5000	900–8500
Power requirement hp	3-7.5	15–25	25–40
Hammers in.	16	20	28
Pulley diameter/face in.	4/5	5/7.5	5/7
Speed rpm	3300–4000	3600	3600
Weight with blower lb	225	625	730
Weight of bagger lb	70	112	112

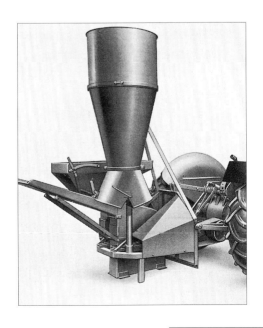

Ferguson pioneered the concept of a tractor-mounted hammer mill on tractor three-point linkage. It was powered from the tractor pto via the belt pulley accessory.

◀ **The Ferguson hammer mill was popular with small livestock farmers in the U.K.**

Specifications of the Ferguson Hammer Mill

Pulley:	width in.	6
	diameter in.	4
	speed rpm	2800–3000
Belt (endless, rubberised) width in.		5
Screens:	width in.	5
	area sq. in.	225
Hopper:	height in.	42
	width in.	13
	length in.	33
	capacity bushels	1.25
Cyclone:	inner diameter in.	11
	outer diameter in.	23
Weight cwt		4.5
Special features	grinds hay, grains, fertilisers etc.	

▲ The MF 15 grinder mixer made in North America was designed for on-farm use to avoid the need for using public facilities. Milled feed could be stored in the 120 cu. ft mixing tank, or, by means of the discharge auger be delivered to other storage bins or fed direct to livestock, 1970. ▼

▲ The M-H Electromatic hammer mill had a horizontal grinding chamber. It was offered with 5 hp or 3 hp electric motors and could mill 3-6 cwt/hr.

▲ The MF 45 combination hammer mill is a high capacity version of the original South African-made Ferguson machine. The MF 45 required the 165, 175 or 178 tractors to drive it, or a 50 hp electric motor. The machine is designed for milling grain or cutting roughage and silage, and silo filling, 1970.

▲ A hand-powered root cutter made by the Blackstone Co. of the U.K. and marketed by M-H, 1930s.

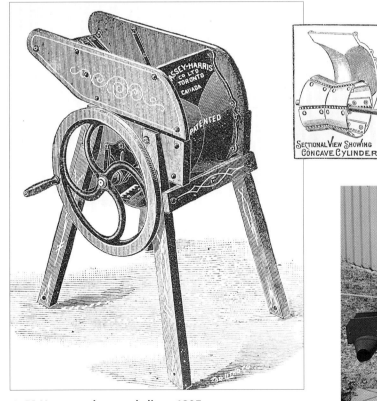

▲ M-H root pulper and slicer, 1895.

▲ M-H maize sheller on display at the Farm Museum, Ontario, at the MF 150th Anniversary event, 1997.

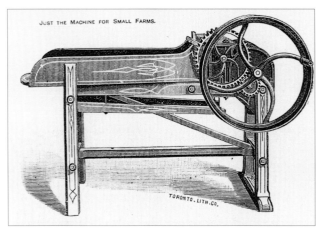

▲ M-H Cummings straw cutter. Hand powered, 1895.

▲ M-H No. 2 Paris straw cutter with engine or hand drive, 1895.

COMPRESSORS AND HEDGECUTTERS

Ferguson offered two sizes of compressors for the TE-20 tractors in the U.K. These were both made by Hydrovane and of 25 and 60 cu. ft/min. They were used to power a range of pneumatic tools of which one of the most common was a hand-held hedge cutter. The reciprocating blade hedge cutters had a saw end for cutting through thicker material. Both compressors were driven by belt from a pulley mounted on the tractor pto.

▲ The Ferguson A-VE-60 hand-held hedge cutter being driven by compressed air from a Ferguson 25 cu. ft/min. compressor.

▲ Ferguson 'Hydrovane' 60 cu. ft/min. compressor showing the belt pulley drive.

CRANES

Simple cranes have been developed for direct attachment to the Ferguson three-point linkage, or for fitting to front loaders. They continued well into the Massey Ferguson era with variants around the world. It is also noted that a crane attachment was made for the industrial version of the 4WD M-H General Purpose tractor, and a front-mounted crane with 1500 lb capacity was offered for the M-H Work Bull tractors.

▲ Ferguson approved Baldwin loader with crane attachment on an industrial Ford Ferguson tractor.

◄ A Ferguson rear-mounted crane photographed in 1953 behind the U.K. Ferguson factory.

The MF 12-10 jib crane was made in India and is derived from the old Ferguson crane. The crane weighs 33 kg but can lift 476 kg, 1980. ►

ELEVATORS

No elevators have been noted in North American M-H literature but M-H sold a range of elevators in the U.K. Many of these were manufactured by Blackstone and Co. and sold under the Massey-Harris Blackstone badge. Earlier types were wooden framed but later ones were all steel. They were all often powered with 1.5 hp Blackstone engines.

Later types in the U.K. were manufactured by Steels Agricultural Machinery of Edinburgh.

▲ **M-H Blackstone timber frame elevator folded for storage.**

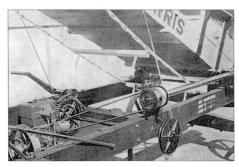

▲ **M-H Blackstone timber frame elevator engine drive.**

M-H Blackstone timber frame elevator in use. ▶

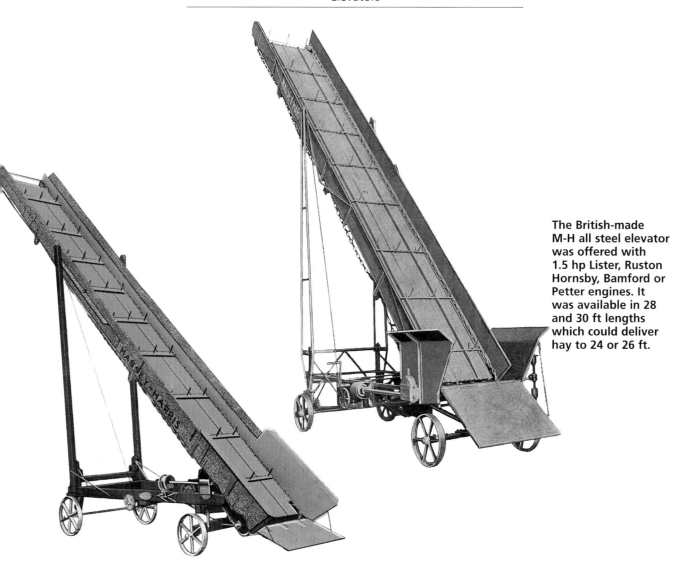

The British-made M-H all steel elevator was offered with 1.5 hp Lister, Ruston Hornsby, Bamford or Petter engines. It was available in 28 and 30 ft lengths which could deliver hay to 24 or 26 ft.

M-H Blackstone timber frame elevator low hopper model.

Specifications of Some Wooden-type Blackstone Elevators

	E	D	B	D.S. Low hopper
Length of trough ft	26	28	30	31
Height to which hay can be delivered ft	22.5	24	26	24.75
Height when folded in.	79	79	79	79
Height over poles ft	16.5	16.5	17	17
Width of elevator when folded in.	78.5	78.5	82	78.5
Length when folded ft	14.5	15.25	16.7	18.25
Weight	19 cwt 1 qr.	19 cwt 3 qr.	22 cwt	23 cwt 1 qr.

ENSILAGE CUTTERS AND FORAGE BLOWERS

The value of silage as a winter stock feed was well recognised by the turn of the century. It had also soon been realised that a better silage could be made if the material was well compacted. This led to the parallel development of high tower silos and cutter blower equipment for delivering chopped fresh forage to the top of the tower.

▲ M-H Cummings ensilage cutter with delivery elevator, 1895.

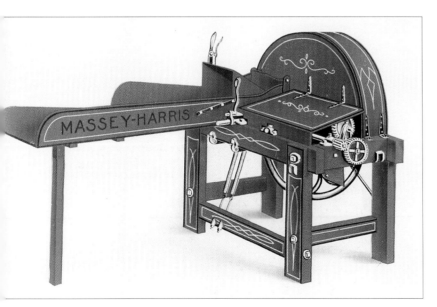

▲ The M-H No. 2 straw and ensilage cutter. A 3-8 hp engine was required to drive it according to the length of carrier fitted which could be up to 24 ft, c. 1917.

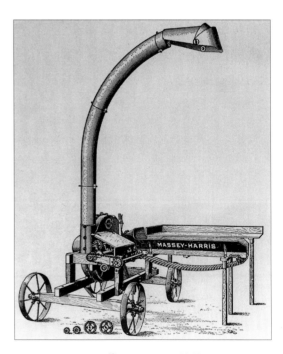

▲ M-H No. 4 ensilage cutter, 1913.

▲ Wallis 20-30 tractor, driving hand-fed ensilage cutter in the U.K.

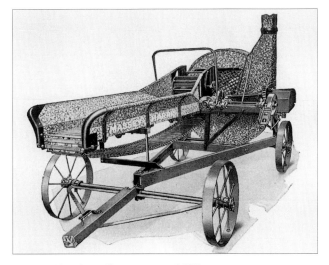

▲ M-H No. 6 ensilage cutter, 1933.

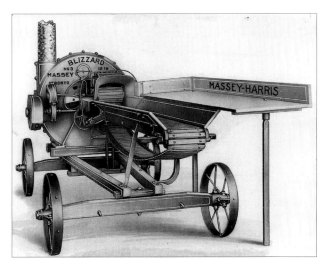

▲ M-H Blizzard No. 3 ensilage cutter.

◀ MF 98 crop blower driven by tractor pto. A 60 hp or larger tractor was required and the machine could fill silos up to 80 ft high through a 9 in. pipe. The machine is seen being fed chopped forage from a self-unloading forage box, 1968.

▲ Manual feeding of fodder into an early M-H forage blower.

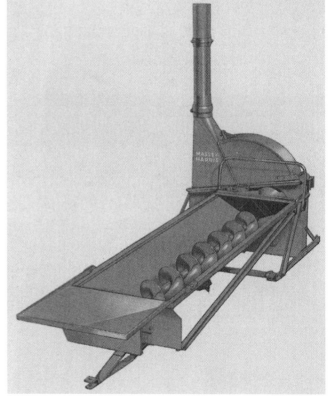

◀▲ The M-H forage blower was pto driven and could be moved by tractor between locations. The 12 in. auger could handle green silage, chopped hay or grain. Capacity was rated at 35 tons/hr of green forage with a 2-plough tractor supplying the power.

FORK LIFTS

Fork lifts for agricultural use were introduced in the M-H and Ferguson merger period to fit the TE and TO, Ferguson 35 and larger tractors. Front-end weights were required to enable full capacity loads to be carried.

In more recent times industrial fork lifts have been adapted for farm work, often in the form of rough terrain 4WD equipment and telescopic handlers (see Chapter 3).

◄ The MF 737 fork lift was first marketed as a Ferguson product. It is shown here mounted on an FE 35 tractor fitted with a prototype weight tray on the front of the tractor.

◄ MF 10 fork lift on TO-35 Ferguson tractor.

IRRIGATION PUMPS

Ferguson marketed two irrigation pumps for mounting on the three-point linkage and taking drive from the pto. One was manufactured by James Beresford and Son Ltd., the other by an Indian company to the design of the U.K.-based Pulsometer Engineering Co.

◄ A Ferguson irrigation pump made by James Beresford and Son. It was self-priming and could raise water from a depth of 25 ft.

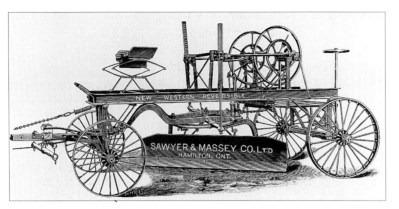

▲ Sawyer and Massey 'new western reversible king of the road' grader, 1906.

ROAD-MAKING AND LAND-FORMING EQUIPMENT

The Sawyer and Massey Co., and no doubt Sawyer before the link with Massey, marketed heavy-duty road-making equipment for use with steam engines and horses. Three examples of such equipment are shown here.

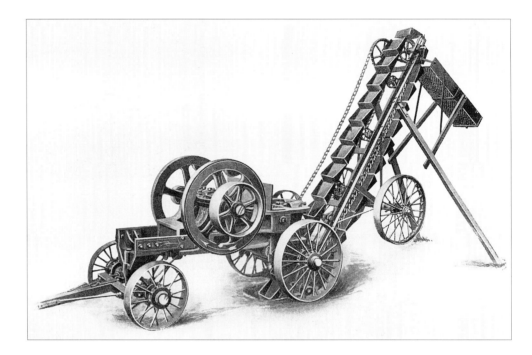

Sawyer and Massey portable rock crusher with chain elevator and chute screen, 1906. ►

▲ Sawyer and Massey reversible road roller, 1906.

▲ Sawyer-Massey sprinkling tank for road construction. The outfit weighed 2000 lb and had 4 in. wide rear wheels of 36 in. diameter.

Ferguson had specialised in this type of equipment and it was developed into the MF era. There was a particular strength in this sector in South Africa and North America. Much of this equipment has a dual application in land forming for agriculture and the construction of rural roads, dams and embankments, etc.

Earth scoops were perhaps the simplest form of earth moving equipment and M-H developed one for use with horses. Ferguson offered an earth scoop mounted on the three-point linkage and many of these were sold. In the MF era a reversible earth scoop was offered, the main feature being that the scoop body could be reversed within the support frame so that it could work in both a

forward and reverse mode for scraping and tipping. Semi-mounted earth scoops were also made. These had a land wheel at the rear to enable a greater machine and load weight.

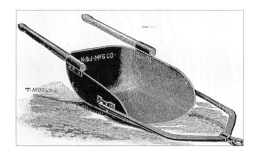

◄ **M-H Columbus solid steel drag scrapers. Made in 7,5 and 3 cu. ft sizes with and without runners, 1895.**

The MF 1 soil scoop made in North America is a development of the original Ferguson implement. It can be used in forward or reverse mode unlike the Ferguson which only operated forwards. A larger machine, the MF 905 was made in South Africa, 1976. ▼

▲ The MF 15 soil scoop was made in South Africa for tractors up to 65 hp. It is semi-mounted with a rear 360 degrees turn castor wheel. The heaped capacity was 0.57 m³, 1976.

▲ A Ferguson wheel-type scoop as sold on the South African market.

One of the most widely adopted pieces of 'Ferguson' type equipment which is still manufactured to this day is the rear-mounted tractor grader. The first version of this was called an earth leveller and blade terracer and was widely sold in India. This was followed by a succession of more robust multi-purpose grader blades. The early implement only had 45 degrees of sideways adjustment, but subsequently most models that have been offered rotated through 360 degrees and could be reversed for reverse pushing, and tilted or angled left or right for terracing and shallow ditch forming. Over the years they have become more robust as tractor power has increased.

▲ M-H 50 tractor with angle dozer terracer.

◄ The MF 685 rear-mounted and hydraulically controlled blade was perhaps the ultimate development of the Ferguson blade. It was made in medium duty (1.8 and 2.5 m width) and heavy duty (2.5 m width) models for tractors of 30-60 and 60-100 hp, 1989.

Front-mounted blades were possibly first offered for the M-H General Purpose 4WD tractor. Ferguson popularised this type of implement when he offered such blades for the Ford Ferguson utilising its hydraulic system.

Many types of trailed or semi-trailed scrapers have been offered which variously combined the activities of earth-moving, grading and fine levelling. They have been used widely in developing and maintaining levelled irrigated areas, as well as in dry-land farming activities.

The MF 830 blade is a Ferguson concept, but upgraded in design for MF tractors of 65-100 hp. It is 1.83 m wide and has a blade height of 0.6 m. When lifted there is 1.2 m clearance beneath the blade, 1989. ▶

The North American MF 18 scarifier was made in 73 and 81 in. widths which were equipped with six or eight scarifier teeth. The unit could be used for scarifying only, scarifying and scraping, scraping only, or for back filling, 1970. ▼

◀ The Ferguson earth mover had a 17 in. blade and was 5 ft wide. It could be angled left or right, or tilted to left and right. It was lifted out of work by linkages reaching back to the rear linkage arms.

▲ Ferguson trip dump scraper as sold on the South African market.

▲ Land plane carrier for the MF 338 drag scraper showing the scraper assembled in position under the carrier frame.

▲ The Australian-made MF 338 was a versatile machine capable, with attachments, of operating as a drag scraper, leveller or land plane. It had a working width of 3.05m, 1976.

▲ Leveller attachment for the MF 338 in action.

Bund formers have been offered as disc or mouldboard units and both have had an application in irrigated and dry-land farming for controlling water flow.

▲ The MF 732 bund former can make bunds of up to 1 m wide and 0.5 m high using tractors of 45-100 hp, 1989.

▲ Disc ridging on the contour using an MF toolbar.

Ditchers have been offered for the construction of shallow water channels where required, in irrigated areas or for diverting run-off water flows.

The Ferguson Disc Terracer was adopted in parts of the U.S.A. and South Africa for forming contour terrace bunds or sometimes initial ploughing of rough land.

For rice growing areas in India, Ferguson marketed Paddy disc harrows (see Chapter 4, Vol. 1) and also a Paddy Disc Planker. The planker was used for levelling the surface of the paddy field in a submerged state.

▲ The MF 731 ditcher/subsoiler is a dual-purpose machine for 40-100 hp tractors. It can ditch to a 24 in. depth. The adjustable mouldboards may be removed for subsoiling, 1989.

▲ Ferguson V trenching tool based on a Ferguson subsoiler.

▲ Ferguson TE-20 tractor with Ferguson AFO-20 disc terrracer. The disc is 28 in. diameter and has a 12 degree adjustment. The 'suck' of the plough was converted into a weight transfer effect on the tractor.

▲ Demonstration of a British-built Ferguson TE-20 planking in an Indian rice paddy.

Rite-way electrical motor-driven Roto-matic pump for Rite-way milking machines. ▶

MILKING MACHINES

'Rite-Way' milkers were marketed by M-H in the 1940s. This comprised an electrically driven Rotamatic vacuum pump unit with V-belt drive, a sanitary vacuum tank, a pipeline to individual cow places and clusters with churns.

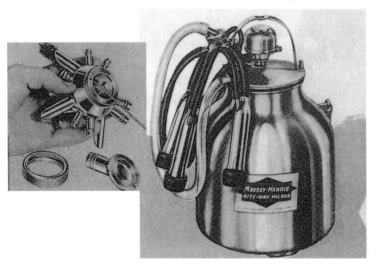

▲ M-H Rite-way milking bucket, 1951.

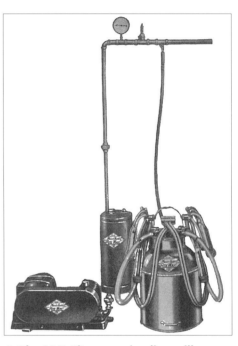

▲ The M-H Rite-way pipe line milker.

▲ M-H Pony tractor with loader, loading M-H No. 10 T muck spreader.

MUCK LOADERS

The company's hydraulic muck loaders appear to have been first developed in the Ferguson line of equipment as far back as the Ford Ferguson days. Ferguson is sometimes credited in the U.K. with having marketed the first hydraulically operated farm tractor manure loader. At the M-H and Ferguson merger, two Ferguson muck loaders went into the M-H-F range—the light duty L-UE-20 and the M-UE-20 High Lift Loader. However, M-H did market hydraulic loaders for some of its post–war series tractors.

◄ M-H hydraulic loaders of 1948. Gravel scoops, snow and ice buckets, bulldozer blades and snow ploughs were also available.

◄ MF 35 tractor with loader and push-off loading fork unloading into Ferguson 3-ton trailer, Kent, U.K., 1958.

French-made MF 825 tractor with loader and rear counterweight, 1960s. ▼

▲ MF 890 loader. At least eight models of agricultural tractor loaders were being produced in the U.K. in 1989 for tractors between 45 and 160 hp. Lift capacity at ground level was 800-2400 kg according to model, 1989.

The MF pallet tipper was a valuable accessory for early MF loaders in the U.K. The pallet, used for vegetables and fruit, could be tipped sideways slowly for unloading. ►

Many outside companies made loaders for M-H, Ferguson and MF tractors which should not be confused with those which were badged by the companies. After the M-H merger there has been continuous production of loaders by MF up to the present day to fit many of its tractor models, including small garden tractors.

They can usually be fitted with muck forks, material buckets, quick attach kits, grapple forks, pallet forks and mechanical self-levelling devices.

The North American MF 95 utility loader shown on a Tricycle type MF 180 tractor had a lift capacity of 3680 lb. Materials buckets and blades were also available, 1970. ►

The TAL Allied front-end loader is a recently announced product of TAFE Access Limited – MF's partner company in India. It has been made in association with a Canadian loader specialist. It is especially suited to the MF 245 tractor, 1996. ►

Attachments available for the 800 series loaders, 1994.

Power Buckets

Width 1.37 m
(54 in)
Capacity 0.55 m³
(19.3 ft³)

Width 1.98 m
(78 in)
Capacity 0.79 m³
(28.1 ft³)

Width 2.03 m
(80 in)
Capacity 1.25 m³
(44 ft³)

Power Digging Buckets

Width 1.37 m
(54 in)
Capacity 0.42 m³
(14.8 ft³)

Width 1.68 m
(66 in)
Capacity 0.65 m³
(22.9 ft³)

Width 2.03 m
(80 in)
Capacity 0.50 m³
(17.8 ft³)

Root Buckets

Width 1.63 m
(64 in)
Capacity 0.75 m³

Width 1.98 m
(78 in)
Capacity 1.43 m³

Hi-tip Buckets

Provide extra 1.0 m
(39 in) height and
0.55 m (22 in)
forward reach.

Width 2.0 m (79 in)
Capacity 0.8 m³
(28.5 ft³)

Width 2.0 m (79 in)
Capacity 1.0 m³
(35.3 ft³)

Width 2.25 m
(89 in)
Capacity 1.5 m³
(53 ft³)

Manure Forks

Width 1.47 m
(58 in)
Capacity 0.6 m³
(21 ft³)

Width 1.47 m
(76 in)
Capacity 0.60 m³
(21 ft³)

Manure Forks

Width 1.93 m
(76 in)
Capacity 0.85³
(30 ft³)

Pallet Forks

Max capacity
1.5 ton (3308 lb)

Max capacity
1.0 ton (1654 lb)

Silage Grabs

Width 1.47 m
(58 in)
Capacity 0.8 m³
(28 ft³)

Bale Spike

Tines fit to pallet
fork frame

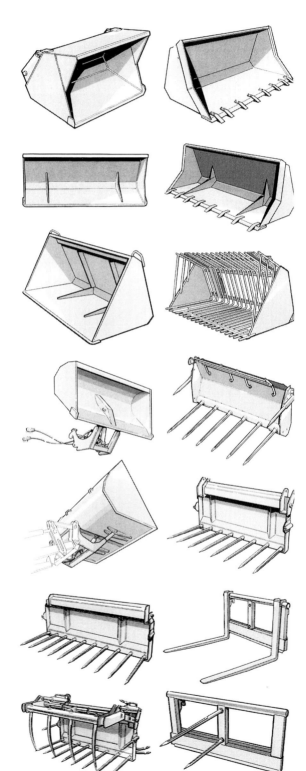

800 series attachment continued.

Width 1.93 m (76 in)
Capacity 1.13 m³ (40 ft³)

Hi-reach Bale Grab

Provides extra 1.8 m (72 in) of li to stack bales up 6 high

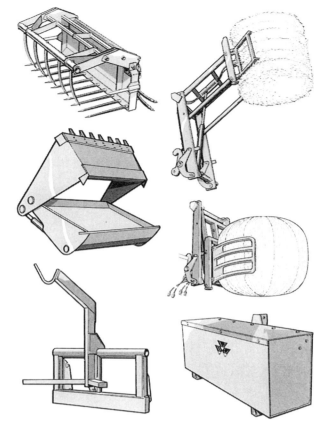

Multi Purpose Bucket

Width 1.93 m (76 in)
Capacity 0.54 m³

Jaws available in place of tines to handle wrapped bales

Bag Hook

Bag hook fits to pallet fork frame

Counter Weights

Ballested up to 680 kg (1499 lb) gross max.

Ballested up to 1360 kg (2998 lb gross max.

▲ MF 1246 loader with materials bucket on MF 1240 tractor. Capacity 476 kg, 1996.

MUCK SPREADERS

M-H first ventured into muck spreaders when it acquired the Kemp Manure Spreader Co. in 1904. These were horse-drawn machines of various sizes which developed through many models. Ultimately tractor hitches became available for these four-wheel machines. Then, in the post-war period, two-wheel tractor-drawn machines were introduced by both M-H and Ferguson before their merger. These were land-wheel drive machines. M-H introduced its first, the No. 11, in 1945 alongside its old four-wheel horse-drawn type. After the merger, pto-drive machines were developed and spreaders have continued to increase in size as higher power tractors have evolved.

▲ Very early M-H No. 3 manure spreader in the Farm Museum, Ontario. In the forground is an M-H sleigh.

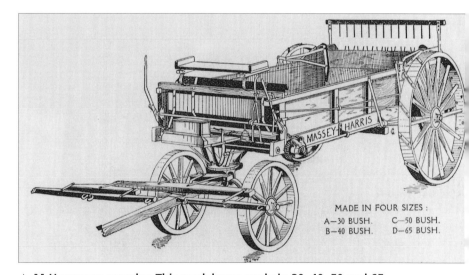

▲ M-H manure speader. This model was made in 30, 40, 50 and 65 bushel sizes, 1913.

▲ M-H 'Rude' No. 4 low down manure spreader, c. 1917.

M-H No. 8 light draft manure spreader, 1933. ▶

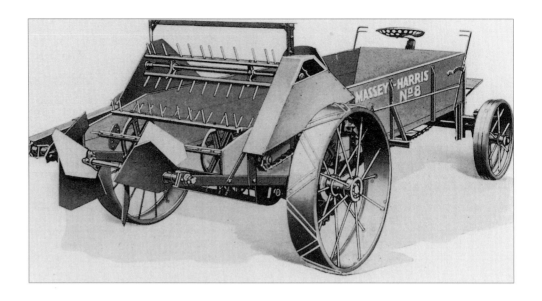

Specifications of the M-H No. 8 Light Draft Four-wheel Spreader (a typical 4-wheel spreader)★

Length of box inside in.	113
Width of box at front in.	39.5
Width of box at beaters inside in.	41.25
Depth of box inside in.	16.5
Height of load in.	18–32
Overall width in.	74.5
Width of tread in.	68.5
Wheel base in.	101
Model 8 wheels diameter × width in.	36 × 7 rear, 26 × 4.5 front
Model 8R rubber tyres in.	7.50 × 24 rear, 5.50 × 16 front
Loading height at rear wheels in.	36
Width of spread ft	7
Loads per acre	6, 8, 12, 16 or 20
Hitches	2-horse with neck-yoke or tractor hitch

M-H 101 tractor and M-H No. 11 spreader. ▼

★ Model 8 = steel wheels. Model 8R = rubber tyres

▲ 744D tractor with M-H 712 U.K.-made muck spreader. (Artist's enlargement of flying muck!)

▲ M-H 50 tractor fitted with Ferguson-style loader and M-H No. 15 spreader. Note spreader fitted with Ferguson-style eye hitch for automatic pick-up hitch.

▲ The British-made MF 19 manure spreader was pto driven and available in 3630 and 4720 litre models. The average maximum loads were 1.96 and 2.95 tonnes, 1980.

▲ MF No. 18 muck spreader. Tandem axle and pto drive.

◀ The MF 110 manure spreader made in North America was a heavy duty, medium capacity pto drive machine. It was typical of a range of pto drive spreaders which replaced the M-H and Ferguson two-wheel and land drive spreaders, 1970.

▲ **MF 900H horizontal spreader.**

Today very large machines, typified by the 900 series spreaders, are available and matched to high hp tractors. The 900 series included rotary spreaders, vertical beater and horizontal beater types.

Capacities of 900 Series Spreaders 1993

Horizontal Beater		Vertical Beater		Rotary	
Model	Volume cu. yd	Model	Volume cu. yd	Model	Volume gals
5 ton★	5.8	8 ton	9.85	5.5 ton★	484
7 ton★	8.5	10 ton	12.5	7 ton★	582
8 ton	10.3	12 ton	15	7 ton	582
10 ton	12.5			8.5 ton★	748
12 ton	15			8.5 ton	748
				10 ton	873
				12 ton	1025

★ single axle models, all others tandem

▲ **MF 900V vertical spreader.**

▲ **MF 900R rotary spreader.**

SLURRY TANKERS

The progressive move away from straw bedding of housed animals to slurry systems prompted the development of slurry transport and spreading tankers. These are now huge machines matched to modern day high-power tractors.

In 1996, MF was offering eleven models of slurry tanker in the U.K. in its 900 series range. There are both single and double axle models.

▲ The British-made MF 100 slurry tanker was made in 3640, 5000, 5910 and 9100 litre sizes which weighed between 1484 and 2672 kg. They were fitted with vane-type pto drive pumps for filling and emptying, 1980.

MF 900 Series Slurry Tankers 1996

Model	Capacity l	Length m	Tractor hp	Unladen weight kg
VT 850	3864	3.02	35	1610
VT 1100	5000	3.56	45	1840
VT 1300	5910	4.17	70	2110
VT 1500	6820	4.24	60	2410
VT 2000	9092	5.16	100	2580
VT 1300T	5910	4.17	70	2380
VT 1500T	6820	4.24	80	2790
VT 2000T	9092	5.16	100	3030
VT 2600T	11820	5.13	120	4490
VT 3000T	13638	5.79	140	4682
VT VT3000STR	13638	5.79	140	5450

◄ An example of an MF 900 series vacuum slurry tanker. Optional equipment included manual top fill lid, remote control for pump, extra sight glass, dribble bar applicator, fully opening rear door and mudguards, 1996.

The Australian-made MF 420 Truline post driver could deal with posts made of wood, concrete or steel. The machine could take posts of up to 300 mm diameter and 2500 mm length. The driver could be angled 25 degrees left or right and 20 degrees forwards or back, 1980. ▶

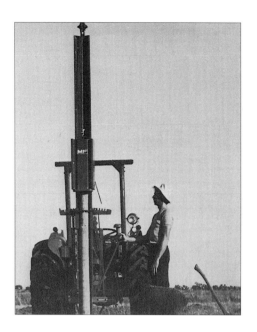

POST-HOLE BORERS, POST DRIVERS

Post-hole borers have been offered from Ford Ferguson days, through the Ferguson tractor era and into the MF era. M-H also offered them for use with their tractors which were fitted with a three-point linkage in the post-war period. They were all of a similar design, driven by the pto and usually available with a range of auger sizes.

MF made a post driver for the Australian market. This was called the 'Tru-Line' post driver and could handle posts of different materials.

An MF 723 post hole digger working on an MF 35 tractor. 6 in., 9 in., 12 in. and 18 in. augers were available. The three smaller augers could bore to a 3ft depth, the large one to 2 ft. ▶

▲ M-H potato cutter, 1930.

POTATO EQUIPMENT

A six to eight bushel per hour Potato Cutter was marketed by M-H. This appears to have been an Aspinwall product (as were some items of cultivation equipment). It was used for cutting potato seed and could halve or quarter potatoes, or cut to any desired size. It could also be used for cutting a range of root vegetables for stock feeding.

Hand or engine powered 'Favorite' Potato Graders were sold by M-H but made by the Mountville Manufacturing Co. Standard equipment included three sizes of screens—1.187 in., 1.5 in. and 1.875 in. The machine could also be used for grading onions or similar crops.

Specifications of Favourite Potato Grader	
Capacity bushel/hr	0–80 (hand model)
	100–125 (power model)
Screen surface sq. in.	882
Overall dimensions in.	76 × 52 × 32
Pulley in	14 × 2
Power required hp	0.5
Shipping weight lb	150

▲ M-H 'Favourite' potato grader, hand powered, 1930.

STATIONARY BALERS AND PRESSES

No literature was found to indicate that the company has ever had a substantial interest in marketing large stationary balers. This may be accounted for by the fact that straw in the major grain growing areas outside Europe had little value, and Europe had its own well developed stationary baler and threshing machine industry.

However, one photograph of North American origin was found in the M-H archives at the Ontario Agricultural Museum which shows horses driving a stationary baler. It is unclear as to whether this is an M-H product.

Hay press powered by horses turning a horse gear. This photograph was found in the M-H archives, but without specific M-H equipment identification. ▼

In the U.K. some interesting photos were found in MF archives of stationary balers and presses. The presses had apparently been marketed by M-H and produced by G. Stephenson and Sons of Newark.

◄ **M-H Stephenson hay press, 1900.**

M-H stationary hay/straw baler, U.K., 1920. ▼

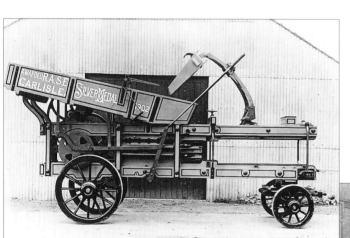

▲ **M-H stationary hay/straw baler, U.K., 1902.**

M-H Stephenson No. 11 press made for the Indian market in teak, 1905. ►

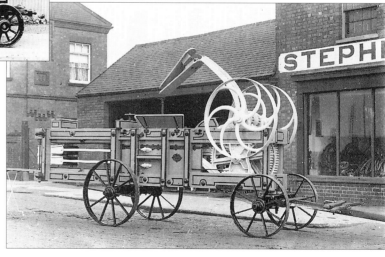

STRAW TRUSSERS

M-H made straw trussers for placing behind threshing machines to truss the loose straw as it was ejected from the thresher unit. These took their drive by belt from the threshing machine. The trusses or bundles, tied automatically with string, were of low density compared with those from a conventional baling machine.

The trusser principle was adapted for use on combine harvesters and used principally on some M-H combines in Europe. They were made in Germany for M-H by Raussendorf (see Chapter 2).

◄ ▲ M-H No. 1 and No. 2 single and double band trussers. These could take straw from a 4-6.5 ft feed width, c. 1910-22.

Ferguson curved tine subsoiler D-BE-28 operated to a depth of 18 in. and weighed 258 lb. ▶

▲ M-H Stephenson horse-drawn mole drainers in two sizes, U.K.

Ferguson straight blade susoiler which was offered in many countries by Ferguson and M-F. This particular example was offered by Ferguson in South Africa. ▶

SUBSOILERS AND PIPELAYERS

In the U.K. Ferguson sold a curved tine subsoiler with a disc ahead of the blade to cut through turf or trash. In South Africa and Australia Ferguson, and later MF, offered a rigid, straight reversible-blade subsoiler. This used a telescopic top link to give improved ground clearance for transport. In the MF era, the use of the subsoiler was extended to incorporate a pipe-laying attachment. Multi-tine subsoilers are referred to in Chapter 4, Vol. 1. In the UK. it appears that M-H marketed the Stephenson horse-drawn mole drainer.

M-H-F 202 work bull laying pipe with Ferguson-type M-H-F subsoiler fitted with pipe laying attachment. ▶

THRESHERS AND MAIZE SHELLERS

Early in its history, the company sold winnowing equipment and progressed to selling large stationary and mobile threshing machines. The latter appear to have been all steel bodies rather than wood as was more usually the case with threshing machines manufactured in Europe. They mostly used the peg-drum threshing mechanism.

▲ Sawyer and Massey 'Monitor' clover huller – sectional view, 1895.

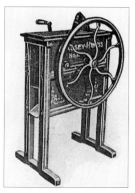 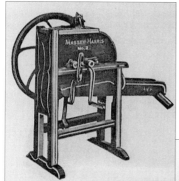

▲ M-H No. 1 and 2 (hand drive), and No. 3 (hand or power drive) maize sheller. No. 1 and 2 can shell 50-70 bushels/day 1913.

▲ Sawyer-Massey steam traction engine threshing in western Canada.

◄ Wallis tractor threshing in western Canada.

▲ Green M-H
Pacemaker tractor
threshing in
western Canada.

Sawyer and Massey
'Peerless' thresher
with Sawyer and
Massey windstacker
and Woods steel
self-feeder, 1906.▶

Sawyer and Massey
'Daisy' thresher with
Sawyer and Massey
blower and Wood
Bros. self-feeder,
1906. ▶

Sawyer and White were the two major suppliers of threshing machines to M-H. In 1944, M-H 'White' Nos. 4 and 5 steel threshers were being offered by M-H. These were of 28 in. × 46 in. and 24 in. × 42 in. sizes.

Some Specifications of Three Models of M-H Steel Threshers

	No. 1	No. 1B	No. 2B
Cylinder width in.	22	24	28
Width rear machine in.	36	44	48
Bars in cylinder	12	12	12
Spikes in cylinder	60	66	78
Bands in cylinder	3	3	3
Cylinder diam. inc. spikes in.	21.625	21.625	21.625
Cylinder speed rpm	1140	1140	1140
Rock surface sq. ft	30.9	37.77	41.36
Riddle surface sq. ft	12.66	13.25	14.46
Belt hp required full spec. machine	10–25	15–30	30–40
Weight fully equipped lb	6570	6800	7070

N.B. 1. Normal equipment: wind stacker, M-H feeder, 9 ft carrier, perfection register.
2. Special order extras: 14 ft carrier for 24 and 28 in. models, M-H feeder, clover attachment, chaff blower, hinged stacker pipe, various types of Hart registers or loaders, Hart or Garden City feeders.

▲ **Restored M-H steel thresher on display at recent Milton steam-era show (photo by J. DeVisser).**

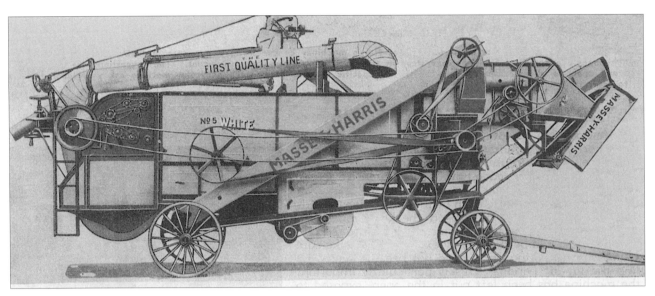

▲ M-H White No. 5 steel thresher.

▲ MF pto drive stationary corn sheller.

The MF 139 South African thresher was pto drawn and capable of threshing maize, sorghum and sunflower. With corn, 5000 kg/hr of grain was possible from unhusked cobs and 5000 kg/hr from husked cobs. Both bagger and bulk models were available. The unit required a 30 hp tractor, sometimes less, 1976. ▶

TRANSPORTERS

Ferguson pioneered the use of his Ferguson tractor for light transport duties, utilising several types of transporters mounted on the hydraulic three-point linkage. These ideas were subsequently adopted around the world in various similar forms. The most famous of these was the transport box, but there were also dump skips and transporters. The range of transporters offered was widened in the MF era.

▲ An original Ferguson transport box still working in north Wales and seen fitted to a 1958 basic model MF 35 petrol/tvo tractor.

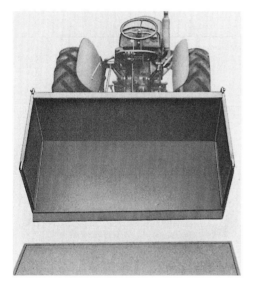

▲ The Ferguson T-JE-21 transporter was made in tipping and non-tipping versions. It had a capacity of 7 cwt or 1 cu. yd.

▲ The Ferguson dump skip R-JE-20 had a capacity of 10 cwt. It was not widely sold and there are few surviving specimens.

▲ Manufactured in Australia, the MF 12 transporter has a capacity of 432 kg and platform size of 743 mm x 1520 mm, 1980.

▲ The Indian-made 2-10 transporter has a capacity of 765 litres or 356 kg. In the raised position the body can be tipped. The rear and side panels are detachable to make an open platform transporter of 1.57 m^2, 1980.

▲ Bain two-horse platform spring lorry, post 1901.

WAGONS

M-H's strength in wagons came from the purchase of the Bain Wagon Co. This gave the company a very diverse range of farm, forestry and personnel wagons. The strength of this acquisition went on to be utilised for the production of wartime wagon equipment for military purposes. At the time, wagon bodies were made almost entirely of timber. The Second World War effort saw M-H moving to steel body wagons and today's range of MF wagons are mostly all steel bodies.

Bain Niagara fruit wagon, post 1901. ▶

Specifications of Two-Horse Bain Platform Spring Lorries

No.	Axle size in.	Skein size in.	Tyre size in.	Wheel Diameter in.		Capacity lb
				Front	Rear	
37	1.75 × 10	3.25 × 10	3 × 0.5	32	37	4000–5000
38	2 × 11	3.5 × 11	3 × 0.75	32	37	6000–8000
39	2.5 × 12	4 × 12	3.5 × 0.5	32	37	10000–12000

Specifications of Bain Niagara Fruit Wagons

No	Skein size in.	Tyre size in.	Wheel diameter in.		Platform dimensions ft.		Capacity lb
			Front	Rear	length	width	
40	2.5 × 8	2 × 0.5	32	34	11	6	1500
41	2.75 × 8	2 × 0.5	32	34	11	6	2500
42	3 × 9	2 × 0.5	32	34	11	6	3500
43	3.25 × 10	2 × 0.5	32	34	11	6	4500

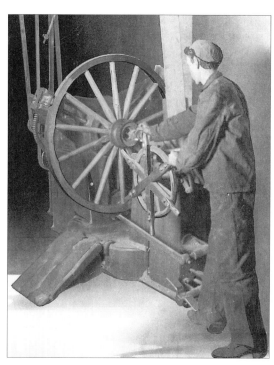

▲ Bain 'New Ontario' adjustable hay and stock wagon, post 1901.

▲ Manufacturing Bain wagon wheels.

The Bain Triple Box Farm Wagon

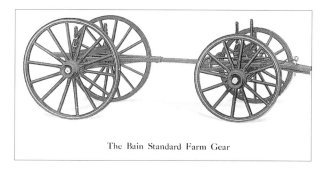

The Bain Standard Farm Gear

Massey-Harris Dump Wagon

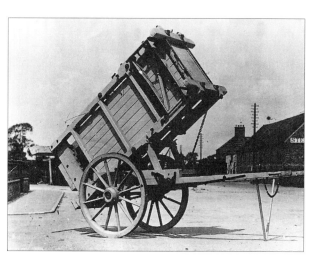

▲ This photo of a Stephenson-made root and manure tipping cart in 1890 may repesent one of the early Massey marketing ventures in the U.K. with another manufacturer (Massey started establishing U.K. branches and agents in 1887).

Early Ferguson hitch for Ford-Ferguson era Ferguson two-wheel trailer. ▶

One of the most important advances in wagon design was the Ferguson concept of a two-wheel wagon with its hitch point under the rear of the tractor back axle. This gave significant weight transfer of the trailer and its load onto the tractor, and so enabled a small tractor to pull a large load. Such weights could not have been pulled in other than flat, good surface conditions using traditional four-wheel trailers which transferred no weight to the tractor. Additionally the Ferguson hydraulic system was used for tipping the trailer. Hitching was also facilitated by an automatic pick-up hitch which used the tractor's hydraulic implement lift arms to automatically hitch the trailer. All these principles are still in use today.

▲ French-made MF tractor with Ferguson design MF 3-ton hydraulic tipping trailer.

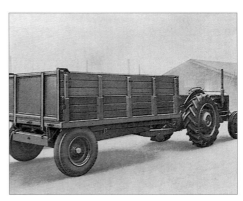

▲ A 3-ton MF 717 trailer. This is the classic two-wheel Ferguson design trailer hitched directly under the tractor rear axle to transfer weight to the tractor. This example is shown fitted with grain sides.

◀ MF 35 tractor with French-made Ferguson trailer, France, c. 1960.

The Ferguson inspired design innovation of the 'Multi-Pull' hitch (Chapter 1, Vol. 1) was particularly applicable to the towing of four-wheel trailers but surprisingly was never widely adopted.

In 1995, MF in the U.K. were offering 700 series trailers in several ranges. The capacity of these is from small one-ton models for compact tractors up to 14-ton models for large agricultural tractors.

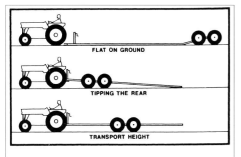

Loading positions.
The wheels can be positioned anywhere along the length of the trailer to balance the load correctly.

▲ The M-H 102 rubber tyred wagon was available with hitch for horses or drawbar for tractors. It was fitted with 6.00 x 16 6-ply tyres and had a capacity of 5000 lb, 1950.

◀ The MF 5,6,7,8 and 65 running gears were of 3.6, 5.45, 7.26, 9.08 and 4.55 tonne capacity. They could be fitted with flat bed, silage or grain bodies,1976.

◀ The North American MF 9 implement carrier/trailer was designed for transport of wide implements and combine tables. It had a 4535 kg load rating. The deck size was 6.4m x 1.5m, 1970.

The British-made MF 200 low loader trailer had a 3 ton load capacity and platform area of 8.8 m². It was specifically designed for carrying pallets, boxes, bales, sacks and implements. The platform height was 610 mm, 1980. ▶

▲ The 5.5 tonne, four-wheel trailer was made for international sales. It has automatic over-run brakes. The drawbar was designed to be strong enough to accept pressure control linkage. The platform size is 4 m x 2 m, 1980.

▲ The MF 200 Monocoque trailer was made in 6.5, 7, 8.5 and 10 tonne capacities. All were twin axle. They were specifically designed for bulk transport. Silage versions were also offered, 1980.

▲ An MF 700 M Monocoque trailer, 1995.

▲ The 4.5 tonne capacity MF 22 high-level tipper made in the U.K. had a double chassis/ram arrangement which could achieve a discharge height of 1.91 m. Optional accessories included grain sides, silage sides, platform extension and hay ladders, 1976. ▼

▲ An MF 12-tonne model 700 B articulated bale trailer, 1995.

MF 700 Series Agricultural Trailers 1995

Range	Type	Capacities t	
700C	compact trailers	1, 1.5, 2, 2.5, 3.5	single axle
700L	Lynx trailers	12, 14	dual axle
700M	Monocoque trailers	5, 6.5, 7, 8, 10, 12	single and dual axle
700B/700P	bale/pallet trailers	4, 5, 6, 8, 10, 12 bale	single and dual axle and articulated
		10, 12, 14 pallet	dual axle
700R	root trailers	8, 10, 12	dual axle
700D	dropside trailers	4, 5, 6, 7, 8, 10, 12, 14	single and dual axle
700AD	articulated dump trailers	6, 8, 10, 12	single and dual axle
700HSM	high specification monocoque trailers	8, 10, 12, 14	dual axle

Specialist type of wagons have included a Tobacco Hauling Truck and Bulk Trailer Bins. The latter were four-wheel grain trucks with built in auger or bagging off chutes for unloading.

Trucks which link integrally with combine harvesters have also been offered. These were for bagged or bulk grain.

Pto Self-Unloading Forage and Bunk Feeder Wagons have also been made. These are high-sided wagons which can receive forage blown into them from forage harvesters and then deliver it, either out of the rear into a silage pit or from the side into livestock troughs. Their unloading mechanisms are pto powered. They can also be used for other materials such as small grain and fertiliser.

The Sunshine M-H 50, trailer bulk bin had a 123 bushel capacity. It hitched to 506 pto headers by a single pin. It could be unloaded by the built-in auger at 20 bushels/min., or grain bagged off. The standard bulk bins in the header were only 30 or 38 bushel capacity. ▼

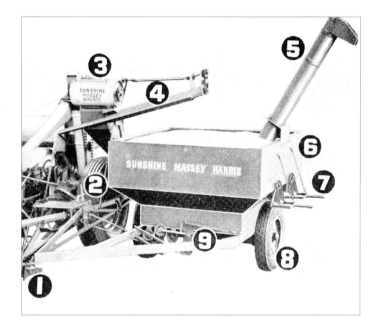

A bagging-off platform was offered for the Sunshine M-H 508 header when it was not equipped with a bulk grain bin. It had a capacity of 16 bags. ▶

▲ MF 23/24 self-unloading forage wagons, shown with top cover to prevent loss of fodder. Capacity up to 700 cu. ft.

▲ MF forage harvester loading into trailed, four-wheel self-unloading forage wagon.

▲ Hand clutch control of unloading on an MF self-unloading wagon.

▲ MF self-unloading wagon delivering fresh forage to feed lot troughs.

▲ Unloading corn from an MF self-unloading wagon into a corn cribber.

▲ The MF 114 and 116 self unloading forage boxes had volumes of 600 and 687 cu. ft respectively. They could be equipped with running gears of 8, 12 and 14 tonne capacities, 1978.

WINCHES

Ford Ferguson offered a front-mounted winch driven by shaft from the pto and having a capacity of 6000 lb. Ferguson, and later MF, offered a light duty pto drive winch fitted to the three-point linkage. This had a capacity of 7000 lb. M-H appear to have never offered a winch for their tractors although, certainly in the U.K., winches were offered for fitting to M-H tractors by outside companies. The MF Skidder made for forestry work was an exception in MF times, in that it had a factory fitted winch (Chapter 6).

▲ Power winch attachment, for the Ford-Ferguson tractor.

PEAT PRESSES

The MF photographic archives in Coventy, U.K. yielded two photographs of peat presses thought to have been marketed by M-H in the U.K.

▲ Ferguson winch (owned by author's son) made by Hesfords of Lancashire, U.K. for Ferguson. It is powered by pto and has a rated pull of 7000 lb. Rope lengths were 60, 80 or 100 ft.

◄ Victorian peat press thought to have been marketed by M-H in the U.K.

Peat press with elevator feed thought to have been marketed by M-H in the U.K. ►

CHAPTER TWO

Harvesting Equipment

From the early days both Massey and Harris specialised in cereal and grass harvesting equipment, starting with simple horse-drawn mowers and reapers. The importance of grain and fodder harvesting equipment to the company's activities over the years cannot be overestimated and is attributable to the fact that area-wise, cereals and grass are the two most important world crops. Notwithstanding this, the company has also marketed harvesting machinery for other important crops.

M-H played a premier role in the development of the mass-produced self-propelled combine harvester. The development took place against a rising world demand for food grains and the bringing of great areas of land around the world into small grain cultivation. It also proceeded against a background of increasing industrialisation in the western world which was causing farm labour to become scarcer and more expensive. These latter pressures were perhaps greater in North America and Australia, where European settlers had brought large tracts of land under the plough, than in Europe itself. The history of the development of the self-propelled combine harvester really has its roots in Australia, one of the early M-H markets for farm machinery, and where from the early days M-H co-operated with Australian engineers.

The Patterson Oxford five-rake reaper. Post 1889. ▼

In the U.K., M–H obtained significant amounts of hay-making machinery from local implement manufacturers. Two of the bigger links were with the Blackstone and Dickie companies. The products of these two companies were jointly badged with M–H. Another such company was Steels Agricultural Machinery, and products were badged Massey-Harris S.A.M.

This chapter reviews the evolution of the various types of harvesting equipment through the ages.

REAPERS

Following the scythe and mower, the reaper was the next stage in the mechanisation of grain cutting. The reaper was a development up from a simple mower blade over which the cut material fell into a wide swath, to a machine which caught the cut material and deposited it to the side of the machine in loose bundles, either by a man with a rake pulling it off, or by action of the sails. Both Massey and Harris acquired rights to the machines manufactured by others to get into the market.

▲ The Johnston Harvester Co.'s wrought-iron harvester.

▲ The Massey reaper harvester, 1895.

The Harris Brantford self-raking reaper. This was available as 4, 4.6 or 5 ft cut. ▶

CEIFEIRA SIMPLES «MASSEY-HARRIS»

◄ Early M-H reaper as advertised in a Portuguese M-H equipment brochure.

The M-H No.2 reaper shown folded for transport. ▼

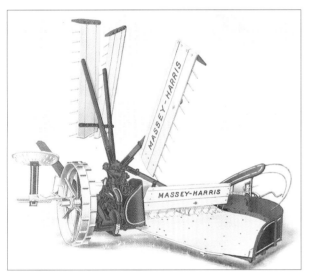

▲ M-H No. 2 reaper. 4, 4.5, 5 and 5.5 ft cut, c. 1917.

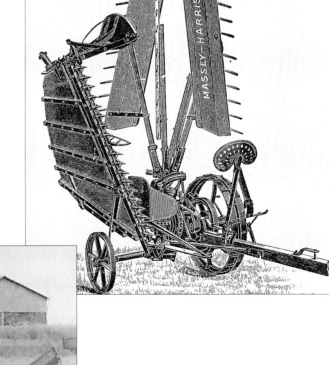

▲ Oxen pulling an M-H reaper, and showing how the men had to manually bundle or 'bind' the crop after cutting.

▲ The Patterson Light Steel binder with improved knotter. Post 1889.

▲ The Harris Brantford No. 2 Light Steel binder. This was available with the new Brantford or Appleby knotter, 1891.

BINDERS

The binder was a development of the reaper. Both Massey and Harris acquired rights to the machines of other manufacturers to establish themselves in this line, then pursued further development. The critical advance which makes a binder superior to a reaper is that it cuts and then ties the cut material in bundles or sheaves. Both Massey and Harris worked hard to advance machinery design and in particular the knotter mechanism. Wire knotters were used at one stage but ultimately all machines came to have twine knotters. Both Massey and Harris had a period of phenomenal success with their binders in the same period. This period of intense competition in marketing two lines of highly successful products may be seen as the catalyst to their merger. In the years just before the merger, Harris had scored notable sales success in Europe with his Brantford Open End Binder. This simple concept—that the rear of the binder elevator and binding platform were not closed in and so allowed any length of straw to pass up through the machine to the knotter—was immensely popular in Europe where straw was a sought-after commodity and cut to its full length.

▲ The Massey Low Down binder.

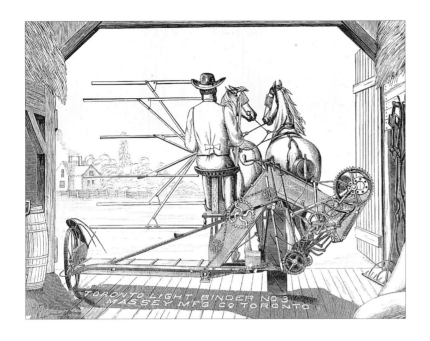

◄ **Massey Toronto Light binder, 1891.**
▼

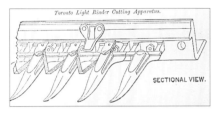

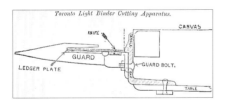

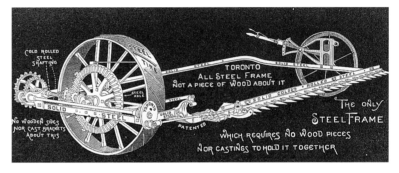

◄ **Oxen pulling M-H binders at Nassanres, France.**

▲ M-H binder pulled by oxen team in Tunisia and cutting oats (and thistles!)

▲ Mule team pulling an M-H No. 16 binder in Western Province, Cape of Good Hope, South Africa.

▲ Horse-drawn binder with sheaf carrier. Note how the sheaves are dropped in regular rows for stooking.

▲ M-H push type binder.

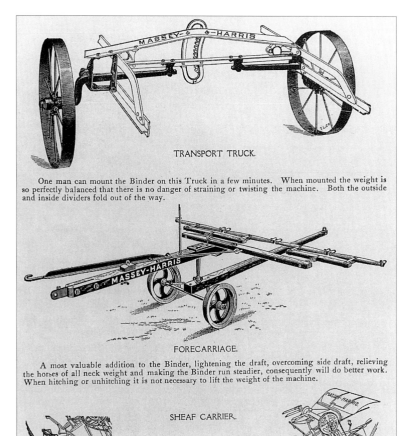

TRANSPORT TRUCK.

One man can mount the Binder on this Truck in a few minutes. When mounted the weight is so perfectly balanced that there is no danger of straining or twisting the machine. Both the outside and inside dividers fold out of the way.

FORECARRIAGE.

A most valuable addition to the Binder, lightening the draft, overcoming side draft, relieving the horses of all neck weight and making the Binder run steadier, consequently will do better work. When hitching or unhitching it is not necessary to lift the weight of the machine.

SHEAF CARRIER.

FOLDED.   READY TO RECEIVE THE SHEAVES.

Simple, strong, does not sag, is easily tripped by the driver's foot and discharges the sheaves without shelling grain. It works satisfactorily on the level or on a hillside. If it strikes a stump or other obstruction it folds automatically and prevents breakage. It is not necessary to climb over or on it to oil the machine as it folds close to side of Binder; it is always ready but never in the way.

▲ Attachments for binders, 1913.

▲ The M-H No. 6 binder – an early example of a pto drive binder.

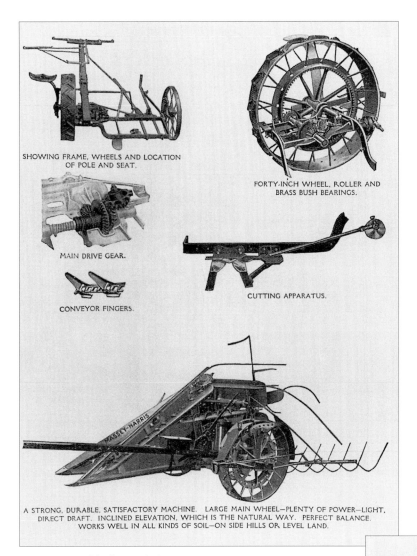

SHOWING FRAME, WHEELS AND LOCATION
OF POLE AND SEAT.

FORTY-INCH WHEEL, ROLLER AND
BRASS BUSH BEARINGS.

MAIN DRIVE GEAR.

CONVEYOR FINGERS.

CUTTING APPARATUS.

A STRONG, DURABLE, SATISFACTORY MACHINE. LARGE MAIN WHEEL—PLENTY OF POWER—LIGHT,
DIRECT DRAFT. INCLINED ELEVATION, WHICH IS THE NATURAL WAY. PERFECT BALANCE.
WORKS WELL IN ALL KINDS OF SOIL—ON SIDE HILLS OR LEVEL LAND.

▲ M-H corn binders, 1913.

▲ M-H 12-20 tractor and binder in the
early 1930s at Wilderspool Farm,
Lancashire, U.K. Owned by the author's
grandfather; author's father on the
binder.

▲ Tractor-drawn binder with sheaf
carrier pulled by a Deering tractor.

▲ M-H Sunshine 6B binder made in
Victoria, Australia shown working in
Scotland, U.K. It is pulled by a British-
made 745 diesel tractor made at
Kilmarnock in Scotland.

◄ M-H corn binder cutting and binding
green corn. The binder is fitted with an
elevator to load the sheaves onto a
trailer travelling alongside.

▲ Testing a binder knotter at the Brantford factory.

Early North American MF 35 cutting and binding undersown oats, Oklahoma, U.S.A. ▶

M-H tractor-drawn, pto drive binder. ▶

SWATHERS

Swathers may be used for grain or forage crops. The basic concept is that the crop is cut and laid in a swath (often of variable width and deposited to the rear or side of the machine) to cure for a period on the stubble of the cut crop. Grain crops would subsequently be picked up with a combine harvester fitted with a pick–up reel table. Forage crops would be picked up by crop loaders, balers, pick–up and chop-forage harvesters or simply turned or tedded for further drying.

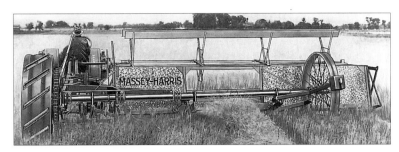

▲ Wallis 20-30 tractor pulling a large M-H swather. This is a land-wheel drive model, the large drive wheel powers the machine. Note the extension wheels fitted to the tractor to give three rows of lugs.

▲ M-H green Model 25 tractor pulling M-H land-drive swather fitted with loading elevator in Western Canada.

▲ M-H tractor and swather. Note the spare wheels for use when the swather is in narrow transport mode.

▲ M-H No. 8 pto drive trailed swather.

◄ Swathing oats with a M-H self-propelled swather.

▲ The MF30 pull-type swather was pto driven and was primarily designed for grain crops. It had a 3.6 m or 4.88 m cut, 1970.

Swathers for forage have evolved from machines which simply cut the crop, to machines which 'condition' the crop to speed the rate of drying. This is achieved by passing the crop through crimper rollers or some form of laceration device.

The MF 220 self-propelled swather of 1996 is a high-output machine built with the comfort of the driver in mind. The cab has an air-conditioner, heater, tinted glass and AM/FM cassette stereo. It is an elegant machine, reflecting how today's machines must have eye appeal to attract the customer. All the header functions, including the knife, are hydraulically operated.

◄ The North American-made MF36 self-propelled swather was propelled by a 53 hp petrol engine. It had a 3.2, 3.66, 4.3, 4.9 or 5.5 m cut. The table was fitted with two canvas elevators which formed a central swath. The machine could be used for forage or grain crops. For the forage crops an optional conditioner could be fitted, 1970.

88hp, triple delivery MF 220 swather, 1996. ▼

▲ The North American-built MF35 pull-type swather had a cut of 6.4 m and was said to be capable of 5 ha/hr. A 0.9 m wide header extension was available, 1980.

Some Specifications of the MF 220 Swather

Wheelbase in.	137
Track width in.	131
Engine	4-cylinder diesel 88 hp
Ground drive	hydrostatic with planetary gear final reduction
Speed range mph	0–14
Headers	draper or auger type
Draper head delivery	centre or double swath
Auger head delivery	single swath
Draper head widths ft	18–30
Auger head widths ft	14–16
Knife type	reciprocating blade, serrated, 1200–1400 strokes/min
Conditioner	for auger head 59 in. wide, timed intermeshing rollers
Optional equipment	rear weights, header-gauge wheels, windshield wiper kit

STRIPPER-HEADERS, REAPER-THRESHERS AND COMBINE HARVESTERS

The Sunshine Harvester of 1901.▼

The first 'combine harvester' was effectively the Australian-made H. V. McKay 'Sunshine Harvester' marketed around the turn of the century. The Sunshine Harvester had a peg-drum threshing mechanism. It was horse-drawn, land-wheel driven and had a stripper-header; hence it took no straw into the threshing mechanism and there were no straw walkers or other straw cleaning devices. It was this harvester which was to influence M-H combine development, and M-H went on to link with the company.

Early combine development ignored the straw component of the crop in terms of both the cutting and cleaning mechanisms. Indeed, straw had no value in many of the grain growing areas of the world. However, farmers near cities and most European growers had a market for straw, and this requirement created a demand for the whole crop to be cut and threshed. This influenced design towards the reciprocating-blade cutting mechanism and straw-walker separators. However, certain areas of the world, where straw remained of no value, continued to use stripper-header harvesters and there has been a recent revival of interest in stripper-headers even in Europe. The change to slurry base rather than straw-bedded animal housing systems has undoubtedly lowered the value of straw in certain grain growing areas.

From the beginnings of the Massey and Harris companies, their endeavours were keenly focused on mowing machines, reapers and binders. Their intense rivalry in this product sector, particularly binders, led to their natural merger to become Massey-Harris. Their joint expertise and strength in the sector subsequently evolved into combine

▲ The first Australian stripping machine – a horse push stripper-header type.

M-H stripper harvester pulled by oxen in Tunisia, North Africa. ▼

harvester development, but initially making use of Australian expertise. This started just before the turn of the century and led to the first M-H Stripper or Header harvester, the M-H No.1, being produced in 1910. This was developed up to the No. 5 reaper-thresher in 1922, which had a mounted gasoline engine to provide the threshing and reaping power. 1939 saw the introduction of the M-H 20 combine harvester, which earned its place in history as the first true M-H commercial self-propelled combine harvester.

▲ M-H reaper-threshers in a 3500 acre wheat crop, West Australia, December 1921.

▲ M-H reaper and thresher in Australia.

▲ M-H reaper and thresher cutting an 8 ft swath in a 40 bushel crop, 1909.

▲ Harvesting with M-H reaper threshers at the Tipperary Estate of Messrs. Burges, York, Australia, 1906.

▲ The M-H reaper
of 1913.

Reaper in the field
unloading into
sacks. ▶

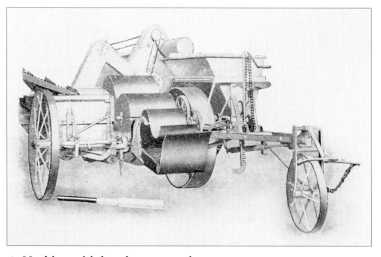

▲ The forecarriage. ▲ Machine with header removed.

▲ **Divider extension comb.**

▲ **Chassis arrangement.**

However, it is interesting to record that the first true self-propelled combine harvester was the Sunshine Auto Header made in Australia and that it was eventually marketed by M-H under the H. V. McKay Massey-Harris badge. This was a 12 ft cut machine with two speeds of 3 and 1.5 mph, which were both used for cutting according to conditions. Forty to fifty acres per day were said to be possible. The machine could be used for stationary threshing by fitting a feed table and straw elevator.

Tom Carroll, an Australian, spearheaded M-H combine research and development through to, and beyond the M-H 20. He has a sure place in history for his work on M-H combine development, which for many years gave M-H an unsurpassable reputation. One of the departures from H. V. McKay thinking was to adopt a rasp bar and concave threshing mechanism rather than McKay's peg drum arrangement. Tom Carroll also

pioneered the use of caterpillar tracks on combines and so took modern harvesting to the rice fields of the world. Several 'Rice' combines were made and rice tracks were an option for several models of combine.

The Sunshine auto header, made in 1935 in Australia. This was the world's first 'self-propelled' combine harvester. ▼

Model Development of Early M-H Reaper-threshers and Combines

Date★	Model	Comments
1901	M-H Stripper-Harvester	Australian, then South American market. 5 ft and 6 ft cut. Heads stripped from stalks. No straw-walker separating mechanism. Pull type ground drive.
1910	No. 1	Horse-drawn powered from main wheel. Knife for cutting grain in combination with long fingers and eccentric reel. Straw walkers and decks for separating kernel and chaff. 8.5 ft cut.
1912	No. 2	Similar to No. 1. Pull type ground drive. 8.5 ft cut.
1912	No. 3	Difference largely in table. Large diameter reel and conventional type knife and guards. 8.5 ft cut.
1915	No. 4	Similar to No. 3. 9 ft cut.
1922	No. 5	Horse or tractor drawn. Powered by auxiliary gasoline engine. Straw rattlers instead of straw walkers. 12 ft cut.
1926	No. 6	Smaller machine with straw walkers. 10 ft cut.
1924	No. 7	Straw walker machine. Pull type, auxiliary engine. 12 ft cut.
	No. 8	One machine partly developed in engineering.
1926	No. 9	Horse or tractor drawn. Auxiliary gasoline engine.
1929	No. 9A	Similar to No. 9. 12 ft cut.
1929	No. 9B	Similar to No. 9. 12-15 ft cut.
1929	No. 9C	Similar to No. 9.
1929	No. 9D	Similar to No. 9.
1927	No. 10	Experimental.
1930	No. 11	Smaller machine. Horse or tractor drawn. Auxiliary gasoline engine. Grain tank model. Quick detach platform. 12 ft cut.
1930	No. 11A	Bagger model.
	No. 12	Experimental only.
1936	No. 14	Largest model ever made. Tractor operated. Pull type auxiliary engine. 12 and 16 ft cut.
1937	No. 15	Smaller machine. First M-H pto-driven machine. Tractor drawn. Engine to special order only. First M-H combine with rubber tyres. 6 and 8 ft cut.
1937	No. 17	Similar to No. 15 but larger. 10 or 12 ft.
1940	No. 18	Streamlined and larger than No. 17. Auger table as special order—a few were sold.
1938-39	No. 20	First M-H self-propelled. 16 ft. Built regardless of weight. Table in front of machine rather than alongside. Grain tank models operated by one man.
1940	No. 21	Self-propelled. Similar to No. 20. Lightweight. 12 and 14 ft. Basis of the Harvest Brigade. Exported to all major grain growing countries.
1942	No 21 A	Self-propelled. Auger table instead of canvas.
1944	No. 22	Self-propelled.
1946-47	No. 221, 222, 223	Self-propelled. 14, 10 and 7 ft cuts, respectively.

★date placed on market. N.B. Nos. 13, 16 and 19 skipped for no apparent reason. Source: *Combine Development* by Massey-Harris, 15 April, 1947. Internal document. Also some data from *The Grain Harvesters*, Quick J.G. and Buchele W., 1978.

◄ Wallis experimental centrifugal combine under construction at Racine. This is probably a project inherited by M-H when they took over Wallis in 1928. Photo 1929.

◄ Wallis 20-30 tractor pulling M-H 9A engine-drive combine in Western Canada. The engine is a Wallis.

◄ M-H No. 9A-9B combine with engine drive and fitted with pick-up. It is pulled by a Wallis 20-30 tractor fitted with rear wheel extensions.

Specifications of M-H Models 9A and 9B Reaper-threshers

	No. 9A	No. 9B
Width of cut ft	12	12 and 15
Width of cylinder in.	33	33
Diameter of cylinder in.	22	22
Width of rear	37	37
Width of platform canvas in.	36	36
Speed of cylinder rpm	1100	1100
Motor	Buda 4-cylinder	Red Seal Continental 4-cylinder
Diameter of front wheels in.	24	24
Width of front wheels in.		4
Diameter of main wheel in.	52.5	52.5
Width of main wheel in.	15	15
Diameter of grain wheel in.	52.5	52.5
Width of grain wheel in.	10	10
Bearings	SKF, Hyatt, M-H	SKF, Hyatt, M-H
Lubrication	Alemite	Alemite
Capacity of grain tank bushels	35	60
Special order equipment	8 or 10 horse-hitch, straw-carrier dump, bagger and platform, brake and clutch for cross conveyor.	

▲ Green M-H Model 25 tractor with M-H No. 14 engine-driven combine.

▲ M-H No. 11 combine with engine drive pulled by an M-H 12-20 tractor.

▲ Front cover of a brochure advertising the M-H No. 14 reaper-thresher, 1937.

▲ No. 15 pto combine working in soya beans. It is pulled by an M-H green Challenger tractor.

▲ M-H No. 16 pto drive combine. Note the tractor has extended rear engine panels – possibly a natural-gas powered model.

▲ M-H 21 combine with pick-up.

▲ M-H No. 21 self-propelled bagger combine at work in the Royal Estate, Windsor Great Park, England, U.K. Note the combine is fitted with steel drive wheels – possibly a wartime economy measure.

▲ The large M-H No. 20 combines fitted with pick-up.

▲ M-H 21A combines harvesting pasture grass seed. Note the toothed pick-up reels for lifting the crop above the knife.

▲ The ladies admire an M-H 21A combine fitted with tracks at a rice festival in Louisiana, U.S.A.

The Clipper Combine was a highly successful post-war small combine and sold as a trailed with engine drive, trailed with pto drive or as a self-propelled model. The first pull types were introduced in 1938 and they stayed in production for 20 years.

Specifications of Some Clipper Combine Models

	Self-Propelled	Trailed 6 ft model	Trailed 7 ft model
Overall width in.	105	132	144
Overall length in.	216	227	227
Weight with bin lb	5200	3200	3300
Cutting height in.	1.5–33	1.5–33	1.5–33
Width of cut in.	81	72	81
Gathering width in.	84	76	84
Cylinder width in.	60	60	60
Cylinder type	rasp	rasp	rasp
Grain tank bushels	22.5	25	25
Engine	4-cylinder gasoline, 1500 rpm, 34.5 hp	4-cylinder V-type gasoline, 2000 rpm, 21 hp	4-cylinder V-type gasoline, 2000 rpm, 21 hp
Speeds mph	on 8.00 × 24 tyres: low 0.75–3, high 2–8, reverse 0.75–5.	according to tractor	according to tractor

Pto drive 'Clipper' tanker combine being pulled by red M-H pacemaker tractor in Canada. ▶

▲ **M-H self-propelled 'Clipper' combine, harvesting peanuts in South Africa with a pick-up on the header.**

▲ **M-H self-propelled 'Clipper' combine fitted with pick-up.**

▲ **M-H 102 Super tractor pulling pto drive 'Clipper' bagger combine.**

POWER DRIVE HARVESTER

▲ The Sunshine M-H power drive harvester had a 10 ft cut and was fitted with a 23 bushel grain tank. The peg drum had 76 teeth and the concave had 78 pegs.

▲ M-H 81 tractor pulling engine drive Clipper combine in France.

The M-H Nos. 21 and 722 self-propelled combines were the first to really invade the British market in the post-war years and set the scene for the later Model Nos. 726 and 780 self-propelled machines which were made in the U.K. The 722 was actually made in the U.K. for one year in 1948. Most were adapted for TVO fuel.

▲ M-H Model 22 combine in New Zealand.

Specifications of M-H 21 and 722 Combines Sold in the U.K.

	No. 21	No. 722
Width of cut ft	12	8
Table	canvas, electrically operated	auger, electrically operated
Engine	Chrysler 6-cylinder 65 hp	Continental 4-cylinder 35 hp
Forward speeds mph	field 1, 1.5, 2, 2.5; road 7	24 speeds from 0.75–6.25
Drum speeds rpm	330–1150 by sprocket changes	330–1080 by sprocket changes
Drum width in.	32	24
Grain tank bushels	45	30
Optional bagger unit	Four spout	Four spout
Optional extras	Pick-up, pick-up reel, straw spreader, dual wheels	Pick-up, pick-up reel, straw spreader

Specifications of the British-made M-H 726 Combine

Width of cut in.	102 or 144
Length in.	266
Working width in.	102 model will pass through 10 ft gateway
Engine	56 bhp Austin 6-cylinder or
	Morris 4-cylinder petrol/TVO engines
Speed range mph	1–7 by two gears with 12 variations in each gear
Type of table	feathering auger with standard reel
Table lift in.	2–28.5, electric
Drum in.	22 diameter and 24.5 wide
Drum speed rpm	380–1160 by sprocket changes
Grain tank capacity bushels	40
Bagger attachment	4 spout with rotary screen; sun canopy optional
Weight lb	6720

▲ The M-H 726 combine was the first to be mass produced in the U.K. with a choice of Austin or Morris engine.

▲ M-H combine harvesting rice in Tanzania, Africa. This appears to be a British-made Model 726.

▲ M-H self-propelled combine, fitted with special reel, harvesting dwarf sorghum in the U.S.A.

▲ M-H No. 60 pto drive combine pulled by M-H 333 diesel tractor.

▲ Over twenty M-H combines at work on a large farm in Turkey.

▲ British-built M-H 780 combine at work in Victoria, Australia, 1953.

M-H 82 combine. Note the development of a lower profile on this model, 1957. ►

▲ **M-H 890 combine in France.**

▲ **M-H No. 60 self-propelled combine with two-row corn header.**

▲ **M-H 80 combine fitted with pick-up for lifting previously swathed crop.**

▲ **M-H 60 self-propelled combine. Note it is fitted with drive pulleys at the rear for use with a straw spreader.**

▲ M-H 90 special combine fitted with pick-up header and Polaris straw cutter/spreader.

▲ M-H 90 rice special combine in U.S.A. Fitted with tracks and larger rear tyres.

▲ M-H 92 hillside combine on tracks. Design advances over the 90 model included the break back unloading auger and cover for the bulk tank.

▲ M-H 90 combine harvesting wheat in Chile, South America.

▲ M-H 90 special combine with pick-up lifting a swathed crop.

▲ M-H 90 special purpose, low ground-pressure combine with straw spreader.

M-H 685 combine. Note the large diameter reel on this model, 1957. ►

M-H 92 hillside combine. ►

M-H Sunshine 585 combine with stripper-header in Victoria, Australia, 1957. ►

M-H 55K tractor with trailed pto drive Sunshine No. 4 header, 1955. ►

Ferguson undertook development work on a tractor side-mounted combine harvester in the U.K. and U.S.A. with the intention of marketing it in 1957. Several prototypes were made. The machine had a 7 ft 6 in. cut and was powered by the tractor pto. The project was killed off by the Ferguson and M-H merger as it was thought that it would affect sales of the M-H 735 combine.

As with tractors, there has been a proliferation of combine harvester models since the merger. This chapter can only endeavour to give a pictorial indication of a selection of the models that have been made. However, a good indication of the range of combine models which have been produced around the world by M-H and MF has been prepared from a French MF wall chart.

▲ British Ferguson mounted combine prototype. Apparently about ten were made.

◄ Experimental Ferguson combine tractor mounted on a Ferguson TO type tractor with auxiliary engine drive, 1951. This North American prototype was similar to U.K. produced prototypes mounted on TE tractors but driven from their ptos. The Project died with the merger of M-H and Ferguson.

Chronology of M-H and MF Combine Harvester Production

Model	Power source	Country of production	Years of production
M-H 1 reaper-thresher	land drive	Canada	1910–1915
M-H 2 reaper-thresher	land drive	Canada (for Australia)	1912–1919
M-H 3 reaper-thresher	land drive	Canada (for Argentina)	1912–1919
M-H 4 reaper-thresher	land drive	Canada	1920–1923
M-H 5 reaper-thresher	engine	Canada	1922–1926
M-H 6 reaper-thresher	engine	Canada	1925–1930
M-H 9 reaper-thresher	engine	Canada	1927–1932
M-H 11 reaper-thresher	engine	Canada	1930–1936
M-H 14 reaper-thresher	engine	Canada	1933–1936
M-H 15 reaper-thresher	engine or pto	Canada	1937–1953
M-H 17 reaper-thresher	engine or pto	Canada	1937–1953
M-H 20	self-propelled	Canada	1938–1940
M-H Clipper (Auger or canvas table)	engine or pto	U.S.A.	1938–1951
M-H 21	self-propelled	Canada	1939–1949
M-H Clipper	self-propelled	U.S.A.	1944–1951
M-H 222	self-propelled	Canada	1947
M-H 722	self-propelled	U.K. (Manchester)	1948
M-H 26	self-propelled	Canada	1948–1952
M-H 27	self-propelled	Canada	1949–1952
M-H 726	self-propelled	U.K. (Kilmarnock)	1949–1953
M-H 27L	self-propelled	Canada	1951
M-H 50 Clipper	self-propelled	U.S.A.	1951–1955
M-H 50	pto	U.S.A.	1951–1954
M-H 890/MF 890	self-propelled	France	1953–1961
M-H 90 special	self-propelled	Canada	1953–1956
M-H 90	self-propelled	Canada	1953–1956
M-H 780	self-propelled	U.K.	1953–1958
M-H 60	pto or engine	Canada	1953–1958
M-H 60 special	self-propelled	Canada	1953–1956
M-H 70	self-propelled	Canada	1953
M-H 630/MF 630	self-propelled	Germany	1956–1964
M-H 82	self-propelled	Canada	1957–1963
M-H 92	self-propelled	Canada	1957–1959
M-F 830	self-propelled, diesel	France	1958–1966
M-F 830	self-propelled, petrol	France	1958–1966
M-H 92 hill side special	self-propelled	Canada	1958
M-H 35	self-propelled	Canada	1958–1963
M-H 35	pto	Canada	1959–1962
MF 685	self-propelled, petrol	Germany	1959–1963
MF 685	self-propelled, diesel	Germany	1959–1963
M-H 72	pto	Canada	1959–1963
M-H 72	self-propelled	Canada	1959–1963
MF super 92	self-propelled, petrol	Canada	1960–1963
MF 892	self-propelled, petrol	France	1960–1964
MF 892	self-propelled, diesel	France	1960–1964
MF 31-6	self-propelled, diesel	Germany	1962–1971
MF 400-7	self-propelled	U.K.	1963–1966
MF 500-7	self-propelled	U.K.	1963–1964
MF 31-6	self-propelled, petrol	Germany	1963–1970
MF 86-6	self-propelled, diesel	Germany	1963–1968
MF 86-6	self-propelled, petrol	Germany	1963–1968
MF 82-6	self-propelled	Germany	1963–1968
MF 410	self-propelled	Canada	1964–1972
MF 510-7	self-propelled	U.K.	1965–1966
MF 510	self-propelled	Canada	1965–1977
MF 99	self-propelled	France	1965–1970
MF 410-7	self-propelled	U.K.	1966–1967
MF 510-8	self-propelled	France	1966–1971
MF 30-6	self-propelled	Germany	1966–1969
MF 205	self-propelled	Canada	1966–1970

Cont. on page 80

▲ MF 585 Sunshine combine at work in Australia. With reeless header.

▲ MF 72 combine fitted with special oversize rice tyres.

◄ MF 65 tractor with MF 35 trailed combine.

▲ MF 892 rice combine, Italy, 1961.

MF 35 pto drive combine, tanker model. ►

MF 405	pto	Canada	1966–1972
MF 410-8	self-propelled	France	1967–1971
MF 187-1	self-propelled	Germany	1968–1973
MF 186-6	self-propelled	Germany	1968–1973
MF 515	self-propelled	France	1970–1971
MF 487-8	self-propelled	France	1970–1974
MF 520/525	self-propelled	France	1970–1980
MF 186-8	self-propelled	France	1971–1975
MF 620/625	self-propelled	U.K.	1971–1977
MF 187-8	self-propelled	France	1972–1974
MF 507	self-propelled	France	1972–1976
MF 520/7	self-propelled	U.K.	1973
MF 307	self-propelled	France	1974–1979
MF 206	self-propelled	France	1975–1979
MF 506	self-propelled	France	1975–1978
MF 760 hydro	self-propelled	Canada	1975–1981
MF 750-M	self-propelled	Canada	1977–1980
MF 750 hydro	self-propelled	Canada	1977–1981
MF 740	self-propelled	Canada	1977–1979
MF 550	self-propelled	Canada	1978–1988
MF 440-QA	self-propelled	France	1978–1984
MF 240	self-propelled	France	1978–1984
MF 751	pto	Canada	1978–1979
MF 540	self-propelled	Canada	1978–1988
MF 620 S II	self-propelled	U.K.	1979–1982
MF 530/535	self-propelled	France	1980–1983
MF 865	self-propelled	Canada	1981–1987
MF 850	self-propelled	Canada	1981–1987
MF 851	pto	Canada	1981–1982
MF 660/665	self-propelled	France	1981–1984
MF 560/565	self-propelled	France	1981–1984
MF 852	pto	Canada	1983–1984
MF 840/845	self-propelled	France	1984–1985
MF 830/835	self-propelled	France	1984–1985
MF 820/825	self-propelled	France	1984–1985
MF 810/815	self-propelled	France	1984
MF 800/805	self-propelled	France	1984–1985
MF 31	self-propelled	Denmark	1985–1987
MF 29	self-propelled	Denmark	1985–1987
MF 27	self-propelled	Denmark	1985–1992
MF 24	self-propelled	Denmark	1985–1994 +
MF 20	self-propelled	Finland	1985–1986
MF 16	self-propelled	Finland	1985–1991
MF 8	self-propelled	Finland	1985–1994 +
MF 8560 rotary	self-propelled	Canada	1986–1987
MF 8590 rotary	self-propelled	Canada	1987
MF 20 XP	self-propelled	Finland	1987–1990
MF 38	self-propelled	Denmark	1988–1994 +
MF 31 XP	self-propelled	Denmark	1988–1992
MF 29 XP	self-propelled	Denmark	1988–1994 +
MF 10	self-propelled	Finland	1988
MF 8570 rotary	self-propelled	Canada	1989–1993
MF 5650	self-propelled	Canada	1989–1993
MF 8460	self-propelled	Germany	1989–1993
MF 8450	self-propelled	Germany	1989–1993
MF 34	self-propelled	Denmark	1990–1994 +
MF 40	self-propelled	Denmark	1991–1994 +
MF 36	self-propelled	Denmark	1991–1994 +
MF 32	self-propelled	Denmark	1991–1994 +
MF 30	self-propelled	Denmark	1991–1994 +

Source: Recherches Conception et Production:Marketing FDC Massey Ferguson. The data is taken from a 1994 wall chart of 28 in. × 50 in. This French chart shows all non self-propelled models as being 'Tractée' or land-drive which was not the case; these have been changed to land-drive, pto or engine-drive according to other sources of information. Models marked + were still in production when the wall chart was prepared.

◄ MF 35 combine with pick-up harvesting a swathed bean crop. Note the combine is fitted with pulleys to drive a straw spreader.

▲ Line drawing of M-H 35 combine.

▲ MF 32 combine in an oat crop.

▲ MF 300 combine with MF 321 corn header.

▲ MF 205 combine with 222 corn header.

▲ MF 760 combine.

▲ The U.K.-made 510 and 515 combines typified the style of the 400 and 500 series combines. Four table sizes of 10, 12, 14, and 16 ft were available. The 515 had an exclusive double action separator to enhance separation of grain from straw. The machines weighed just over 5 tons and were fitted with Perkins A6.354 engines, 1970

▲ The MF 39 rice combine was made in Germany with a 38 bhp engine. It had a 2.13 m table and weighed 3000 kg. It had a peg tooth drum as used on other rice combines, 1970.

▲ Prototype MF 410-510 type combine undergoing evaluation.

▲ Australian-made MF 3342 trailed pto drive combine with Quick Attach comb-type header. The machine can cut between 51 and 914 mm high, it weighs 4790 kg and has a 3400 litre tank, 1980.

◄ MF Pickups were available in 1980 in 2.67 and 3.44 m widths. They were available with conventional or electrical Vari-Speed drive.

◄ The MF 206 combine shows the typical design and livery of French and U.K.-made combines of the day. The 206 was available with 2.5 or 3 m tables and was fitted with a 68 hp Perkins A4.236 engine. The machine weighed 3500 kg with a 2.5 m table and had a 2300 litre grain tank, 1976.

◄ The South African-made MF 52 rotary recleaner was fitted to tanker combines to provide a clean grain sample straight off the field. It could handle 8 tons/hr. The basic unit weighed 144 kg, 1976.

Today's combines are often huge machines. They are typified by the 8000 series combines which are produced for MF by Claas. This series includes both conventional rasp-bar machines and the 8570 rotary combine.

Some Specifications of 8450 and 8460 Combines

	MF 8450	MF 8460
Engine	Perkins 6.0L	Mercedes 366LA
hp	162 DIN	221 DIN
Cylinder diameter/width in.	18/52	18/62
Total concave area sq. in.	960	1109
Straw walker area sq. in.	8900	10850
Total cleaning area sq. in.	6560	7905
Grain tank bushels	180	215

1. Grain header.
2. Feed elevator.
3. Front feed beater.
4. Rotor drive.
5. Rotor intake.
6. Guide vanes.
7. Concaves.
8. Threshing lobes and rasp bars.
9. Separating.
10. Sweeps and guides.
11. Grain sample door in tank.
12. Direct discharge.
13. Returns auger.
14. Cleaning fan.
15. Pressurised cleaning shoe.
16. Clean grain auger.
17. 227 bu. grain tank.
18. Turret unloader.
19. Straw chopper (optional).

▲ MF 8460 Claas-made combine with Mercedes engine, 1993.

▲ Sectional view of MF 8570 rotary combine fitted with Cummins 6 CTA 8.3 250 hp engine. It can be fitted with a range of grain and corn headers and pick-ups from 13 ft to 30 ft wide, 1993.

Headers have been retained in some parts of the world where straw is of no value. In the early MF period headers were still widely used in Australia and badged with the MF Sunshine label. One of the larger models was the 585 pto Header.

Specifications of 585 pto Header Combine

Cutting width ft	12.25
Cutting height in.	4–28
Drum	rasp bar 31.25 in. wide × 18 in. diameter
	12 speeds from 396–1455 rpm
Concave	4 rasp bars
Beater	5 sided with 1 in. lips
Riddles in.	2, 1.25, 0.75, 0.625 standard with options
Straw walkers in.	10.125 × 108
Grain tank bushels	50
Unloading auger, unloading height in.	116
Tyres	10 × 28 in. × 8 ply, options available
Transport width in.	187
Weight lb	6000

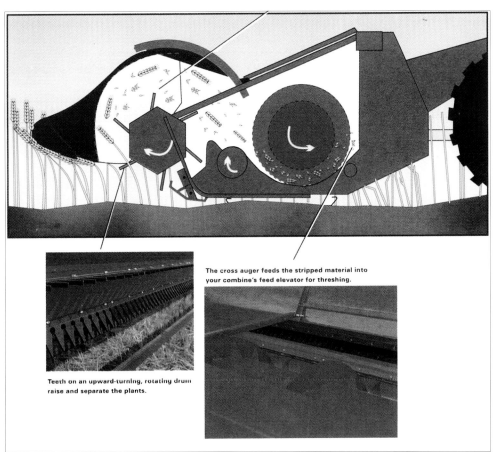

Teeth on an upward-turning, rotating drum raise and separate the plants.

The cross auger feeds the stripped material into your combine's feed elevator for threshing.

◀ Diagrammatical section of MF 6000 Series 'Harvest Hustler' stripper-header which fits MF 8400, 800 and rotary series combines (also other makes), 1994.

THE RAUSSENDORF STRAW PRESS

A straw press was offered in Europe for attachment to M-H Nos. 726 and 780 and other combines. It was made in Germany and could be fitted to the rear of the combine, positioned to catch the straw as it dropped for the straw walkers. At the time this offered a cheaper option than investing in a separate pick-up baler, but the bales were of lower density.

▲ **M-H 630 combine with rear-mounted Raussendorf straw trusser.**

The M-H Raussendorf straw press was offered for fitting to M-H 726 and 780 combines in the U.K. and other countries in Europe. ▶

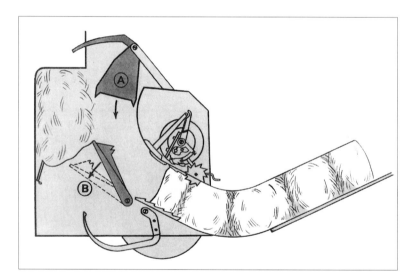

Specifications of the Raussendorf Straw Press

Size of feed chamber in.	40 × 14
Size of bale	Adjustable
Weight of bale lb	16–28
Number of knotters	2
Total weight approx. lb	800
Maximum power required hp	2

CORN PICKERS

Before corn (maize) was harvested by combine harvesters which thresh the grain from the cob, pickers were used to harvest the whole cob which was then threshed in a second operation back at the farmyard. The first self-propelled M-H corn picker was introduced in 1946. Trailed corn pickers were available before self-propelled. Ferguson marketed one in his implement line in North America. This was the single row 'Belle City' corn-picker husker or corn-picker snapper which was pto driven.

Specifications of the M-H Self-propelled Corn Picker

Engine cu. in.	162 industrial★
Corn saver width in.	28
Row spacing in.	38–42
No. of rows	2
Speeds mph	Up to 9.5
Brakes	Individual steering brakes
Header	Power-lift control from platform
Capacity	20–30 acre/day of 50 bushel corn

★ It is reported that 9216 corn pickers were produced and that they initially had 4-cylinder engines which changed to 6 at serial no. 12001.

▲ M-H two-row corn picker mounted on an M-H 44 tractor.

▲ Rear view of M-H self-propelled corn picker, 1957.

▲ M-H No. 3 three-row corn picker especially adapted for Argentina.

◄ M-H self-propelled corn picker-sheller at work in the snow.

▲ M-H self-propelled corn picker being demonstrated in Southern Zimbabwe.

▲ M-H trailed pto drive corn picker pulled by M-H 50 tractor.

In the 1970s the No. 159 tractor-drawn and pto-powered Maize Combine, was manufactured for dry-land harvesting of large grain crops. It had a one-row maize header and could thresh up to 4 ton/hr. Bagger and bulk models were offered.

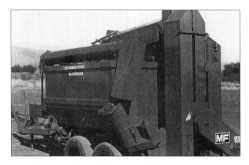

▲ The South African-made MF 159 pto maize combine was designed for dryland harvesting of large grain crops such as maize and sorghum. It could be fitted with one- or two-row headers. Whole plants were taken into the combine and threshed in a longitudinal, perforated rotating cylinder containing ratating beating bars. 400 kg/hr of maize was possible in good conditions with a 65 hp tractor, 1976.

The MF 8, 2 m plot combine harvester was used for harvesting experimental plots and had easy clean features to ensure sample purity, 1987. ▶

MOWERS AND CONDITIONERS

Mowers have been a staple part of the product line since Massey and Harris days with each company obtaining rights to other manufacturers' mowers. The reciprocating blade mower remained standard until after the M-H and Ferguson merger. Increasing standards of crop husbandry have meant that crops, particularly grass in temperate areas, have become too dense for rapid mowing with reciprocating blades. Higher tractor horse power has enabled the development of high speed flail and revolving blade mowers (drum or disc) with very high outputs and freedom from blockages.

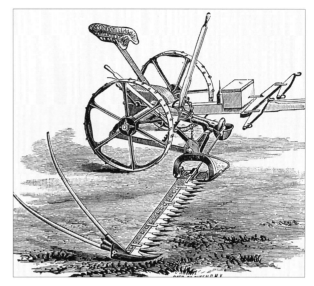

▲ Patterson 'Queen of the Meadow' mower. Post 1889.

◀ Patterson rear cut changeable speed mower. This machine had two speeds for the knife to suit different crop conditions. Post 1889.

◀ Brantford No. 1 mower, 1891.

▲ **The Harris Brantford No. 3 mower which was available in 4.6 ft or 5.6 ft width with 2.5 in. or 3 in. blade sections, 1891.** ▶

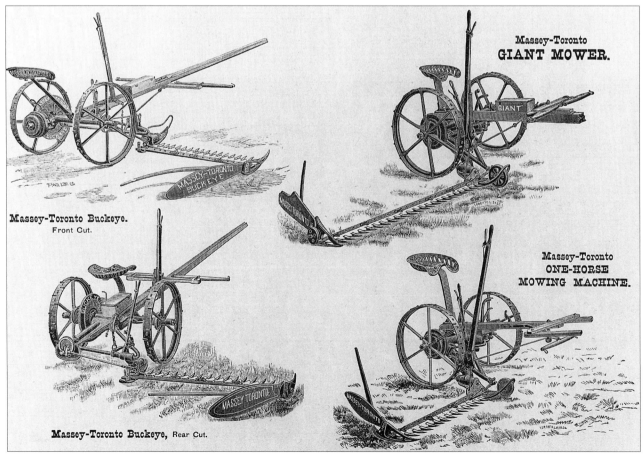

▲ **Massey mower line-up of 1891.**

▲ The famous Massey Toronto mower, 1891.

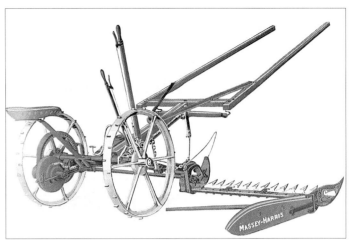

▲ M-H No. 14 mower, 3.5 ft and 4 ft cut, c. 1917.

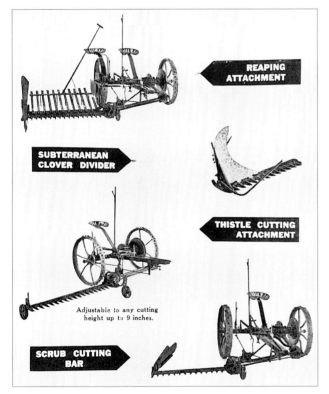

▲ Attachments for the M-H 5.5 ft and 6 ft cut tractor trailer mowers marketed by H. V. McKay M-H in Australia.

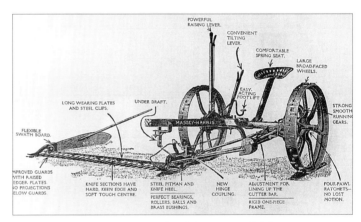

▲ M-H No. 16 mower details. This was available in 5, 6 and 7 ft cut models, 1913.

▲ M-H horse-drawn mower.

Most mowers of the M-H era were trailed. Ferguson marketed mounted pto-driven mowers which were very successful around the world. At the end of the M-H tractor era, M-H offered a pto-driven semi-mounted mower, but at the merger MF adopted the Ferguson fully mounted concept for all but swather-type mowers. There were also mounted mowers for the four-wheel drive and Challenger tractors, and some mid-mounted mowers. M-H also made a self-propelled 'Hay Maker'.

Soon after the merger 'conditioners' came into fashion for speeding the curing of hay crops. Conditioning of crops is essentially the bruising of stem and/or leaf to cause more rapid drying. The two principal mechanisms used are flails or rollers, which are made from a variety of materials. One of the first pto-drive trailed machines appeared in the U.K. in the MF 35 and 65 tractor era as the MF 37-7 and related models. This early machine picked up the forage from a cut swath, but after this conditioners were usually incorporated in drum and disc mowers, and swathers. The MF 37-7 was probably the first MF type of conditioner to be marketed.

▲ Tractor-drawn wheel drive mower.

▲ Early example of an M-H old style trailed mower with tractor pto drive pulled by green Pacemaker tractor.

▲ M-H general purpose 4WD tractor with M-H pto drive mounted mower.

▲ M-H green tricycle type Challenger tractor with pto drive mounted mower.

▲ M-H 745 diesel tractor with M-H 706 pto drive mower turning the field corner in England, U.K.

▲ M-H 50 and fully mounted pto drive 'Dyna Balance' mower.

▲ M-H Colt tractor fitted with a pto drive mid-mounted mower.

▲ M-H 50 tractor with pto drive linkage-mounted version of the semi-mounted mower.

▲ M-H Pony tractor with M-H semi-mounted pto drive mower.

▲ M-H 20 self-propelled hay maker, 1957.

The Ferguson
PA-EE-20 game
flusher shown
mounted on a 'grey-
gold' Ferguson 35
diesel tractor.
Nine chains with
weights on the ends
are dragged through
the grass to frighten
the birds ahead of
the mower. ▶

◀ MF 50 tricycle-type tractor and
semi-mounted pto drive mower.

MF 825 tractor with agricultural ▶
mid-mounted mower in France, 1960s.

◄ **MF 50 tractor and MF No. 6 pto drive semi-mounted mower with hydraulic lift control.**

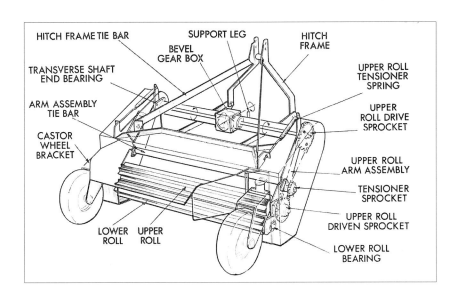

▲ **MF 65 gasoline tractor and MF 30 mower in heavy crop of an annual cereal forage.**

HITCH FRAME TIE BAR

SUPPORT LEG

BEVEL GEAR BOX

HITCH FRAME

TRANSVERSE SHAFT END BEARING

UPPER ROLL TENSIONER SPRING

ARM ASSEMBLY TIE BAR

UPPER ROLL DRIVE SPROCKET

CASTOR WHEEL BRACKET

UPPER ROLL ARM ASSEMBLY

TENSIONER SPROCKET

UPPER ROLL DRIVEN SPROCKET

LOWER ROLL   UPPER ROLL

LOWER ROLL BEARING

◄ **The MF 37-7 hay conditioner.**

Some Specifications of the MF 37-7 Hay Conditioner

Pick–up width ft	Up to 4
Conditioned swath width ft	3
Machine width in.	67
Upper roller in.	53 long, 7.375 diameter, 12 flutes
Lower roller in.	53 long, 6.375 diameter, 10 flutes
Forward operating speed mph	4–8
pto operating speed rpm	350–650
Machine weight lb	970

The Australian-made MF 41 mower was available as 1.53, 1.83 or 2.14 m cut. The 1970s effectively saw the end of the cutter bar mower evolution and the rapid change to rotary drum and disc mowers. This mower has Dyna-Balance drive and is a descendant of the original Ferguson mounted mower, 1976. ▶

The MF 82 is a four-disc rotary mower requiring a minimum of 30 hp and capable of 2 ha/hr. The discs are driven by an oil-immersed gear train drive which can work at +/- 30° from the horizontal, 1976. ▼

MF 81 mower conditioner. This machine crimped the forage between a rubber carcass and fluted steel rollers to cause quicker drying, 1968. ▶

▲ The American-made MF 40 hay conditioner uses an upper rubber and lower steel roller to gently crush the stems of the forage. Best results were obtained by conditioning immediately after mowing. It could operate at up to 10 mph. It is shown here working in tandem with an MF mid-mounted mower in an alfalfa crop, 1970.

▲ The MF 164/6 and 165/7 trailed pto drive mower conditioners were of 2.75 and 3.20 m cutting width and required a minimum of 70 and 90 hp. They were both two-drum machines and were available with flail or roller conditioners according to model, 1989.

◄ MF 122/124/126 mounted drum mowers with flail conditioner both cut and condition the crop. Respectively they require a minimum of 35, 45 and 50 hp for their 1.65, 1.85 and 2.1m widths of cut. All models have two drums with three knives/drum, except the larger model which has four, 1989.

◄ The MF 725 and 925 'Haytender' mower conditioners were 2210 and 2820 mm cut machines. Conditioning was through a pair of rollers and cutting was by reciprocating blade, 1980.

FORAGE HARVESTERS

By the mid-1940s M-H were offering their pto-drive Forage Clipper. This was an advance in the handling of green and dry fodder. Ferguson also offered a tractor side-mounted forage harvester—'The Tractor Mate'—for his Ferguson tractors in North America. This machine could be equipped with an auxiliary engine for extra power. Chop length was adjustable between 0.375 and 3.563 in. The Forage Clipper was upgraded to larger capacity models such as the No. 20 Forage Clipper.

Specifications of M-H Forage Clipper

Width of cut in.	15, reciprocating blade
Cylinder in.	36 wide, 15 diameter
Drive	pto with over-running clutch
Capacity	in forage crops of 3–8 tons/acre the machine would cut 4–12 tons/hr depending on conditions
Wheels	5.50 × 16 implement pneumatic tyres
Overall width ft	7
Length of cut in.	0.375, 1.5 or 3.5 long
Delivery	side or rear with 24 in. elevator
Special equipment	pto attachments for various tractors; auxiliary motor; knife grinding attachment; pick-up for windrowed or cured hay and straw; blower

◄ Ferguson side-mounted 'Tractor Mate' forage harvester. This had a 52 in. width cut and a 48 in. windrow width pick-up. It was available as pto or auxiliary engine drive.

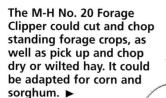

The M-H No. 20 Forage Clipper could cut and chop standing forage crops, as well as pick up and chop dry or wilted hay. It could be adapted for corn and sorghum. ►

Specifications of the M-H 20 Forage Clipper

Cutter bar width ft	5
Cylinder width in.	36
Cylinder speed rpm	450–1800
Drive, pto rpm	534
Drive, engine	6-cylinder Continental, 226 cu. in.
Table lift	hand or hydraulic
Tyre size	6.50 × 16
Chop length in.	0.218–1.25 or double by removing two knives and running cylinder at lower speed

▲ M-H 201 tractor and M-H forage harvester with forage elevator to trailer. The tractor has an unexplained widened rear engine panel.

▲ M-H 30 tractor pulling engine-drive forage harvester and trailer in corn crop, Pembroke, Ontario, Canada.

▲ M-H 44 tractor forage harvesting pre-cut grass in Ontario, Canada.

▲ M-H 33 tractor and forage harvester cutting standing grass crop, 1953.

M-H 44 tractor with forage harvester. ▶

M-H 50 tractor with forage harvester cutting lucerne. ▼

Forage harvesters evolved away from reciprocating blade mowers through flail mowers to the point where many of today's machines are in fact pick-up and chop machines. These pick up a crop from a swath made by a high capacity mower. Today's MF self-propelled forage harvesters are high output machines of up to 480 hp.

Some Specifications of MF Self-propelled Forage Harvesters 1996

	MF 5130	MF 5150	MF 5170
kW/hp	250/340	302/410	353/480
Pick up widths m	2.1, 3, 4.2	2.1, 3, 4.2	2.1, 3, 4.2
No. of cutters	40	48	48
Nominal length of cut mm	5–16 according to no. of cutters		
Max. height of fodder throw mm	5020	5020	5020
Transport height mm	3535	3535	3535
Machine length mm	6420	6420	6420
Wheelbase mm	2700	2700	2700
Weight kg	8950	9210	9280

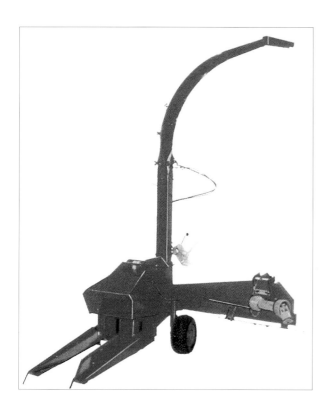

◄ The MF 620 forage chopper was a special-purpose single row, semi-mounted pto drive forage harvester for maize. It was rated as having a capacity of up to 41 t/hr, 1989.

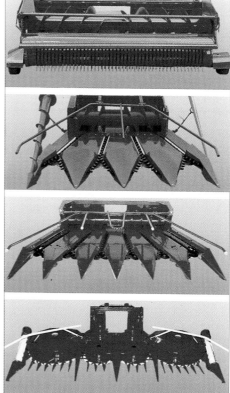

◄▲ The giant MF 5100 series self-propelled forage harvesters have engines of 340, 410 or 480 hp. They are available with four types of header unit, 1996.

WHOLE CROP HARVESTER

In 1991 MF announced a new concept in combine harvesters—the No. 1 Whole Crop Harvester. It was mounted on the tractor linkage and designed for countries where wheat or barley is a major crop and where finely broken straw is an important animal feed. The crop is cut and threshed in the usual manner of a combine harvester, but straw was broken down into small pieces. Both grain and straw were bagged off.

▲ The No. 1 Whole Crop Harvester came with 1.4 or 2 m tables, 1991.

PICK-UP BALERS

The first M-H pick-up baler was the No. 1 'Slicer' Baler announced in 1952. Tom Carroll, the combine developer, was involved with the design of this machine. It has a somewhat classic design in that it retained the overhead packer which was a more or less universal feature of traditional stationary balers. The No. 1 was powered by a mounted air-cooled Wisconsin engine. Later versions were to be offered with an Armstrong Siddley diesel engine, a Ferguson tractor (Standard) engine or a pto drive.

▲ M-H Pacer tractor with M-H engine-driven baler No. 3 undergoing evaluation on the Toronto test track.

▲ The M-H No. 1 hay baler. This was the first M-H pick-up baler, 1946.

▲ M-H 44K tractor with Sunshine self-tying pick-up baler, Australia, 1953.

◄ Meeting of the lines! M-H 780 combine and Ferguson tractor with M-H 701 baler in Warwickshire, England, U.K., near the Coventry Ferguson tractor production plant.

Specifications of No. 1 'Slicer' Baler

Overall length in.	223
Overall height in.	104
Overall width in.	111
Effective pick-up width in.	52
Wheel size	left 7.50 × 16, right 6.00 × 16
Bale size in.	14 × 18 × 37
Type of drive	flat belt
Power hp	24
Plunger speed strokes/min.	50
Twine carrier lb balls	4 × 24
Capacity	5–6 tons hay or 3–4 tons straw/hr
Weight lb	3820
Extra order items	wagon hitch and loader; automatic bale counter

▲ **Ferguson F-12 baler which is similar to M-H's first 'conventional' pick-up baler, the M-H No. 3.**

Following this first model, baler design became more conventional and as we know it for today's 'small balers'—and pto-driven. At the M-H and Ferguson merger, Ferguson was offering such a machine—the F-12. In the merger period this appears to have evolved into the MF No. 3 baler in North America and the MF 703 in the U.K. Ferguson had also been developing, and indeed produced, a tractor side-mounted baler which was made available for the 1955 season in North America. This was fitted to the Ferguson TO series tractors but soon dropped from the MF product line. It had bale length options of 32, 36 or 40 in.

M-H 33 rowcrop tractor and M-H engine-driven M-H hay baler. This is one of the early type of 'conventional' pick-up balers and is probably related to the Ferguson F12 baler. ▶

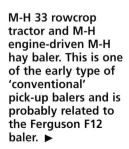

▲ MF 65 tractor and MF No. 10 baler baling alfalfa. The No. 10 was one of the early MF balers. This appears to be a slightly modified version of the Ferguson F12 and M-H No.3.

◄ MF No. 3 engine-driven baler – probably a derivative of the Ferguson F12 baler.

A Ferguson 'Tractor Mate' side-mounted baler, shown fitted to a Ferguson 40 tractor. This model is pto driven, but for the smaller Ferguson tractors an auxiliary engine was available. ▼

Baler development has progressed from the No. 1 to high capacity 'small' rectangular balers, large round balers and big square balers. Low density balers have also been offered.

Some Specifications of MF High-density Large Square Balers 1996

		MF 185	MF 190
hp requirement		90	135
Bale dimensions mm	width	800	1180
	height	875	1270
	length	up to 2500	up to 2800
pto speed rpm		1000	1000
Piston strokes/min		41	25
Piston stroke mm		710	780
Machine weight kg		5108	8440
Width mm		2729	3190
Working length mm		8532	8900

MF 825 tractor with MF low-density baler baling lucerne in France. Note the 'straight through' baler mechanism. Low- density balers had a phase of popularity as they allowed hay to be baled at a higher moisture content than is possible with high density balers. This also avoided much leaf loss in crops such as lucerne and clover, 1960s. ▶

◀ Baling irrigated green alfalfa for direct feeding to livestock in Saudi Arabia with Australian-made MF12 baler and U.K.-made MF Ferguson 35 four-cylinder diesel tractor, 1972.

▲ The North American MF 12 baler was classed as a medium output machine. It was operated at 80 plunger strokes per minute. Bale density was controlled by the pressure control on the tractor hydraulics. Note the pto bale thrower and drive on this baler, 1976.

▲ The North American-made MF 560 giant round baler required a minimum of 50 hp to drive it. Bales were 1.52 m long, had a diameter variable between 760 and 1830 mm and could weigh up to 681 kg. In good conditions a bale could be made and ejected in 3.75 minutes, 1976.

▲ The Spanish-made MF 124 and 126 balers are twine and wire tying models respectively. The pick-up width is 1420 mm, transport 2540 mm and the machine weighed 1400 kg, 1980.

▲ The MF 5 large square baler required a minimum of 90 hp and produced bales of 80 x 80 x 80-250 cm. It weighed 5010 kg, 1989.

◄ The MF 822 and 828 round baler 3 and 1.8 m diameter and 1.2 m width. They required a minimum of 50 and 55 hp and weighed 1680 kg and 1925 kg, 1989.

▲ **M-H 744 diesel tractor and M-H 701 baler in England, U.K. In the U.K. the 701s were available with Wisconsin or Armstrong Siddley diesel engines.**

The almost 8.5 tonne MF 180 big square baler is the largest of all MF's balers. ▶

▲ **The MF 146 is the largest of MF's 1996 round balers. Bales of up to almost 0.75 tonnes with a volume of 3.4 cu. m are possible.**

Some Specifications of MF Round Balers 1996

	MF 140	MF 142	MF 144	MF 146
Min. power requirement kW	22	34	37	37
pto rpm	540	540	540	540
Machine weight kg	1442	1551	4177	4177
Bale length mm	991	1194	1905	1905
Bale min. diameter mm	762	762	1270	1270
Bale max. diameter mm	1372	1295	1905	1905
Bale max. weight kg	249	454	748	748
Bale max. vol. cu. m	1.4	1.6	3.4	3.4

BALE HANDLING

In their basic form pick-up balers, making traditional small rectangular bales, simply drop them on the ground singly. They then had to be manhandled onto trailers. Several devices have been used over the years to cut out this hand labour. They have included bale throwers, bale loaders and bale chutes and also accessories for tractor loaders for lifting round bales.

▲ MF 44 tricycle tractor and 701 pick-up baler. The baler is fitted with a bale chute to raise the bales to the trailed wagon.

◄ M-F hay baler with loading chute. Note the baler is a left-hand model – or maybe a reversed photograph!

◄ ▲ **MF 512 bale loader. Shown in action and as the unhitched machine.**

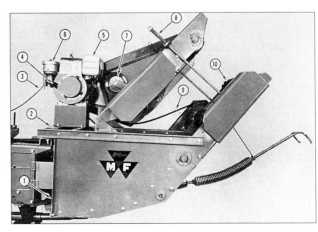

▲ **The MF 21 bale thrower powered by a Briggs and Stratton engine.**

▲ MF 165 tractor and No. 9 baler fitted with No. 6 bale thrower.

▲ An MF 14 medium density baler.

▲ The MF 22 bale thrower made in North America takes power from the pto unlike earlier types which used an auxiliary engine. The thrower could handle 34 kg twine-tied bales up to 900 mm long, 1976.

▲ M-H Sharp rake, 1895.

M-H Ithaca rake, 1895. ▼

TEDDERS, RAKES etc.

These machines are variously used to turn, scatter or collect the cut hay or green forage crop, or sometimes straw from cereal crops. They have evolved through the horse era to the sophisticated high output machines of today.

▲ M-H hay tedder. The forks could be adjusted to higher or lower positions whilst in motion and the outer forks would ted any hay run over by the wheels, 1897.

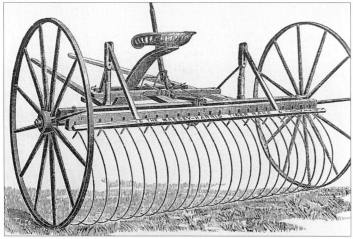

▲ M-H improved Tiger rake, 1895.

◄ Early type of M-H hay tedder, 1895.

▲ M-H horse-drawn rake working a heavy crop in eastern Canada.

▲ M-H 44 tractor with M-H No. 11 side rake.

▲ An M-H hay tedder made in U.K. by the Blackstone Co.

▲ MH No. 6 oil bath hay tedder. Note the cut out lettering on the seat. The machine had 15 settings.

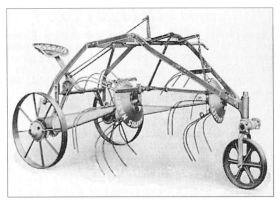

▲ **M-H Blackstone high frame combined swath turner, collector and side delivery rake, 1938.**

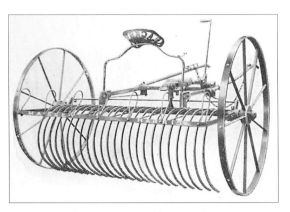

▲ **M-H Blackstone manual horse rake, 1938.**

▲ **M-H Blackstone forward action haymaker, 1938.**

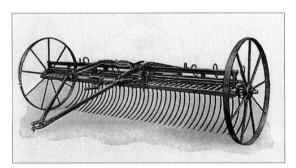

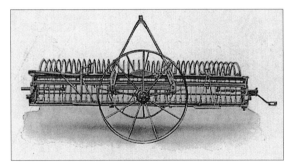

▲ **M-H Blackstone self-acting tractor rake shown in work and transport positions, 1938.**

◄ **M-H No. 517 side-delivery rakes at work in Australia, 1953.**

▲ The M-H Dickie swath turner and hay collector could handle two swaths from a 5ft mower. The turning heads were adjustable for transport and swath widths.

▲ The M-H Dickie side-delivery rake and swath turner had an overall width of 8 ft 7.75 in. and weighed 1334 lb.

▲ The M-H Dickie No. 716 tractor rake had 48 tines and a working width of 14 ft 2 in. The two end sections fold up for transport to reduce the width to 8 ft 4 in.

▲ MF front-mounted Windrow turner on an MF 65 diesel tractor, 1962.

◄ MF 50 tractor with MF 36 semi-mounted side rake.

▲ M-H 33 tractor with M-H No. 11 side rake.

Made in South Africa, the MF 19 mounted dump rake was originally designed for Ferguson tractors. It is 3.05 m wide and weighs 160 kg, 1976. ▶

Trailed and mounted versions of the French-made MF 85 gyro swather were available in 2.3 and 2.8 m widths. They could be operated at up to 14 km/hr, 1976. ▶

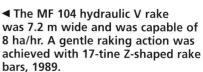

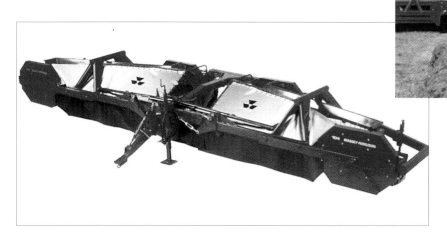

◄ The MF 104 hydraulic V rake was 7.2 m wide and was capable of 8 ha/hr. A gentle raking action was achieved with 17-tine Z-shaped rake bars, 1989.

◄ The MF 35/36/38/40 finger wheel rakes were of 3.65, 4.6, 5.5 and 7.6 m width with 7, 8, 9 and 10 rake wheels respectively. The MF 38 was mounted and the others trailed. Ten ha per hour was claimed to be possible with the large machine. Tractors of 30-35 hp were required, 1989.

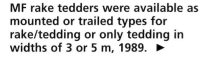

MF rake tedders were available as mounted or trailed types for rake/tedding or only tedding in widths of 3 or 5 m, 1989. ►

HAY LOADERS

Hay loaders were a big advance in the mechanisation of hay and green forage handling. They removed the need for hand labour to load cut material onto wagons. These machines were introduced at the turn of the century so have seen use in both horse and tractor drawn modes. Today they are not made and older ones are only rarely seen in use.

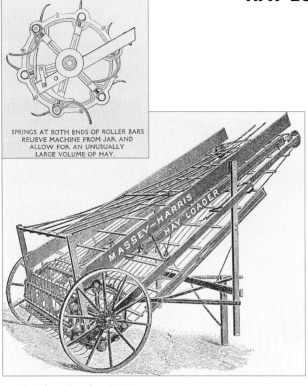

SPRINGS AT BOTH ENDS OF ROLLER BARS RELIEVE MACHINE FROM JAR AND ALLOW FOR AN UNUSUALLY LARGE VOLUME OF HAY.

▲ M-H hay loader, 1913.

▲ M-H No. 7 cylinder hayloader, 1944.

▲ M-H horse-drawn hay loader. Note the extension conveyor to deliver fodder across to the wagon.

▲ M-H tractor and M-H hay loader in a heavy crop.

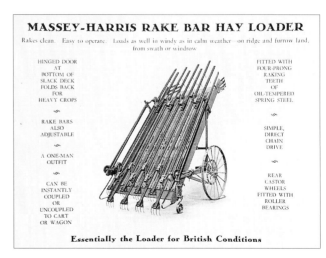

MASSEY-HARRIS RAKE BAR HAY LOADER

Rakes clean. Easy to operate. Loads as well in windy as in calm weather—on ridge and furrow land, from swath or windrow

HINGED DOOR AT BOTTOM OF SLACK DECK FOLDS BACK FOR HEAVY CROPS

RAKE BARS ALSO ADJUSTABLE

A ONE-MAN OUTFIT

CAN BE INSTANTLY COUPLED OR UNCOUPLED TO CART OR WAGON

FITTED WITH FOUR-PRONG RAKING TEETH OF OIL-TEMPERED SPRING STEEL

SIMPLE, DIRECT CHAIN DRIVE

REAR CASTOR WHEELS FITTED WITH ROLLER BEARINGS

Essentially the Loader for British Conditions

HAYPACKER

The M-F 48 Haypacker was heralded as a completely new way of harvesting, handling and feeding hay. It made hay wafers directly from dry hay in the field. The principle of the machine was the pick-up and flail chopping of dry hay which was then pressed through packing chambers by pressure rollers. In the chambers the hay is compressed by hydraulic pressure. Deflector plates allowed the adjustment of wafer length, but standard length was $2 \times 2 \times 2$ in. The machine had a water tank reservoir to enable controlled application of moisture to ensure good binding of the hay. The machine was powered by a 150 hp heavy duty Chrysler industrial gasoline engine. The machine weighed 4850 lb. Wafers were elevated into a following trailer and could then be handled mechanically into store or feeding places, or marketed long distances. Wafers weighed about 27 lb/cu. ft compared with 12–14 lb/cu. ft for baled hay and 3.5–5 lb/cu. ft for loose hay.

MF No. 48 haypacker powered by Chrysler engine. The machine picks up dry hay directly from swaths in the field, then chops and presses it into hay wafers. ▼

▲ Machine with trailed wagon.

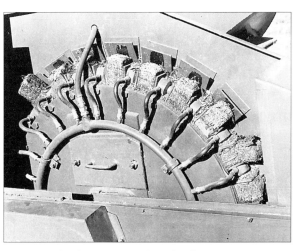

▲ Hydraulically controlled wafer-forming presses.

▲ The M-H 723 rear-mounted buck rake was virtually identical to that offered by Ferguson. It had a carrying capacity of 750 lb.

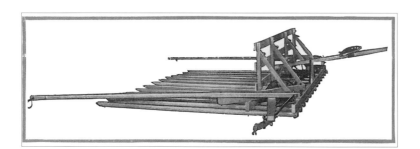

HAY STACKERS AND HAY SWEEPS, BUCKRAKES

M-H marketed both horse-push and tractor-push sweep rakes for collecting hay and straw of various crop types. These were fabricated mainly of high quality woods such as oak, hickory and firs. An advance on these were hay stackers for front mounting on tractors which could lift hay to over 20 ft (according to model) and so mechanised to a high degree the building of hay stacks. Both M-H and Ferguson made a rear-mounted buckrake for use on the three-point linkage. This type of machine was very popular for placing green material in silage pits.

◀ The M-H Grain King No. 85 extension arm overshot stacker was an extra-heavy-duty stacker which could lift hay to 20.5 ft.

◀ The M-H Grain King No. 16 4-wheel power lift sweep rake was of the horse push type.

M-H sky rake on an M-H No. 44 tractor. The loader is hydraulically operated. ▶

PEANUT HARVESTING

Trailed pto-driven and self-propelled Clipper Peanut Harvesters were made and modelled on the Clipper combine. The self-propelled model was similar in appearance to the first self-propelled M-H Corn Picker. Main features of these peanut harvesters were the spring tine pick-up for lifting pre-pulled and dried whole plants from the soil surface, and an eight-bar spring-tooth cylinder to comb the mass of stems and leaves and take it through the concave teeth in a steady flow. Both bagger and bulk machines were available.

Specialist peanut pickers, in effect mobile threshers powered by tractor pto, have also been marketed. These machines were taken into the field and hand labour used to feed previously dried peanut plants into the machine.

The South African-made peanut picker MF 149 was pto driven and designed to thresh sun-dried whole peanut plants to produce unshelled peanuts. Output was 600-800 kg/hr. The standard model was hand fed but it could be fitted with a self feeder kit, also a peanut haulm elevator. The unit required a 30 hp tractor, sometimes less, or could be fitted with an 8 hp auxiliary engine, 1976. ▶

▲ The MF 129 South African-made peanut sheller is a pto drive stationary thresher. It was capable of shelling 1800 kg/hr. Alternatively the unit could be powered by a 10 hp auxiliary engine.

◀ M-H Clipper peanut picker. This specially adapted clipper combine has a special pick-up to lift whole dried pre-lifted peanut plants on to the canvas elevator.

▲ M-H shaker potato digger. The shaker is agitated up and down by the lug wheel beneath the shaker.

POTATO HARVESTING

Simple modified horse ploughs marked the first mechanisation of potato harvesting. M-H went on to market both spinner and elevator diggers for the horse and tractor age as part of their line of potato production machinery. Some of these had auxiliary engines. Ferguson marketed a pto-drive mounted spinner-digger which was highly successful and was marketed well into the MF era. The Junior and King diggers preceded the No. 1 range of potato diggers.

Specifications of M-H 'Junior' and 'King' Potato Diggers

	Junior	King
Elevator ft	5	6
Wheel height in.	31	31
Wheel face in.	4	4
Width of apron in.	21	21
Equipment	2-horse hitch, auto truck, road rims special order	extension elevator or shaker, vine turner and kicker, auto truck; road rims and 4-horse hitch to special order

▲ M-H Junior potato digger, 1930.

▲ The Sunshine M-H power-drive potato digger was marketed in Australia. It had a 24 in. digging share and the wheels could be adjusted to accommodate rows of 27-36 in. width.

◀ M-H No. 1 potato digger. Horse drawn but with engine to power the elevator mechanisms, 1926.

▲ M-H No. 1 pto potato digger. This version is equipped with a three speed automotive transmission to facilitate different elevator speeds according to conditions and forward speed.

◀ M-H Blackstone No. 4 potato digger. This was made by the Blackstone Co. for M-H. Note the Blackstone seat and M-H badging, 1938.

Specifications of M-H No. 1 Potato Diggers

Size	Power source	Regular equipment	Special equipment
6 ft 22 in.	traction	extension elevator, short turn auto type forecarriage	vine turner and kicker, road rims, drum truck forecarriage, rolling coulters
7 ft 24 in.	traction	two-horse hitch 6 ft, four-horse hitch 7 ft	drive parts and motor to convert 7 ft 24 in. digger to engine power
7 ft 24 in.	engine	extension elevator, short turn auto type forecarriage and two-horse hitch	vine turner and kicker, drum truck forecarriage, rolling coulters, 6 or 8 hp Novo or 6 hp M-H engine
7 ft 24 in.	pto	extension elevator, 1.125 or 1.375 in. spline connection	vine turner and kicker, three-speed automotive type gear shift

After the merger, MF marketed a potato harvester—the 711—which had a good reputation for producing a clean, undamaged sample but had a low work rate. This appears to have been MF's first and only involvement in fully mechanised potato harvesting equipment. The harvester was available as a bagger or bulk delivery model. It required only a 35 hp tractor and was capable of 2–2.5 acres a day depending on the crop, with four sorters plus tractor drivers. The potatoes were lifted by a large disc onto a finger rotor and then delivered into the drum-cleaner elevator. Sorters received the potatoes and dirt on a revolving table and then picked the potatoes from the dirt.

▲ The MF 711 potato harvester shown in bulk delivery model form. Note how the sorters picked the potatoes from the dirt rather than vice versa. This ensured an exceptionally clean crop sample.

Specifications of the MF 711 Potato Harvester

	Bulk Delivery	Bagger
Drive	pto through reduction gear	
Tyre size	6.50 × 16	6.50 × 16
Wheel track in.	88.5	88.5
Width of headland required yds	6	6
Overall transport width in.	108	100
Overall height fully raised in.	112	77
Overall length in.	159	157
Max. elevator reach from side of harvester ft	4	
Max. elevator vertical clearance ft	6	
Weight cwt	27	24

▲ Soyabean harvesting, Ontario, Canada. This photo shows the difficulty for unmodified combines harvesting the crop.

SOYA BEAN HARVESTING

Soya beans are harvested by conventional combines with modified tables. The principal problem with soya is that some of the pods are borne very close to ground level and low cutting is required. The problem of low hanging pods can be particularly acute in low rainfall areas where plants can be quite dwarfed in some seasons. For a long time MF has marketed a selection of tables to suit different crop conditions, including pick-up tables for swathed crops.

◄ In the 1970s, Quick-Attach combine tables became a feature of MF combine design. Shown in the picture are three table types for North American MF 300, 510, 750 and 760 combines. They were available in various widths, 1976.

SUGAR BEET LIFTER AND TOPPER

Ferguson offered simple sugar beet lifters and toppers in the days before elevator digger type harvesting machines. They greatly reduced the amount of hand-work involved in hand harvesting the crop. The lifter was made in single and two-row forms.

▲ The Ferguson L-HE-21 beet topper, showing the front guide shoes, hoizontal topping knife and feeler wheel.

◄ The Ferguson IL-HE-20 single-row beet lifter could be used on a range of root crops with row widths of 16-28 in.

SUGAR CANE HARVESTING

MF played a key role in the mechanisation of sugar cane harvesting. Their initial development work took place in Australia where they linked with the Crichton Co., which they bought in 1966. This led to the production of a tractor-drawn harvester. By 1968 they were introducing their first self-propelled cane harvester to the market.

In the mid-1970s two self-propelled machines, the MF 102 and 201, were offered, which had a capacity of 15,000 t/yr and over.

▲ M-H prototype sugar cane harvester in Australia, c. 1959. The rig is pulled by a British-made M-H 745 four-cylinder diesel tractor.

Specifications of 102 and 201 Cane Harvesters

	102	201 Cane Commander
Engine	Perkins 6 cylinder A6. 372	Perkins V8
Max. hp	110	140
Transmission	hydrostatic	Dowmatic hydrostatic
Speeds, F and R km/hr	infinitely variable 0–19.2	infinitely variable 0–19.2
Topper height m	0.76–4.27 above cutters	0.76–4.27 above cutters
Weight kg	6350	8380
Basecutters	2 × contra rotating discs	2 × contra rotating discs
Choppers	4-blade contra rotating	4-blade contra rotating

▲ The MF 205 sugar cane harvester was powered by a Perkins V8-640 engine. The weight of the wheeled version was 9000 kg, and a tracked version was also available, 1980.

▲ The MF 65 R tractor was made in Brazil for operations in sugar cane fields. The loader is standard equipment and it has an instant reverse transmission. The engine is a 56.5 hp Perkins AD4.203, and the tractor weighs 2320 kg, 1980.

◄ MF 515 sugar cane harvesters pulled by MF 65 tractors (high clearance models). Note that the MF 35 tractor pulling the second trailer is an unusual high-clearance model. Queensland, Australia, c. 1963.

COTTON HARVESTING

The Rust Cotton Picker was, as far as can be ascertained, M-H's only venture into cotton picking machinery. Two models were made, namely the single-row model M and the two-row model MT. Both could be fitted on the 44, 44 special and 444 row-crop tractors; additionally the model M could be fitted to the 33 and 333 row-crop tractors. Both had a picker mounted on the front left side of the tractor and the model MT had a second unit on the rear right of the tractor.

▲ M-H 'Rust' Model M single-row cotton picker mounted on an M-H 44D special tractor. The machine was apparently made by Ben Pearson Inc. This probably marked M-H's first and only venture into this sector.

Some Specifications of the Rust Cotton Harvesters

Feature	Model M single unit for 33, 44 and 44 special tractors	Model MT tandem unit for 44 and 44 special tractors
Picking speed mph	3.3	3.3
Row width in.	36–42	36–42
Turning radius ft	9	9
Max. height wagon side for dumping ft	9	10
Basket capacity	155 cu. ft, 600–800 lb seed cotton	210 cu. ft, 1000–1200 lb seed cotton
Picking unit: No	1	2
No. of slats	80	160
No. picking fingers	1280	2560
Finger picking speed rpm	1275	1275
Length	18 ft	17 ft 10 in.
Width with basket	9 ft	8 ft 3 in.
Weight of picker lb	3625	6000

▲ **Ferguson kale cutrake made in the U.K. The machine is reversed into the standing green crop which is cut and collected on the rake, then carried to the livestock.**

KALE HARVESTING

On the U.K. market, Ferguson offered a Kale Cutrake. This essentially comprised a buckrake with cutter blade mounted on the end of the tines and driven by the pto. It had an 8 ft wide cut.

◀ **The Ferguson kale cutrake G-HE-20 shown with a load of cut kale.**

TOBACCO HARVESTING

◀ **M-H 744 diesel tractor in rare tricycle form working in the tobacco harvest in the Gold Coast, Africa.**

SWEET CORN HARVESTING

About 50 sweet corn harvesters were made in 1970. As can be seen from the photograph they were used for harvesting fresh cobs as a vegetable.

Some Specifications of the MF 540 Corn Harvester

Engine	Perkins A6.354 diesel, 6-cylinder
hp	110
Transmission	Three ranges with variable speed control
Ground speed mph	1.02 – 14.54
Tyres	23.1 × 26 front; 11 × 16 rear
Overall length with corn head ft/in.	26 × 11
Width ft/in.	11 × 9
Wheel base in.	138.5
Shipping weight without corn head lb	12,000
Rated capacity tons/hr	18
Corn heads	4 or 3-row (44-S or 43-S)
Hopper capacity tons	3

▲ An MF sweet corn harvester. Very few of these machines were made.

OIL PALM HARVESTING

A request by an oil palm estate in Malysia led to MF designing a tractor-based collection system for fruit bunches from oil palms. Based around an MF 240 tractor, the unit comprises a broad deflection frame and half tonne Quick-Attach baskets for the front-end loader and rear linkage. It was reported that an added advantage of the system over manual methods was that the noise of the tractor scared away the snakes!

◄ An MF 240 tractor fitted with half-tonne baskets for carrying oil palm fruit bunches, Malaysia, 1994.

BEAN HARVESTING

In South Africa MF offered a cowpea or bean lifter in the merger period. It could cut crops or weeds 1-3 in. below the surface. Normally it was used to cut two rows simultaneously. The double-sided sweep blade had a total width of 48 in. and the coulter was of 20 in. diameter.

◄ The South African-made cowpea or bean lifter weighed 194 lb and was widely used for hay or ensilage work.

CHAPTER THREE

Industrial Equipment

The original concept of industrial equipment by agricultural tractor manufacturers was the provision of basic agricultural tractors with perhaps some added weight, non-agricultural tyres, larger fenders and push/pull equipment. Such tractors were produced as far back as in the Wallis, Ferguson Brown and Ford Ferguson pedigrees which gave the main tractor lines to the MF history. The Ferguson hydraulic system enabled the early development of hydraulically operated loaders. These early pioneers did however realise the need for specialist industrial implement lines to be developed and all offered implements that were additional to the normal agricultural ones.

At the end of the Massey-Harris tractor line in the Massey-Harris-Ferguson period, the 'Work Bull' tractors were launched, based on the 333/444/555 style tractors. These were advertised as being able to 'handle scores of jobs reserved for expensive, single purpose machines' and 'cut costs on work and run jobs … digs, lifts, loads, cleans up around construction sites, factories, roads and streets'. Thus was shown increasing recognition of the ability of tractors to play off-farm roles. The Work Bull 202 was also available and based on the Ferguson TO 35 tractor.

The M-H Wallis 20-30 "Certified" Industrial tractor. 1929. ▼

M-H-F's first significant entry into the industrial market, with purpose built, heavy duty loaders and backhoes, was when they acquired Midwestern Industries in 1957. They made Davis loading and digger equipment, which was then offered by M-H-F and subsequently Massey Ferguson for fitting to tractors of the day such as the M-H 50, MF 35 and 65 type tractors. It is noted that the MF 65 tractor was offered as the 65R and 65S industrial models. The 65R had a torque converter and shuttle transmission.

Besides recognising the growing need to clearly define industrial equipment, another MF marketing ploy was to define a group of industrial machines as being 'Snow Moving Equipment'; these were in fact unmodified industrials offered with various dozer and loading attachments.

In 1966 MF made a policy decision to establish a separate Industrial and Construction Machinery Division. However, even before this MF was offering a sizeable range of industrial equipment. In the following years this policy evolved into the establishment of manufacturing plants in Italy, the U.S.A. and the U.K., and the takeover of Hanomag in Germany. The latter was sold after only five years. By 1983 production had been rationalised and the U.K. operation became the main centre.

In 1992 the MF industrial division was sold off to FERMEC but the use of the MF name and livery on its products continued into early 1997, notwithstanding the takeover of FERMEC by CASE in late 1996. The U.K. factory at Trafford Park in Manchester was by then the only plant making 'MF' industrials; significantly it was originally a Massey-Harris plant.

However, later in 1997 the MF badge was dropped.

INDUSTRIAL MODELS OF THE WALLIS DESIGN TRACTORS

Industrial models of the Model 12 and 25 tractors were sold in limited numbers. There was also an industrial version of the Wallis 20–30 tractor.

▲ **Wallis 12-20 industrial tractor. Spoke wheels were also available,1928.**

Specifications of the M-H Wallis 12-20 Industrial Tractor Differing from those of the Standard 12-20

Front axle	special extra heavy industrial axle
Wheels and solid tyres in.	spoke type wheels with tyres: rear 40 × 10,490 lb;
	front 29 × 5,160 lb solid cast wheels with tyres: rear 40 × 5,480 lb; front 29 × 5,190 lb
Wheelbase in.	73
Tread in.	spoke wheels 44.5 front; 47 rear solid wheels 44.5 front; 45 rear
Turning radius ft	10 outside
Height/length overall in.	50.5/107.5
Power	12 hp at drawbar
Forward road speeds mph	2.33, 4.5 and 10
Accelerator	foot operated
Brakes	hand emergency brake, foot brake for rear wheels (differential type)
Platform	special with sides next to wheels
Seat	adjustable spring cushion with side arms and adjustable back
Extra equipment	extension wheels to make dual equipment 840 lb each wheel weights for solid cast wheels: 1 set of 6 × 100 lb each or 1 set of 12 × 100 lb each wheel weights for spoke wheels: 1 set of 2 × 250 lb or 1 set 2 × 500 lb or 1 set 2 × 250 lb + 2 × 500 lb or 1 set 4 × 500 lb
Extra equipment	gas or electric lighting equipment, belt pulley, radiator screen, swinging drawbar, axle sleeves with groove for mounting cranes, derricks, winches etc.

◄ **M-H Model 25 industrial tractor, 1936.**

Industrial 25 Specifications

Low pressure tyres:	12.75 × 28 rear	
	7.50 × 18 front	
Solid cast wheels and rubber tyres		Weight 5876 lb
	42 × 9 rear	
	30 × 5 front	
As above with dual rear wheels		Weight 8123 lb
Speeds mph:	Forward	2.5, 4, 7, or 10
	Reverse	2.5
Wheel weights		one 300 lb per rear wheel possible

An industrial version of the Pacemaker tractor was made but details of it are scarce. Two distinguishing features are reported to be a foot throttle and a seat with backrest.

INDUSTRIAL GENERAL PURPOSE TRACTOR

An industrial model of the M-H General Purpose tractor was available with forward speeds of 2.75, 4.25 and 9

▲ **Industrial general purpose 4 WD tractor with snow plough and cab.**

mph, reverse speed of 3.25 mph and in widths of 50 to 60 in. They had cast centre wheels and pneumatic or solid rubber tyres, and an outside turning radius of 10 ft. The tractor weighed 4000–7000 lb depending upon weight of wheels and tyre equipment. It was reputed to give 4 lb of drawbar pull for each 1 lb of total tractor weight. Special industrial attachments for the tractor were a rear-mounted crane, 18 ft telescopic boom, rear- or front-mounted sweeper, rear-mounted 5000 lb pull winch with 700 ft of 0.5 in. cable and two snow ploughs. Special wide, smooth, steel airport wheels were also available to create what was designated the 'Aviation model'. Lights, starter, front and rear bumpers, cab, vertical adjustment hitch and automatic coupler were available to special order.

Specifications of Snow Plows and Sweepers for General Purpose Tractors

Large plow		Small plow		Sweeper	
Height at front of V in.	31	Height of plow in.	24	Two-way brush	Angles to either side
Width at top of plow ft	8	Length of plow ft	8		
Width of cutting edge of plow ft	7	Cutting width of plow in.	78	Sweeping width in.	66 cut
		Thickness of moldboard in.	0.25	Rotating speed rpm	125
Height at rear of V in.	43	Shipping weight lb	1500	Weight lb	800
Height overall ft★	5				
Thickness of moldboard in.	0.375				
Shipping weight lb	1400				

★lifting gear

WARTIME AND POST-WAR MASSEY-HARRIS INDUSTRIALS

80 and 81 Tractors

During wartime the M-H 80 and 81 tractors came closest to being an industrial tractor. These were extensively offered with shunting equipment for use on airfields. These were a lightweight tractor which were to evolve into the

M-H 20 and 22 tractors at the end of the war. Photographs show them with considerable rear-wheel weighting and often with front pushing gear.

'I' Designation Tractors

Serial number records show that in the period 1953–1957 a few 'I' designation tractors were produced. These were the I 162, I 330G, I 244 and FSI 244, which were apparently made for military applications.

◀ M-H Model 81 'industrialized' tractors shown in their wartime role.

▲ An unknown M-H tractor! It is possibly an Industrial (I) version of a 44 tractor.

▲ An I 162 tractor made for the U.S army.

Work Bull Tractors

M-H-F Work Bulls were M-H tractors made in the period 1956–1958 and styled like the 333/444/555 tractors or MHF 35 and 65 based tractors.

The M-H tractors were designated the 303 and 404 of 42 and 52 belt hp respectively. Power steering was optional on both models. They were offered with loaders and backhoes. The early loader was designated the 500 and the

◀ The M-H-F Work Bull tractor of 42 belt hp.

early backhoe was the Davis 185. Subsequently, Davis 101 and 102 loaders were offered.

The MF Work Bull based on the TO 35 tractor was designated the MHF 202 Work Bull. The first of these were produced with a normal TO 35 bonnet, but these were restyled in the MF era to become the MF 202 Work Bull with heavy duty front grille and restyled bonnet.

Some Specifications of M-H Work Bull 303 and 404 Tractors

▲ An M-H-F 404
Work Bull tractor of
52 hp.

	303	404
Belt hp	42	52
Drawbar hp	40.5	46
Engine: gasoline model	208 cu. in. 1500 rpm	277 cu. in. 1500 rpm
Wheelbase in.	85.5	85.5
Weight gasoline/diesel lb	5260/5410	5420/5560
Gears	5F + 1R	5F + 1R
Tyres, front: standard/optional	7.50 × 18/7.50 × 15	7.50 × 15/ 7.50 × 18
Tyres, rear: standard/optional	13.00 × 18/13.00 × 24	14.00 × 24/14.00 × 30
Attachments available	front-end loader 0.75 cu. yd capacity, backhoe with 12–36 in. buckets, fork lift, front-end sweeper, front-end 1500 lb capacity crane, angle dozer, scarifier, pintle hook kit, swinging drawbar kit, radiator shutters, all weather steel cabs, snow plows	

An M-H-F 202 Work
Bull tractor of 34 hp.
▼

▲ An M-H-F 202 Work Bull tractor fitted with approved rotary trencher. This could trench u[ ] deep and be fitted with 12 or 18" buckets. W[ ] travel speeds of 1.5–5mph were possible.

Some Specifications of the MHF 202 Work Bull (TO 35 style)

Engine hp	34 belt
Weight lb	2900
Front tyres: standard/optional	6.00 × 16/6.50 × 16
Rear tyres: standard/optional	11 × 28/13 × 24
Wheelbase in.	72
Front axle	modified and strengthened
Power steering	standard
Extra equipment	lighting, belt pulley, wheel weights, dual rear wheel kit, vertical muffler, swinging drawbar and clevis

A Pit Bull industrial tractor complemented the basic Work Bull range and was designed as a single purpose machine. This was a rear control tractor adaption with torque converter. It had five forward and five reverse speeds. It also had hydraulic turning and parking brakes with optional power steering. Standard equipment was a loader shovel of Davis design. The shovel could be removed and the hydraulic arms utilised for a dozer blade, a Davis broom (rotary brush), a Pit Bull backhoe, a Pit Bull 2000 lb capacity fork lift and a loader scarifier.

▲ **The Pit Bull loader was made by Midwestern Industries Inc. and available only through M-H-F sales outlets. It appears to be based on an M-H design tractor and had hydraulic reversing clutches which permitted direction changes without stops to change gears.**

FERGUSON INDUSTRIALS

The first Ferguson industrial was a Ferguson Brown tractor of which only a few were produced. Details on these are scarce but they apparently had larger rear wheels and front wheels of pressed steel. Surviving examples in South Africa have an offset steering wheel, but it is not clear whether this feature is factory original or otherwise. The next Ferguson industrials were modified Ford Ferguson tractors. These were offered with various types of loading equipment which utilised the tractor's hydraulic equipment.

▲ A Ferguson Brown industrial with offset steering. The transport box is definitely not original. In South Africa it is considered as an 'Air Force' type.

▲ Ford Ferguson 'all purpose' tractor.

▲ The Ford Ferguson 'Moto-Tug' marked the start of Ferguson's development of industrial tractors. It was available as a 5640 lb or 3720 lb tractor, the heavier one being fitted with dual rear wheels.

▲ Bulldozer and road grader attachments on a Ford Ferguson tractor. Other industrial equipment included front angle dozer, snow ploughs and front blades.

▲ Ford Ferguson tractor with Baldwin loader (Ferguson approved accessory).

▲ The TE 20 basic industrial tractor was the least modified of the normal agricultural tractors.

Ferguson tractors made in the U.K. were offered in three models: basic, semi and full industrial. They were available with petrol, tvo, lamp oil or diesel engines. An 'Industrial–Council Type' was also offered. This was a slightly modified full industrial to allow a lighting rearrangement at the front to accommodate a front-end loader. One single headlight was placed centrally on top of the bonnet and the other in the right-hand side of the grille. All industrials had dual hydraulic and mechanical rear brakes, and a hand brake. The MHF 202 Work Bull was of course really a 'Ferguson' industrial and has been noted earlier.

▲ Ferguson TEF (diesel) semi-industrial tractor.

▲ British-made full industrial TE-20 Ferguson tractor.

◄ A 'Council type' TE 20 industrial. Note the extra headlight positioned in the grill.

Some Specifications of the Ferguson TE Industrial Tractors

	Full Industrial	Semi Industrial	Basic Industrial
Models	TE-P20, TE-R20, TE-S20, TE-T20	TE-P20-T, TE-R20-T, TE-S20-T, TE-T20-T	TEP-ZD, TET-ZD, TEP-ZE, TET-ZE
Features	front bumper full front fenders full rear fenders side cover for rear fenders footboards headlamps side lamps rear floodlight (optional) tipping seat radiator grill guard 6.00 × 16 in. front tyres Industrial-tread rear tyres horn	agricultural tractor fitted with dual brakes, industrial tyres, front bumper and radiator grille guard identical to those fitted on the full industrial	ZD tractors had agricultural rear fenders and ZE types were without rear fenders. They all had dual brakes, horn and mirror. The basic industrial was offered with accessories of bumper, grille guard, stepboards, front and rear cutaway industrial fenders.
Weight lb	3070–3320		3030–3280

◄ The U.S.A-made Ferguson TO 20 '85' special industrial tractor.

Ferguson utility loader (Davis design) on Ferguson TO tractor, c. 1956. ►

▲ This photograph of a TE 20 Ferguson tractor powering a small trailed excavator was found in the MF archives in the UK. It may represent evaluation work of an excavator for listing as Ferguson approved equipment – but no records have been found of this.

INDUSTRIALS OF THE MASSEY FERGUSON ERA

The present day concept of industrial tractors being heavy duty diggers and loaders really started in the M-H and Ferguson merger period, when Davis loaders and backhoes were first adopted for tractors of that era. Initially, they were fitted to M-H Work Bulls, MF 50, Ferguson TO-40 and TO-35 tractors. Beside the backhoes and shovels, other implements were offered for the range, including fork lifts, grader blades (Ferguson type), reel mowers, heavy-duty rotary mowers, pipe and cable layers (Ferguson type), post-hole borers (Ferguson type), rotary trenchers, brooms or sweepers, angle-dozers and ditchers.

An M-H 444 tractor with Davis 102/202 loader. The two loaders were identical except that for the 102 the hydraulic pump was front-mounted whereas on the 202 it was rear-mounted. ▼

▲ Wills ditcher (Ferguson approved accessory) on TO tractor.

This heavy-duty Davis equipment was firstly fitted to little modified agricultural tractors. However, the age of the yellow livery MF industrials was born after MF acquired Davis and fitted the Davis equipment to yellow MF industrial tractors of the 35 and 65 types. One early type was based on the MF 35 tractor in the UK. This was the 702 tractor with 702 power shovel and 710 digger—the tractor being strengthened to take the loader and shovel. This was a design allied to the MF 202 Work Bull produced in North America and based on the TO 35 tractor. It was an acclaimed advance in industrial machinery design, being the first of its kind to be able to dig flush alongside buildings, fences and other obstructions. In the U.K. the MF 35 tractors were also offered in a more basic industrial

▲ (Top) Davis utility loader of 7 cu. ft. 1000-1500 lb lift seen fitted to an MF 50 tractor. (Bottom) Davis 101 and 201 loaders. 1000-2000 lb capacity, single or double action rams. Seen fitted to a TO 35 tractor, 1975.

▲ MF 202 Work Bulls coming off the Detroit factory line, 1958.

form and given fenders and guards etc., more or less the same as had been offered for the Ferguson industrials.

Initially backhoes had a central pivot point, but this was soon superseded by a pivot point which could be moved from one side of the tractor to the other and be operated from any position along this line. This was a feature of the 702 tractor loader and 710 digger. The digger, when set to the side, had an operational arc of 200 degrees.

▲ A U.K-made M-H-F FE 35 industrial tractor.

▲ Rear of an M-H-F FE 35 industrial tractor showing industrial-type fenders.

◄ MF 35 tractor fitted with Shawnee loader and bucket, loading coke at Corby, Northamptonshire, U.K. 1958.

Some Specifications of the MF 702 Tractor Loader with 710 Digger and 702 Power Shovel

702 Tractor:

Engine bhp	Standard 23C. 37.4
Tractor weight lb	3785

702 Power Shovel:

Lift capacity lb	2000
Lift height to top of bucket in.	140.5
Lift height to bucket underside in.	116
Dump height with bucket tipped in.	102
Standard material bucket capacity cu. ft	11

710 Digger:

Digging depth ft	12
Back reach from tractor axle in.	209
Dumping height (underside of bucket) in.	122
Dumping height (bucket folded back) ft	8
Side reach (central) in.	164
Side reach (side) in.	200
Bucket sizes: Utility in.	36
Trench in.	12, 16, 20, 24
Clay in.	12, 16, 20, 24
Shovel in.	24
Machine weight lb	2548

During the MF 35 era in the U.K., MF offered a range of 'Specialised' equipment for use with its 35 and 65 agricultural or industrial tractors in the industrial and amenity services environment. These comprised implements from the existing agricultural range and equipment of other manufacturers which was promoted in MF literature. One brochure lists 14 MF catalogued products and 14 products of other manufacturers.

(Above and right) Examples of MF 'specialised equipment' for industrial purposes. Atkinson road gritter (top), MF 16 trailed dumper (centre), verge trimmer (bottom). ▶

MF 'Specialised' Equipment for Industrial-style Versions of MF 35 and 65 Tractors in the U.K.

MF Catalogue equipment	Equipment of other makers
MF 736 mid-mounted mower	Twose Tractamount roller
MF 727 subsoiler/cable layer	Sturiluxe road brush—front mounted
MF 72 compressor	refuse collector (two-wheel refuse cart)
MF 723 post-hole borer	Boughton winch
MF 737 fork lift	Pattison Parkover gang mower—2 side + 1 rear
MF 17 3-ton trailer	Scrapette scraper—trailed
MF 735 loader	Ibbett Eezion trailer—single-axle low loader
MF 727 subsoiler	Bunger trailer—four wheel
MF 704 winch	Beresford Watermaster pump
MF 16 trailed dumper	Hargreaves Sisis turf piercer
MF 706 earth scoop	Small Electric Motors welding generator
MF 721 multi-purpose blade	Atkinson road gritter
MF 65 rotary cutter	Bomford and Evershed blade—front mounted
MF dump skip	Twose Somerset verge trimmer

▲ **MF 205 industrial tractor with MF 702 loader shovel, 1965.**

In the U.K. the 702 tractor was superseded by the 203 and 205 tractors. The 205 was fitted with a torque convertor and instant reverse which substantially improved output over that obtained from conventional gearboxes.

The instant reverse transmission was built by the Funk Manufacturing Company. A major feature was the use of footpedals for forward and reverse directional changes. It was ideal for loader work as it left the operator's hands free for steering and loader operation. MF were one of the first to introduce a hydraulic shuttle for light industrial equipment.

An early, purpose-built, heavy industrial loader shovel was the MF 356 which was available with gasoline or diesel engines and rated at around 65 hp. This was followed by the MF 470 loader shovel. Each had several bucket size options and a fork-lift attachment was available for the 470.

◄ **MF 205 tractor with loader and backhoe in action, U.K. 1961.**

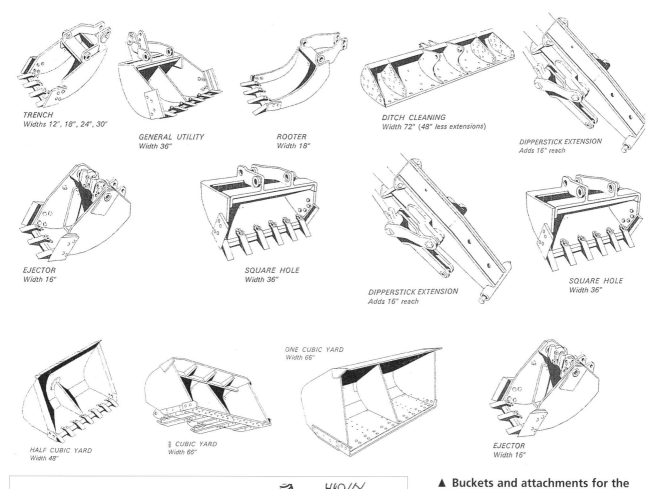

TRENCH
Widths 12", 18", 24", 30"

GENERAL UTILITY
Width 36"

ROOTER
Width 18"

DITCH CLEANING
Width 72" (48" less extensions)

DIPPERSTICK EXTENSION
Adds 16" reach

EJECTOR
Width 16"

SQUARE HOLE
Width 36"

DIPPERSTICK EXTENSION
Adds 16" reach

SQUARE HOLE
Width 36"

ONE CUBIC YARD
Width 66"

HALF CUBIC YARD
Width 48"

¾ CUBIC YARD
Width 66"

EJECTOR
Width 16"

▲ **Buckets and attachments for the MF 220 digger-loader.**

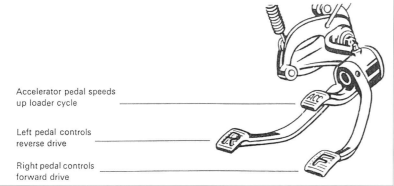

Accelerator pedal speeds up loader cycle

Left pedal controls reverse drive

Right pedal controls forward drive

◄ **The instant reverse pedal on an MF 205 tractor.**

▲ **MF 356 shovel-loader with instant reverse and torque converter. 7000 lb lift capacity.**

▲ **MF 356 shovel loader – front view.**

Brief Specifications of the MF 356 and 470 Loader Shovels 1966

	MF 356	MF 470
Gasoline engine hp bare engine	67.7	66.5
Diesel engine hp bare engine	65.5	71
Max. lift capacity with counterweight lb	7000	7550
Digging force lb	7050	6800
Digging depth below grade in.	1.5	4
Traction	2WD	4WD

In the U.K. the MF 20, 30, 40 and 50 industrial tractors were the second generation of industrials. Two derivatives of the 100 series agricultural tractor range were the 2135 and 2165 Turf Special tractors. These were frequently listed in industrial equipment catalogues before the concept of specialised garden and landscape tractors came about.

The MF 50 C tractor loader produced in North America and of 62 pto hp, 1977. ▶

◀ **MF 20 industrial
multi-power tractor.
It is fitted with a
fibre glass cab – the
first ever type of MF
fitted cab in the U.K.**

Specifications of MF 30 and 50 Industrial Tractors on the U.K Market

	MF 30	MF 50
Weight less cab lb	4400	4700
Wheelbase in.	82	81.75
Engine hp	Perkins A4.212	Perkins A4.212
Cylinders	4	4
BHP at governed speed rpm	60 at 2000	60 at 2000
Transmission	dual clutch Auburn ventilated type	dual clutch Laycock Spicer type
Gears	dual range 4F + R in each range	dual range 3F + R in each range
Instant reverse transmission	no	yes, optional, 4F + 4R
Torque converter	no	yes
Multipower transmission	yes, optional	no
Speeds at 2000 rpm mph	forward 1.26–13.89	forward 1.06–11.39 (std); 1.49–15.45 (instant reverse)
Hydraulic system max. load lb/sq. in.	3000 (tractor pump) 2,925 (auxiliary pump)	3550 (linkage operating pump)
Hydraulic flow output Imperial gals/min.	3.1 (tractor pump) 6.3 (auxiliary pump)	3.1

In North America in the mid-1960s, early industrial versions of the 100 agricultural tractor series were the 2135, 3165, 202, 204, 302 and 304 tractors. By adding loaders and backhoes to these, fifteen backhoe/loader machines were made available to the North American market.

A range of fork lifts was also offered in North America in the mid-1960s in the 202–204 series and the 356 series. Different rigs were available to handle lumber, bricks, cement blocks, building materials, sewer pipes, mortar, parts bins, poles and logs, charging hoppers and yard maintenance.

▲ MF 200 industrial tractor with crane attachment and backhoe.

▲ An MF 3305 industrial tractor with 250 loader working at Ryton in the U.K, 1967.

▲ MF 2135 tractor with mid-mounted mower, 1964.

▲ An example of an early North American-made MF industrial tractor spotted in a collective farm machinery (grave)yard in South Yemen. The backhoe had only a centre position. Possibly an MF 320 or 325.

▲ An MF 204 fork lift, 1965.

▲ **The 1965 range of MF fork lifts and rigs offered in North America.**

Brief Specifications of the 202–204 and 356 Fork Lifts 1966

	MF 202-204	MF 356
Engine hp	gasoline 42 bare engine	gasoline 67.7 bare engine
		diesel 65.5 bare engine
Weight lb	204: 8430	
	202: 8380	
Transmission	204: torque converter	instant reverse
	202: standard or manual shuttle	
Power steering	standard	standard
Differential lock	no	standard
Mast capacities	4000/10.5	6000/12
lb lift/ft height	4000/14	8000/14
	4000/21.5	4000/21.5
	5000/10	2500/31.5
	5000/12	
	5000/14	

MF 2135 TRACTOR
42 hp Gas—43.5 hp Diesel
Standard Transmission
6 Speeds Forward, 2 Reverse
Single or Dual Clutch
Manual or Power Steering

MF 202/3 TRACTOR
42 hp Gas—43.5 hp Diesel
Dual Range (or)
Manual Shuttle Transmission
6 Speeds Forward, 6 Reverse
Power Steering

MF 204/5 TRACTOR
42 hp Gas—43.5 hp Diesel
Torque Converter with
Instant Reverse Transmission
4 Speeds Forward, 4 Reverse
Power Steering

MF 3165 TRACTOR
57.2 hp Gas—60.5 hp Diesel
Standard Transmission (or)
Manual Shuttle Transmission
6 Speeds Forward, 6 Reverse
Power Steering

MF 302 TRACTOR
67.7 hp Gas—65.5 hp Diesel
Manual Shuttle Transmission
6 Speeds Forward, 6 Reverse
Hydrostatic Power Steering
Hydraulic Double Disc Brakes

MF 304 TRACTOR
67.7 hp Gas—65.5 hp Diesel
Torque Converter with
Instant Reverse Transmission
4 Speeds Forward, 4 Reverse
Hydrostatic Power Steering

MF 100 LOADER
Lifting Capacity—2,700 lbs.
Carrying Cap. at 3′—3,400 lbs.
Breakaway Force—4,300 lbs.
Max. Lift Height—10 ft.

MF 185 BACKHOE
Maximum Digging Depth—11½ ft.
Loading Height—8′-6″
Reaches Out to 17′-0″
Exerts Digging Force of 7,250 lbs.
Operates on a 180° swing arc.

MF 200 LOADER
Lifting Capacity—3,300 lbs.
Carrying Cap. at 3′—4,200 lbs.
Breakaway Force—5,300 lbs.
Max. Lift Height—10 ft.

MF 220 BACKHOE
Maximum Digging Depth—12 ft.
Loading Height—8′-6″
Reaches Out to 17′-5″
Exerts Digging Force of 8,500 lbs.
Operates on a continuous 200° arc.

MF 300 LOADER
Lifting Capacity—4,070 lbs.
Carrying Cap. at 3′—6,325 lbs.
Breakaway Force—7,340 lbs.
Max. Lift Height—11½ ft.

MF 320 BACKHOE
Maximum Digging Depth—14′-9″
Loading Height—11′-7″
Reaches Out to 19′-0″
Exerts Digging Force of 9,850 lbs.
Operates on a 200° swing arc.

1
MF 2135 TRACTOR
MF 100 LOADER
MF 185 BACKHOE
• 42 hp Gas—43.5 hp Diesel
• Loading Cap.—2,700 lbs.
• Digging Depth—11½ ft.

2
MF 202/3 TRACTOR
MF 100 LOADER
MF 185 BACKHOE
• 42 hp Gas—43.5 hp Diesel
• Loading Cap.—2,700 lbs.
• Digging Depth—11½ ft.

3
MF 2135 TRACTOR
MF 200 LOADER
MF 185 BACKHOE
• 42 hp Gas—43.5 hp Diesel
• Loading Cap.—3,300 lbs.
• Digging Depth—11½ ft.

4
MF 202/3 TRACTOR
MF 200 LOADER
MF 185 BACKHOE
• 42 hp Gas—43.5 hp Diesel
• Loading Cap.—3,300 lbs.
• Digging Depth—11½ ft.

5
MF 2135 TRACTOR
MF 200 LOADER
MF 220 BACKHOE
• 42 hp Gas—43.5 hp Diesel
• Loading Cap.—3,300 lbs.
• Digging Depth—12 ft.

6
MF 202/3 TRACTOR
MF 200 LOADER
MF 220 BACKHOE
• 42 hp Gas—43.5 hp Diesel
• Loading Cap.—3,300 lbs.
• Digging Depth—12 ft.

7
MF 204/5 TRACTOR
MF 100 LOADER
MF 185 BACKHOE
• 42 hp Gas—43.5 hp Diesel
• Loading Cap.—2,700 lbs.
• Digging Depth—11½ ft.

8
MF 3165 TRACTOR
MF 100 LOADER
MF 185 BACKHOE
• 57.2 hp Gas—60.5 hp Diesel
• Loading Cap.—2,700 lbs.
• Digging Depth—11½ ft.

9
MF 3165 TRACTOR
MF 100 LOADER
MF 220 BACKHOE
• 57.2 hp Gas—60.5 hp Diesel
• Loading Cap.—2,700 lbs.
• Digging Depth—12 ft.

10
MF 204/5 TRACTOR
MF 200 LOADER
MF 185 BACKHOE
• 42 hp Gas—43.5 hp Diesel
• Loading Cap.—3,300 lbs.
• Digging Depth—11½ ft.

11
MF 3165 TRACTOR
MF 200 LOADER
MF 185 BACKHOE
• 57.2 hp Gas—60.5 hp Diesel
• Loading Cap.—3,300 lbs.
• Digging Depth—11½ ft.

12
MF 204/5 TRACTOR
MF 200 LOADER
MF 220 BACKHOE
• 42 hp Gas—43.5 hp Diesel
• Loading Cap.—3,300 lbs.
• Digging Depth—12 ft.

13
MF 3165 TRACTOR
MF 200 LOADER
MF 220 BACKHOE
• 57.2 hp Gas—60.5 hp Diesel
• Loading Cap.—3,300 lbs.
• Digging Depth—12 ft.

14
MF 302 TRACTOR
MF 300 LOADER
MF 320 BACKHOE
• 67.7 hp Gas—65.5 hp Diesel
• Loading Cap.—4,070 lbs.
• Digging Depth—14′-9″

15
MF 304 TRACTOR
MF 300 LOADER
MF 320 BACKHOE
• 67.7 hp Gas—65.5 hp Diesel
• Loading Cap.—4,070 lbs.
• Digging Depth—14′-9″

NOTE: Backhoe-Loader Specifications Calculated to I.E.M.C. Standards.   Horsepower ratings are bare engine without accessories.

▲ **The 1965 MF range of tractors, backhoes and loaders offered in North America.**

From these beginnings came the rapid growth in industrial machines for which the power units became ever more heavy duty and ultimately different from their agricultural counterparts. This was due to the need for heavier duty hydraulics than are required in agriculture, a stronger structure upon which to mount digger and loader units and the different requirements of the construction industry. There also came a requirement for heavy tracked loader and excavation machinery for the construction industry.

◄ A 1970 line-up of industrial and construction machinery, photographed in the U.K.

◄ Display of industrial and construction machines at the opening of the Akron Ohio plant. (Akron Sunday Beacon Journal magazine, April 21, 1968).

Tractors Loaders Backhoes 42hp to 100hp	MF20	MF30	MF40	MF50	MF70	MF80		
Forklifts 42hp to 61hp	MF40	MF2500	MF4500	MF6500	Industrial Wheel Loaders 30hp to 74hp	MF711	MF911	MF11
Wheel Loaders 62hp to 286hp	MF22	MF33	MF44	MF55	MF66	MF77	MF88	
Crawler Loaders 42hp to 180hp	MF200	MF300	MF400	MF500	MF600	MF700	Log Skidders 80hp	MF220
Crawler Dozers 42hp to 180hp	MF200	MF300	MF400	MF500	MF600	MF700	Rubber Tired Dozers 230hp	MF66
Hydraulic Excavators 54hp to 106hp	MF250	MF450	MF450	MF550	Compactors 113hp to 230hp	MF44	MF55	MF66

◄ Industrial equipment line as shown in the 1974 MF annual report.

▲ MF 3366 bulldozer as sold in the U.K. and fitted with three rear-mounted ripper blades.

▲ MF 600 C crawler dozer of Hanomag design, 1975-76.

MF 3366 industrial crawler shovel. In front of St. Apollinare in Classe Church, Ravenna, Italy, 1965. ▶

One of the earliest and more unusual examples of heavy construction equipment that was to be generated by MF's 1966 decision to specialise in this business was the MF 350 Truck Mounted Hydraulic Excavator. Unfortunately no details of this machine have been traced other than that it was based on the 350 hydraulic crawler excavator. By 1974 MF were offering a wide range of heavy industrial equipment.

▲ MF 350 truck-mounted hydraulic excavator, 1967.

▲ MF 450 hydraulic excavator.

▲ MF 450 excavator fitted with hydraulic grab loading scrap, U.K.

▲ MF 55 industrial loader tractor in action at Kendal, U.K. 1969.

Ever increasing mechanisation on farms caused the industrial sector to turn back to agriculture and provide equipment for materials handling in agriculture in the form of skid steer loaders, rough terrain loaders and fork lifts etc. Articulated steering became incorporated on some industrial machines.

An important acquisition during the course of the development of industrial and construction machines was the German Hanomag Co. in 1974. This gave MF a rubber-tyred dozer, a small-wheeled dozer and three large compactors. However, Hanomag was disposed of in 1979.

The range of industrial products offered reached its peak in the late 1970s and by the early 1980s the range had been trimmed considerably and came to include compact tractors. MF eventually sold off its industrial division to FERMEC but the products retained MF badging and the yellow livery.

▲ MF 11 wheel loader fitted with torque convertor and instant reverse. The standard bucket has a capacity of 1.33 cu. yd.

▲ A 1977 MF 300 crawler dozer which had a shipping weight of up to 18,250 lb depending on equipment.

▲ The North American-made 711 B skid steel loader had a 30 hp gasoline engine. It had a 1250 lb operating capacity and 2100 lb lift capacity to full height. Utility, dirt, fertiliser and snow buckets were available, 1976.

▲ An MF 6500 fork lift. This was available with manual or instant reverse transmission, diesel or gasoline engines and two or three stage masts. Maximum lift was 6500 lb.

▲ The MF 32 industrial loader is a derivative of the original Davis loaders. It was offered in North America for heavy duty farm work. It had a break-out force of 4,000 lb, and full height lift of 2,500 lb, 1976.

1980 and 1977 Industrial Machinery Ranges offered in North America

1980			1977		
Range	Model	HP	Range	Model	HP
Tractor backhoe loader	60	68 flywheel	Wheel loaders	33	74 flywheel
	50C	62 flywheel		11	74 flywheel
	40B	54 flywheel	Skid steer loader	811	38.5 max.
	30B	45 flywheel		711B	30 max.
Tractor loader	50C	62 flywheel	Crawler dozer	300	63 flywheel
	40B	54 flywheel		200B	44 flywheel
	30B	45 flywheel	Crawler loader	300	63 flywheel
	20C	45 flywheel		200B	44 flywheel
Industrial tractors	50C	62 flywheel	Skidder	320	80 flywheel
	40B	54 flywheel	Tractor backhoe loaders	80	100 flywheel
	30B	45 flywheel		70	84 flywheel
	20C	45 flywheel		50C	62 flywheel
	20C Turf	45 flywheel		40B	54 flywheel
Compact tractors	205	16 pto		30B	45 flywheel
	210	21 pto		20C	45 flywheel
	220	26 pto	Tractor loaders	50C	62 flywheel
				40B	54 flywheel
				30B	45 flywheel (d)
				20C	45 flywheel (d)
			Tractors	50C	62 flywheel
				40B	54 flywheel
				30B	45 flywheel (d)
				20C	45 flywheel (d)
				20C Turf	45 flywheel (d)
			Forklifts	6500	61 flywheel (d)
				4500	42 flywheel (d)

NB (d) = diesel engine; gasoline engine also available on these models

One of MF's major innovations was the introduction of its Powershuttle transmission system in 1984, fitted first to industrial machinery. Powershuttle is a pressure lubricated hydraulic torque converter system with full synchromesh which revolutionised repetitive forward and reversing operations by enabling soft, clutchless changes between forward and reverse to be made at full engine power with an electronic control. This was the replacement system for the original torque converter/instant reverse system which had been introduced in the late 1950s. Today FERMEC in the U.K. still fit the footpedal system (used on the old instant reverse type transmissions) on loaders destined for the North American market. Landscapers prefer the facility as they can steer with one hand, work the three-point hitch with the other and use the right foot for fast directional changes.

MF 24 Powershuttle telescopic handler, 1984. ▼

MF 14 Fork lift, 1984. ▶

Some Specifications of MF 24 Powershuttle Telescopic Handler 1984

Engine	Perkins A4.236
HP at 2200 rpm	72
Transmission	4/4 Powershuttle torque converter; soft shift forward/reverse; synchro on all gears
Drives	2 and 4WD models
Weight, 4WD version kg	5650
Max. lift to full height t	2.25
Max. lift height m	7.01
Max. lift capacity at full reach t	0.6
Max. reach m	3.71

Some Specifications of MF Fork Lifts 1984

	MF 10	MF 12	MF 14	MF 14	MF 16	MF 16	MF 18	MF 18
Drive	2WD	2WD	2WD	4WD	2WD	4WD	2WD	4WD
Engine	All models option of Perkins A3.152 47 hp or Perkins A4.236 70 hp							
Weight★	4490	4790	4970	5610	5685	5985	6520	6820
Lift★★ capacity t	2	2.2	2.5	2.5	3	3	3.5	3.5
Lift height m★★★	3.6	3.6	3.6	3.6	3.6	3.6	3.6	3.6

★with 2 stage mast   ★★at 0.5 m from heel of fork   ★★★2 stage mast; 3 and super 3 stage masts were also available
N.B. A wide range of agricultural and industrial equipment and accessories were available.

MASSEY FERGUSON INDUSTRIAL EQUIPMENT IN THE VARITY PERIOD

The Varity period of production of MF industrial equipment was between 1985 and 1992. It would appear that construction of tracked equipment had finished before this period. Seven equipment lines appeared in a Varity industrial equipment brochure of 1989.

▲ The 80 hp 4WD 'Farm Handler' was designed specifically for farm materials handling. The loader had a 6017 lb lift capacity and could be used with a range of MF buckets, manure and silage forks, large and small bale grabs, grain and root buckets, pallet forks etc, 1989.

Range Guide to MF Industrial Equipment 1989

Range	Model	Specifications
Backhoe loaders	MF 30H	36.5 kW, 0.75 cu. yd loader, sideshift
	MF 40H	45 kW, 0.75 cu. yd loader, sideshift
	MF 50E	52 kW, 1.05 cu. yd loader, sideshift or centremount
	MF 50H Series S	52 kW, 1.05 cu. yd loader, sideshift or centremount
	MF 50HX Series S	60 kW, 1.25 cu. yd loader, sideshift or centremount
	MF 60 H Series S	60 kW, 0.95 cu. yd loader, centremount
Highways	MF 20F	35 kW
	MF 40E	45 kW
	MF 50E	52 kW
	MF 50EX	60 kW
Articulated backhoe loader	MF 65A	68 kW, articulated frame, 1 cu. yd loader, sideshift
Industrial tractor loaders	MF 20F	35 kW, 0.75 cu. yd loader
	MF 30E	36.5 kW, 0.75 cu. yd loader
	MF 40E	45 kW, 0.75 cu. yd loader
	MF 50E	52 kW, 1.05 cu. yd loader
	MF 50EX Farm Handler	60 kW, loader with range of attachments
	MF 50H Series S	52 kW, 1.05 cu. yd loader
	MF 50HX Series S	60 kW, 1.25 cu. yd loader
Wheeled loaders	MF 613	40 kW, 0.85 cu. yd loader, articulated
	MF 615	53 kW, 1.05 cu. yd loader, articulated
Skid steer loaders	MF 505 Scat Loader	23.4 kW, 0.39 cu. yd loader, range of attachments
	MF 506 Scat Loader	29.8 kW, 0.39 cu. yd loader, range of attachments
Materials handlers	MF 14K	52 kW, 2.6 tonne capacity
	MF 16K	52 kW, 3 tonne capacity
	MF 25	54 kW or 70 kW, 2.5 tonne capacity

MASSEY FERGUSON INDUSTRIAL EQUIPMENT IN THE FERMEC PERIOD

In the 1992–1996 period in which FERMEC owned and managed MF industrial equipment manufacturing and its marketing, the product range was quite contracted compared with the extensive range which MF had offered in the 1960s and 1970s.

Today MF industrials are concentrated in the product ranges of mini-excavators, skid-steer loaders, tractor loaders and backhoe loaders. A feature of today's industrial range is the variety of implements that can be fitted. Like the agricultural tractor, they have come to be viewed as power units that can take on a wide range of tasks. In the last two decades there has been a proliferation of 'optional' equipment for industrial tractors, extending their original roles of loading and digging. Fork lifts, augers, chain excavators, pavement cutters and hole borers are but a few of the range of industrial implements now available.

The MF 128 mini excavator has an overall width of only 1450 mm and crawler length of 1870 mm, 1996. ►

Some Specifications of Mini-excavators 1996

	MF 114	MF 115	MF 128	MF 130	MF 135
Engine hp	17	17	22.5	26.5	28.5
Engine, Perkins model	103.10	103.10	103.13	103.15	103.15
Operating weight kg	1450	1550	2810	3110	3430
Max. dig depth mm	2160	2160	2600	2850	3105
Track speed kph	2.2	2.2	2.7/4.7	2.7/4.7	2.6/4.6

▲ **The MF 515 XP skidsteer loader shown with pallet and auger attachments, 1996.**

AGRICULTURE & LANDSCAPING

The versatile fork and grab can handle a wide range of materials, from bundles of fence posts to hay, silage, manure and hedge trimmings or loose vegetation.

An MF516 with auger gives a compact, effective machine for fence laying operations.

The pallet forks attachment allows palletised material to be handled in and around the farm, and enables trucks to be loaded or unloaded quickly and safely.

INDUSTRIAL & MATERIAL HANDLING

Specialised material handling buckets for industrial applications are available, including high tip and light material buckets.

Where sites must be kept clean and free from debris, the sweeper collector attachment turns the MF516 into a highly effective tool for keeping even the most restricted areas clean.

The scrap grapple allows for the safe handling of all manner of waste materials, from swarf to scrap paper.

CONSTRUCTION & DEMOLITION

The MF516 with backhoe attachment is equipped to accurately trench in extremely confined spaces, but, unlike a mini excavator, still has the versatility to carry other attachments required on the site.

Many additional attachments are available for the MF516, including rock breakers and compactors.

A variety of specialised buckets are available to suit specific tasks, examples include side-tip and high tip buckets, light material buckets and 4-in-1 buckets.

▲ **Some attachments for skidsteer loaders, 1996.**

Some Specifications of Skid–steer Loaders 1996

	MF 513	MF 514	MF 516	MF 516XP	MF 518
Engine hp	13.7	20.2	47.9	47.9	80.5
Engine, Perkins model	103.07	103.10	104.22	104.22	1004.4
Operating weight kg	829	1338	2387	2387	3134
Lift capacity kg	266	385	655	655	855
Max. dump height mm	1823	2110	2248	2248	2400

Some Specifications of Tractor Loaders 1996

	MF 640	MF 650	MF 680
Engine hp	73	78	88
Engine, Perkins model	4.41	1004.4	1004.4T
Drive	2 or 4WD, optional creeper	2 or 4WD, optional creeper	4WD, optional creeper
Loader lift to full height kg	2500	2500	2500
Transmission	4 speed powershuttle, torque converter		

▲ The MF 660 90 hp industrial tractor has powershuttle transmission, hydro-static steering and electro-hydraulic differential lock. A 1200 kg ballast box is recommended. Both 2 and 4WD models are available, 1996.

The MF 860 backhoe loader is turbocharged and available as 2 or 4WD models. The standard cabbed machine weight is 7627 kg, 1996. ▶

Some Specifications of Backhoe Loaders 1996

	MF 750	MF 760	MF 860	MF 865	MF 960	MF 965
Engine hp	80.5	90	90	90	90	90
Engine, Perkins model	1004.4	1004.4T	1004.4T	1004.4T	1004.4T	1004.4T
Backhoe dig depth m	4.89	4.89	4.89	4.89	4.89	4.89
Loader lift capacity kg	3350★	3050★★	3350★	3350★	3350★	3350★
Loader and backhoe controls	Mechanical	Mechanical	Mechanical	Electronic	Electronic/ mechanical	Electronic

★standard bucket   ★★multipurpose bucket

HIGHWAY TRACTORS

A class of industrial tractors has come to be known as 'Highway tractors'. These are essentially tractors with lighter specifications than heavy industrials and designed to meet the highway maintenance sector, parks and sports ground usage, and around factory use.

The MF 2130 and 2135 tractors marketed in the U.K. were advertised as 'equipped for the highway' and sold in yellow and grey livery. These were fitted with 30 and 45.5 hp engines repectively. Standard equipment included dual brakes, dual clutch, live engine and ground speed pto, road lights, reflectors, numberplate and instrument panel illumination, horn and rear view mirror, tractormeter, speedometer, fuel and oil pressure gauges, ammeter and screw-type top link.

▲ **MF 2135 highway tractor fitted with early type MF fibre glass cab.**

The MF 2130 and 2135 tractors shown 'equipped for the highway'. ▶

Some Specifications of MF 2135 and 2130 Highway Tractors

	MF 2135	MF 2130*
Engine	Perkins AD3.152 3 cylinders	Perkins A4.107 4 cylinders
Max. gross hp	45.5	30
Gears	6F + 2R. Multi-power option gave a 30% faster speed choice in each gear	8F + 2R
Hydraulic lift capacity lb	2850	1825
Front tyres	6.00 × 16	5.50 × 16
Rear tyres	11 × 28	10 × 28
Weight lb	3200	3000
Optional and variable equipment	Dual clutch (live pto) Multi-power/auxiliary hydraulics Dual spool valve/combining valve/pipe kit Cab Spring suspension seat Automatic trailer hitch Cigarette lighter 10 × 28 grassland tyres 11 × 28 agricultural tyres 13 × 24 and 6.50 × 16 industrial tyres	Automatic trailer hitch 10 × 28 grassland tyres Trailer pipe hydraulic kit

* There was also an 'economy' model of this tractor with slightly lower specification

Highway tractors were included in the 1989 MF industrial tractor range noted earlier in the Varity ownership period. Four models were included in a 1991 range. These had high specification cabs, including stereo radio/cassette. Variable equipment according to model included a range of agricultural and grassland tyres, hydraulic trailer brakes, front-end weights, wheel weights, high-flow hydraulic pump, electro hydraulic 4WD clutch, automatic 4WD engagement when brakes applied and two-speed shiftable pto.

The MF 362 H highway tractor designed for use around parks and sports grounds, around factories and for highway maintenance, 1991. ▶

An MF 390 H highway tractor, 1966. ▶

Some Specifications of Highway Tractors 1991

	MF 350H	MF 362H	MF 375H	MF 390H
Engine, Perkins	AD3.152S	A4.236	A4.236	A4.248
Engine power ps	>47	>60	>71	>80
pto power ps	42	55	64	73
Std transmission	8F 2R synchro	8F 2R synchro	8F 2R synchro	8F 2R synchro
Front tyres 2WD/4WD	7.50 × 16	7.50 × 16/10.5×18	7.50 × 16	11.2 × 24
Rear tyres	14.9 × 24	14.9 × 24 or 16.9 × 24	16.9 × 28	16.9 × 28
Weight kg 2WD/4WD	2637	2660/3009	3121	3442

A 'High Visibility' highway tractor is offered in France as the MF 'Visioporteur'. It has a sloping bonnet to give good visibility for front-mounted implements and is available in four models.

◄ **Made in France, the MF 3065 'Visioporteur' tractor is of 85 hp rating and shown here with front linkage. It is targetted at the highways tractor market for roads, roadside and parks maintenance duties, 1996.**

Some Specifications of Visioporteur Tractors 1993

	MF 3050	MF 3060	MF 3065	MF 3065 S
Engine	A4.236	A4. 248	AC4 236	AT4 236 WG
DIN hp	70	80	85	93
Gears	16/16 speedshift as standard; 24/24 speedshift option			
Max. hydraulic lift kg	4550	4550	6230	6230
pto rpm	540/1000	540/1000	540/100	540/1000
Weight kg	3840	3840	3840	3840

TOWING TRACTORS

In Argentina, two towing tractors were manufactured in the late 1970s. These were developments of the 1000 series agricultural tractors and designed for earth-moving duties with such implements as compactors, scrapers, graders, etc.

▲ MF 9500 and 8500 towing tractors of 90 and 180 hp respectively were made in Argentina. They weighed 5270 and 6350 kg. Both were fitted with Perkins 6-cylinder diesel engines, 1980.

Some Specifications of Argentinean Towing Tractors 1980

	MF 8500 (derivative of MF 1088)	MF 9500 (derivative of MF 1098)
Engine	Perkins A6.305S	Perkins A6.354
hp	90	180
Gears	8F, 2R	8F, 2R
pto rpm	540	540
Tyres, front	7.50 × 18	11.00 × 16
Tyres, rear	23.1 × 30	24.5 × 32
Wheelbase mm	2300	2540
Forward speeds km/hr	2.3–31.2	2.6–35
Weight (without wheel weights) kg	5270	5350

INDUSTRIAL TRAILERS

In the U.S.A. MF offered trailers designed for carrying industrial equipment which were advertised either as Industrial or Multi-Purpose trailers. They were made for MF by Fayette. Twenty-three types were offered in the 1980 MF industrial catalogue.

Specifications of MF Multi-purpose Trailers 1980

MF Type/Code number	Axle type	Bed length ft-in.	Capacity lb
STEEL RUNWAY			
1635–129	2	15-0	12,000
1625–130	3	15-0	18,000
WOOD DECK			
1635–116	2	15-0	12,000
1635–117	3	15-0	18,000
1635–118	2	16-0	12,000
1635–119	3	16-0	18,000
1635–120	2	20-0	12,000
1635–121	3	20-0	18,000
1635–122	3	24-0	18,000
BOGIE AXLE, WOOD DECK			
1635–123	Bogie	18-0	24,000
1635–125	Bogie	24-0	24,000
LAWN AND GARDEN			
1635–127	1	9-0	1400
1635–115	1	10-0	4000
COMPACTS AND L & G			
1635–126	2	10-0	3000
1635–252	2	12-0	5000
1635–253	2	14-0	6000
SKID STEER			
1635–136	2	13-0	7000
PICKUP GOOSENECK			
1635–250	2	20-8	16,100
1635–251	3	20-8	24,150
5th WHEEL GOOSENECK—10,000 lb AXLE			
1635–254	2	21-10	26,000
1635–255	3	25-0	36,000
TAG-A-LONG—10,000 lb AXLE			
1635–256	2	24-8	20,000
1635–257	3	24-8	30,000

▲ **An example of an MF contractor dump-trailer in yellow livery, 1995.**

CONTRACTOR DUMP-TRAILERS

In recent years MF has offered trailers for industrial applications and heavy site use. Nine models were offered in the U.K. in 1995 by MF (not FERMEC) and these were all in yellow livery.

**Skid steer loader ►
trailer.**

**Three axle wood
deck trailer. ►**

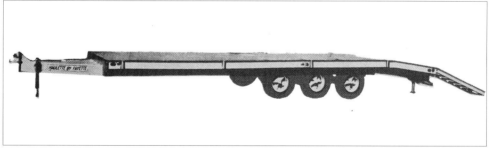

Contractor and Site Dump-trailer Ranges in the U.K. 1995

Range	Model	Axles	Capacity t
Contractor dump-trailers	700CD	single	5
	700CD	single	6.5
	700CD	single	8
	700CD	tandem	8
	700CD	tandem	10
	700CD	tandem	12
Site dump-trailers		tandem	11
		tandem	13
		tandem	15

In South Africa a 9 ton dump trailer was made to conform with road regulations of the day. It had a 7 cu. yd capacity and was linked to MF 165 or 175 tractors fitted with air brake kits.

An MF 79 9-ton dumper. South Africa, 1969. ▶

CHAPTER FOUR

Massey-Harris in Wartime

Massey-Harris, like most other major industrial groups of the day, undertook wartime government contracts to produce a range of products required for both world wars. M-H produced far more for the Second World War than for the First, perhaps reflecting the advance of mechanisation, and hence the greater degree of mechanised fighting which took place in the Second World War.

▲ **Bain wagons in the Boer War.**

WORLD WAR I

Records of M-H production of first world war equipment are fairly scant. One of the first contracts was for production of 18-pounder high-explosive shells. Two floors of a factory were converted for the purpose, turning out 2000 shells per day. The final tally of production was 844,062 shells. Eighteen-pounder shrapnel shells were also made.

The Bain wagon factory played a major role in M-H efforts in the First World War. Their horse-drawn wagons were reportedly superior in some respects to British wagons of the day.

The Bain wagons were made of more seasoned timber, had a better turning circle and made less noise on hard roads; but they did not carry such heavy loads. These were the opinions expressed about the Bain wagons when they were being used in France. Bain ambulance wagons were also made. They were used by the British and Canadian armies. To meet a British government order, a 100/day production rate was achieved.

M-H improved the specification of their normal wagon range for war models (apparently above those required by the government) as follows:

- hickory axles instead of hard maple
- steel skeins instead of cast skeins
- hickory wheel spokes
- much heavier tyres
- poles and reaches reinforced by steel
- grease cups to enable the wheels to be greased without being removed (a feature which was patented).

A sleigh runner was also designed which could quickly be attached to transport wagons or gun carriages. These were utilised by the military in considerable numbers.

In Australia, the H. V. McKay Sunshine works produced great numbers of rigid and springless 'G.S.' wagons and 'Furphy' water carts for the Commonwealth war effort.

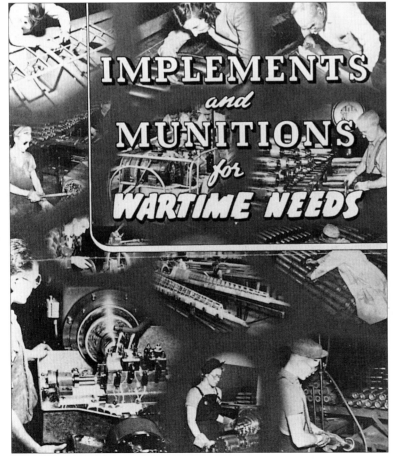

▲ **Front cover of an M-H brochure.**

WORLD WAR II

A great range of products were made by M-H for the Second World War. These included:

Tanks and related products

Tanks:
   M5 light tank (1942–1944)
   M44 155-mm howitzer
   (This may have been an M41)
   M24 light tank
   This was known in the British army
   as the 'General Chaffee'

Tank spares:
   Links for tank tracks — 14 million
   were made
   Tank destroyers (30-ton M10A1 gun
   motor carriages rebuilt into M–36
   tank destroyers)
   Tank recovery vehicles

▲ **M24 tank christened 'General Chaffee' by the troops.**
(Reproduced by kind permission of the Tank Museum, Dorset, U.K.)

An M-H M5 tank at the Kenosha Military Museum, a short distance from where it was made at the Racine M-H factory. ▶

Some specifications of M5 and M24 tanks

	M5	M24
Crew	4	4 or 5
Gross length in.	174.8	219
Width in.	88.3 w/o sand shields	118 over sandshields
Weight, loaded lb	33,100	40,500
Ground pressure psi	12.2	11.3
Power:weight gross hp/t	17.9	14.6
Engines	Twin Cadillac series 42	Twin Cadillac series 44T24
Electrical	12V DC	24V DC
Net max. hp/engine	110	110
Fuel	80 octane gasoline	80 octane gasoline
Max. road speed mph	36	35
Max. fording depth in.	36	40
Max. vertical wall in.	18	36
Max. trench ft	5.3	8

▲ **M5 tank taking shape,1943.**

▲ **M44 155 mm self-propelled Howitzer, Fort Knox, Kentucky, U.S.A., 1954.**

Aircraft products

Tail planes for Mosquito fighter bombers
Wings for Avro–Anson trainer planes
Wings for Mosquito fighter bombers — 15,000 screws and 200 lb of glue were used in making a single wing
Metal fittings for aircraft
Spars for trainer planes

Racine-made tank leaving the factory for the U.S. army. ▶

Manufacture of bomber aircraft wings. ▶

TO VICTORY!

WITH OUR HELP

Truck products

Ambulance bodies
Cargo truck bodies
Four-wheel drive axle assemblies
Cargo truck bodies
Carrier bodies
Personnel carrier bodies
Workshop carriers
Army trailer vans
Radio trailer vans
Bodies for anti-aircraft carriers
Anti-tank gun portees

▲ M-H produced trailer van awaiting fitting with radio equipment.

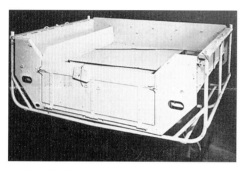

▲ M-H built vehicle bodies saw much active service in the Libyan Desert, North Africa.

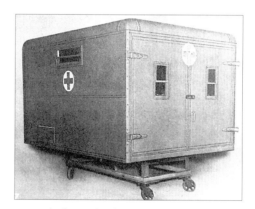

▲ Ambulance body. These were fitted with fans, lights, blanket boxes, heaters and holders for plasma containers.

Welding Military

Truck Bodies

◄ Truck bodies for World War II, 1943.

▲ Shell production at the M-H plant.

Munitions, etc.

40 mm shell and shot — 5,660,000
shells were made
4.5 in. shells
Penetrative nose caps for armour
piercing shot to penetrate 3.5 in.
armour — 2,657,000 were made
25 lb shells — 1,358,000 were made
60 lb shells — 700,000 were made
4.2 in. mortar bombs — 73,000
were made
Ammunition boxes
Transit boxes for shells

Gun equipment

Trainer turrets
Naval gun mounts for 4 in. guns
Sights for anti-aircraft machine guns
Anti-aircraft machine gun mounts

▲ M-H ammunition
box of World War II
vintage.

▲ Final assembly of mounts being made
with gun barrel and breech in position.

▲ Sawyer-Massey modifications of
Mk. XXIII mount adds a sight setter.

● A LINE-UP of Massey-Harris Tractors at the factory ready for shipment to various air fields.

● MEMBERS of the ground crews are saved a great deal of time and labor when there is a Massey-Harris Tractor to haul equipment used in servicing aircraft.

Communications equipment

Aerial towers and masts
Cable reels and racks

Tractors

The 81 and 82 tractors were widely used on British Commonwealth airfields.

Other activities by M-H in Canada

- In 1942 M-H employees pledged 15 minutes of each week's pay to charitable purposes.
- A blood donor clinic was set up in the Toronto factory.
- Clothing was collected for U.K. bomb victims and employees contributed to the Victory loan campaigns.
- An entertainment group from M-H entertained troops in Canada, the U.K. and Europe.
- Massey-Harris even loaned company executives to the Canadian government.

It is reported that during the war period, war production accounted for more than 50 per cent of the total product range value. In 1943 it reached 80 per cent. Subcontracting also became a very important feature of M-H operations developed in the war period and which remained thereafter.

In Australia, H. V. McKay Massey-Harris placed the full resources of the Sunshine factory at the disposal of the Commonwealth and geared up for maximum production. They made aircraft components, forgings for modern weapons, tracks and driving parts for troop carriers and tanks, ammunition of various types, torpedo control gears and radar equipment. Additionally, agricultural machinery manufacture was boosted and over 20,000 Sunshine seed drills were sent to the U.K. A full range of flax harvesting machinery was also developed for the Australian market.

THE HARVEST BRIGADE

No account of M-H in wartime would be complete without reference to the 'Harvest Brigade'. This activity served as a huge publicity coup for M-H. It was achieved by the valuable activity of demonstrating and organising for the first time a highly organised, fuel-efficient grain harvesting operation through agroclimatic zones of the U.S.A. as a major contribution to the war food production drive. Importantly, it launched M-H firmly and in a big way into the North American market — something which at this juncture was long overdue. By 1948 M-H had captured 48 per cent of the U.S. market for self-propelled combines.

The essence of the operation was that M-H made available 500 self-propelled combines with the collusion of the U.S. and Canadian governments' food planners, and co-operation of machine operators who guaranteed to harvest at least 2000 acres each. In the spring of 1944, combines started work on wheat in the south of the U.S.A., moving up through Texas to the central plains by June. This was the 'southern' brigade and it was to meet with a 'central' brigade in the central plains. The two teams spread out over the three state fronts of Colorado, Kansas and Missouri. Another brigade had started in the Imperial Valley in California and joined the main team. Attended by repair crews and spares suppliers, the combines often worked day and night northwards up through Oklahoma, Nebraska, Wyoming and the Dakotas to reach the Canadian border by September.

The statistics for the brigade are worth recording and stand as:

- 500 combines took part in the brigade.
- 1500 miles were covered from the start to the Canadian border.

▲ Advertising the 1944 harvest brigade. This was both a highly successful technical and organisational feat, and advertising success.

- 1,019,500 acres were harvested.
- over 300,000 man hours were saved by the use of self-propelled machines.
- 500,000 gallons of fuel were saved.
- 25,000,000 bushels of wheat and other grains were harvested.
- crops harvested included wheat, oats, barley, flax, sorghum, alfalfa, onion, lettuce, beet, carrots, peas, beans and maize.
- the top operator harvested 3438 acres.
- more than 5000 farmers had their crops harvested.

 *Why*

are Massey-Harris Self-Propelled Combines best fitted for this job?

There are, generally speaking, three different types of combines available to harvest the huge 1944 grain crop:

1. 6-ft. cut and under P. T. O. models.

2. Conventional design combines of 10-ft. cut or larger capacity.

3. Massey-Harris Self-Propelled Combines.

Which Type

can do the job most effectively with a minimum drain on manpower and materials?

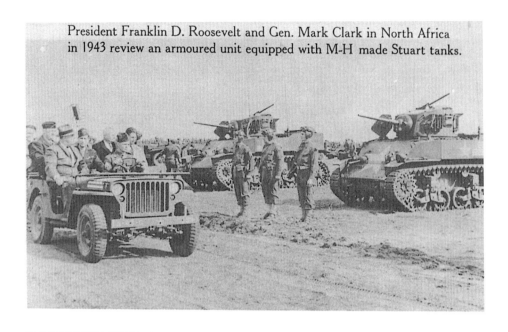

President Franklin D. Roosevelt and Gen. Mark Clark in North Africa in 1943 review an armoured unit equipped with M-H made Stuart tanks.

"The Harvest Brigade," organized by Massey-Harris in World War II to make most efficient use of machines and labour across North America, was the forerunner of today's custom harvesting business.

CHAPTER FIVE

Household, Farmyard and Other Equipment

A considerable range of household articles were sold by Massey–Harris over the years and also to a lesser extent by Massey Ferguson. M-H made a major policy decision after the war to develop a totally new line of products for the North American domestic market, but this was never seriously acted upon. The following is a selection of these, together with those for the farmyard and other sundry equipment.

From a 1913 M-H farm implement catalogue. ▶

MASSEY-HARRIS FARM IMPLEMENTS

STRAW CUTTERS FOR HAND OR POWER.

GASOLINE ENGINES.
ROOT CUTTERS AND PULPERS.

BAG TRUCKS.

CREAM SEPARATORS
200 TO 1000 LBS CAPACITY

VEHICLE JACKS.

WHEEL BARROWS.

FULL LINE OF ENSILAGE CUTTERS

MANURE SPREADERS—4 SIZES

BICYCLES

M-H started manufacturing bicycles based on acquired Columbia Bicycle Co. patents in 1895. Apparently the racing bicycles became world famous. The range of optional seats and handlebars increased as new models were developed. Ladies' models could be had with a lace chainguard. The bicycles were marketed under a safety bicycle concept with the brand name of 'Silver Jubilee'.

▲ **Production of M-H gents' bicycles.**

M-H ladies' bicycle on display at the Ontario Agricultural Museum. ▶

Bicycle Models

Model	Price	Specification
1896		
Gents A	$85	28 in. wheel, 23 in. frame
Ladies A	$85	28 in. wheel, 19 in. frame
1897		
Gents 2		optional brakes; black or maroon
Ladies 2		optional brakes; black or maroon
1898		
Ladies C		19, 22, 24 in. frame; 28 in. wheel
Gents 3		22, 24, 26 in. frame; 28 in. wheel
4. Light roadster		6 chain gear options—71.5 standard. Weight 24 lb
4. Road racer		
1899		
Ladies D		6 chain gear options—66.5 standard; lace chain guard optional
6. Std. Roadster		
7. Light roadster		
7. Special racing machine		

BUTTER CHURNS

Butter churns were made from early days in box and barrel form. Two notable product lines were the 'Lightning' churns and the 'Barrel' churns.

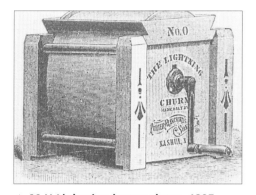

▲ **M-H Lightning butter churn, 1895.**

▲ **M-H Barrel butter churn, 1895.**

Specifications of Lightning and Barrel Churns (gals)

Lightning churns				Barrel churns		
	Holds	Churns			Holds	Churns
No. 0	4	2		No. 0	5	2
No. 1	6	3		No. 1	9	4
No. 2	8	4		No. 2	15	7
No. 3	10	5		No. 3	20	9
				No. 4	25	12
				No. 5	35	16
				No. 6	60	28

COOKING UTENSILS

Bi-metal cooking utensils were made by the Sunshine Waterloo Co., starting in 1956. This was the company which M H F had acquired for the production of office furniture. No details of this venture have been found, but the bi-metal product was based on a patent acquisition valid only for Canada.

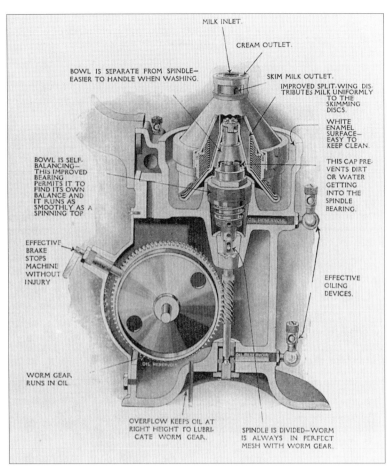

MILK INLET.

CREAM OUTLET.

BOWL IS SEPARATE FROM SPINDLE—
EASIER TO HANDLE WHEN WASHING.

SKIM MILK OUTLET.

IMPROVED SPLIT-WING DIS-
TRIBUTES MILK UNIFORMLY
TO THE
SKIMMING
DISCS.

WHITE
ENAMEL
SURFACE—
EASY TO
KEEP CLEAN

BOWL IS SELF-
BALANCING—
THIS IMPROVED
BEARING
PERMITS IT TO
FIND ITS OWN
BALANCE AND
IT RUNS AS
SMOOTHLY AS A
SPINNING TOP

THIS CAP PRE-
VENTS DIRT
OR WATER
GETTING
INTO THE
SPINDLE
BEARING.

EFFECTIVE
BRAKE
STOPS
MACHINE
WITHOUT
INJURY

EFFECTIVE
OILING
DEVICES.

WORM GEAR
RUNS IN OIL

OVERFLOW KEEPS OIL AT
RIGHT HEIGHT TO LUBRI-
CATE WORM GEAR.

SPINDLE IS DIVIDED—WORM
IS ALWAYS IN PERFECT
MESH WITH WORM GEAR.

▲ Cut away drawing of 1913 M-H cream separator.

CREAM SEPARATORS

A range of cream separators was sold for many years by M-H and the line appears to have been very successful. They were available as hand drive or electric drive models of various capacities.

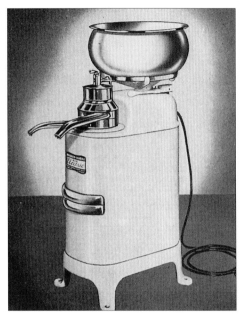

▲ M-H No. 11 Console Model electric motor-driven cream separator.

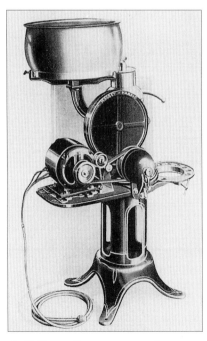

▲ M-H No. 6 cream separators. Hand and electric motor drive (with governor pulley), 1933. ▶

GARDEN GATES

An H. V. McKay Massey-Harris Pty. Ltd. catalogue shows a wide range of double and single ornate garden gates and field gates being offered—often with rabbit or chicken mesh fitted. The range included Sunshine X gates, Sunshine X Stay gates, Sunshine Double X Stay gates, Sunshine Bar gates and Sunshine Garden Gates.

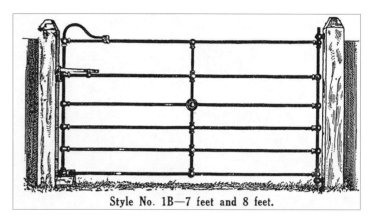

Style No. 1B—7 feet and 8 feet.

Style No. 13—3 feet and 3½ feet (Pipe 1⅛ in. external).

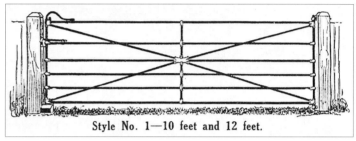

Style No. 1—10 feet and 12 feet.

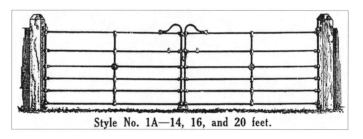

Style No. 1A—14, 16, and 20 feet.

Style No. 13A—3 feet and 3½ feet (Pipe 1⅛ in. external).

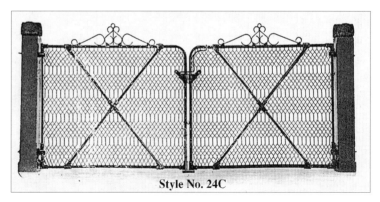

Style No. 24C

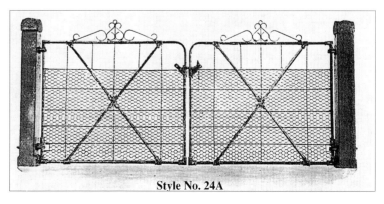

Style No. 24A

Sunshine car and garden gates by H. V. McKay Massey-Harris Pty Ltd.

▲ **MF 700 and 1000 high pressure washers.**

HIGH PRESSURE WASHERS, CHEMICALS AND DETERGENTS

For a period in North America, MF marketed four sizes of power washers. They were driven by electric motors. To cope with various washing jobs, they also marketed a range of chemicals and detergents which included a general purpose cleaner, heavy duty general purpose cleaner, engine degreaser and multi-purpose cleaner, concrete floor cleaner, germicidal sanitizer and a spray wax for metal surfaces.

Specifications of MF Power Washers

	500	600	700	1000
Motor	115 volt; 10 amp	115 volt; 15 amp	1.5 hp, 17 amp	3 hp; 17 amp
Pump gall/min.	1.8	2.1	2.5	4
Pump pressure psi	500–550	600–650	700–750	1000–1100
Hose ft	24	30	30	50
Wand ft	4 or 8	4 or 8	4 or 8	2 (stainless steel)
Weight 1b	65	115	115	272

Massey-Harris 16 cu. ft. Home Freezer.   Massey-Harris 10 cu. ft. Home Freezer.

HOME FREEZERS

At a time when deep freeze units were virtually unknown in European households, M-H was offering its North American customers 'Home Freezers' in their 1946 M-H Farmer's Handy Catalogue. They were offered in 10 and 15 cu. ft sizes.

MILK COOLERS

M-H electrical milk coolers were designed to pull the temperature of milk in churns down to about 40° Fahrenheit. They were available in three sizes and rated as 5, 7 or 9 gallon models, which presumably referred to the volume of the ice bank.

▲ The M-H electric milk cooler. ►

HAND PUMPS

A range of hand pumps of the lift or force type were marketed and many could be adapted for connection to windmill power. Some pumps had iron cylinders, others were brass, and a range of sizes was available. Surprisingly high outputs of up to 760 gals/hr at 40 strokes/min. were possible.

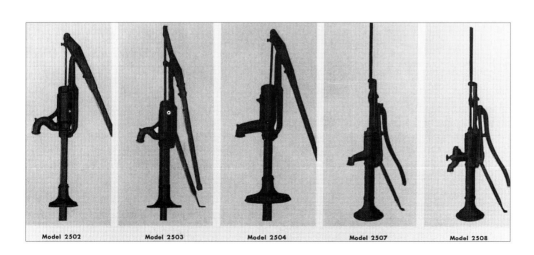

Model 2502   Model 2503   Model 2504   Model 2507   Model 2508

◄ Silhouettes of M-H hand pumps, 1947.

POWERED PUMPS

A gear type water pump was sold to be run from an engine or electric motor at 1400 rpm. It could deliver 400 gals/hr at 50 psi. Depending on discharge pressure, power requirement was 0.25–0.5 hp at 20 ft suction lift. M-H engines were also used to power centrifugal pump units.

◄ M-H centrifugal pumping unit driven by M-H stationary engine, 1946.

SACK TRUCKS

Sack trucks were offered by both the Verity Plow Co. and M-H.

◄ Verity Plow Co. sack truck.

SAFES

Whilst no advertising material or other reference was found for M-H safes, an M-H enthusiast came across a surviving example of one in the U.S.A.

◄ A fine surviving example of an M-H safe made by J. & J. Taylor Ltd. at the Toronto Safe Works.

SCALES

Counter, platform or a union of the two types were manufactured at the end of the nineteenth century.

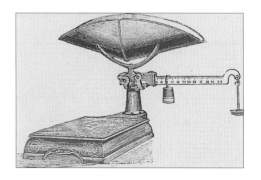

◄ M-H union scale, weighs from 0.5 oz to 240 lb, 1895.

SLEIGHS

This line of products came into the company's product line principally through the acquisition of the Bain Wagon Co. The range of sleighs offered was very extensive. Models were available for domestic, agricultural and forestry use.

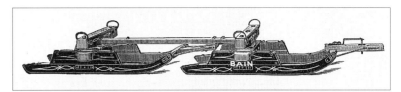

▲ **The Bain Improved Sloop Sleigh – with steel shoes, after 1901.** ▼

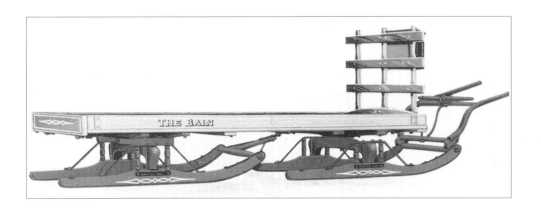

◀ **The Bain Improved One-Horse Sleigh with double bend shifting shafts, c. 1917.**

Specifications of Bain Improved One Horse Sleigh with Double-bend Shifting Shafts

Extreme length of runners in.	70.5
Depth of runners in.	3
Face of runners in.	1.75
Runner length of bearing in.	50
Platform length in.	116
Platform width in.	54
Width of track in.	36
Usage	Very convenient in rough land and bush

Specifications of Bain Improved Sloop Sleigh with Steel Shoes

Bolsters in.	38, 40 or 42, or 60 log bunks and clevises
Runner extreme length in.	82.5
Runner depth in.	4.5
Runner faces in.	2, 2.5 or 3
Runner length of bearing in.	62

▲ **An example of one of the MF Snowblowers fitted with upper and lower augers.**

SNOW BLOWERS

Snow blowers were made by MF as heavy duty equipment for rear mounting on tractors of between 12 and 125 hp and targeted at commercial snow clearance from roads. The machines comprised one or two revolving auger-type blades which cut into the snow and delivered it to a central fan for blowing to the side or loading into carts. Many optional accessories were offered, including chute deflectors, manual, electric or hydraulically rotated chutes, truck-loading chutes and a front-mount assembly with hydraulic lift.

Some Specifications of MF Snow Blowers

	MF 751/763	MF 773	MF 784	MF 796	MF 808
hp range required	12–30	30–45	50–80	80–125	80–125
Cutting width in.	51/63	73	84	96	108
Cutting height, single auger in.	23	27	34	36	36
Cutting height, double auger in.	n/a	n/a	40	42	42
Fan housing diameter in.	18	24	28	30	30
Fan width in.	6.875	8.875	10	10	10
Auger diameter, main in.	14	15	20	20	20
Auger diameter, upper in.	n/a	n/a	15	15	15

SNOWMOBILES

Snowmobiles have evolved from the demand for sleighs, which they have replaced both as a workhorse and leisure product. They are basically high-speed, motorised personal sledges. The first range of snowmobiles was the 'Ski Whiz' range introduced to North America in 1968. There were apparently three initial models, then a more powerful 'Formula' range was introduced.

▲ **MF Ski Whiz, Formula model snowmobile.**

Specifications of the First 'Ski Whiz' Series

	300 S	350 S	500 S
Engine cc	JLO 292	JLO 336	JLO 433.8
hp	18.5	22	28
Starter	Recoil, electric option	Recoil, electric option	Recoil, electric option
Speed, optimum conditions mph	48	50	55
Weight kg	147	161	179
Length cm	253	269	269
Width cm	81	81	81
Seat capacity	2	2 or 3	2 or 3
Track area on ground sq. in.	589	690	690
Ski width/length cm	12.7/105	12.7/105	12.7/105

Brief Specifications of the Formula Ski Whiz Series

	Formula IV	Formula III	Formula I
Engine cc	JLO 440	JLO 399	JLO 399
hp	37	33	28.3
Max. speed mph	80	70	60
Seat capacity	2	2	2
Length/width in.	99.5/32	99.5/32	99.5/32
Weight approx. lb	335	335	335
Track area on ground sq. in.	589	589	589

In 1976 the Cyclone, Whirlwind and Chinook models were available. The Cyclone used a Brooten liquid-cooled engine and the other two a Cuyana axial fan-cooled engine.

◄ **MF Cyclone snowmobile with Brooten engine, 1976.**

SNOW THROWERS

A Snow Thrower for clearing pathways was announced in the 1964 Farmer's Handy Catalogue. It was available for fitting to the M-F Executive garden tractor or as a smaller, self-propelled, walk-behind version based on the rotary tiller and powered by a 4-hp Briggs and Stratton engine. For both, the machine comprised a horizontal auger which collected the snow, and a chute up which the snow was blown. The thrower for the Executive tractor was 48 in. wide and the chute could rotate 270°. On the self-propelled version, the width of machine was 20 in. and the chute could be rotated 180°.

◄ **MF self-propelled snow thrower, 1964.**

▲ **MF 1655 snow thrower.**

STOVES AND HOME HEATERS

◄ **Massey-Harris Superior 'Standard' range No. 1982.**

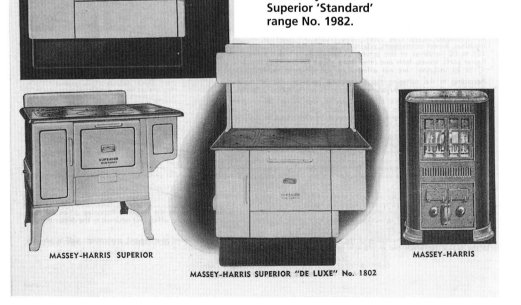

MASSEY-HARRIS SUPERIOR

MASSEY-HARRIS SUPERIOR "DE LUXE" No. 1802

MASSEY-HARRIS

STOVES AND HOME HEATERS

Stoves were offered in a range of sizes for either coal or wood burning. The stoves of the 1940s were available with or without reservoirs, which probably indicates that they could be used for water heating as well. The home heater was essentially a freestanding fire with front doors. This did not seem to have an optional water heating function. The largest size de luxe model had a 19.75 wide × 20.5 deep × 13.5 in. high oven whilst the economy model's oven measured 16 × 18 × 9.75 in. Stoves generally bore the 'Superior' badge.

▲ M-H Standard washer, 1895.

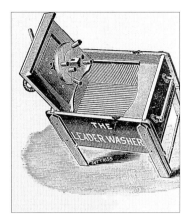

▲ M-H Leader washer, 1895.

◄ M-H Royal Canadian wringer, 1895.

WASHING MACHINES

M-H Snowhite washers. ▼

The first washing machines were of timber construction and operated by hand. Standard and Leader machines were offered at the end of the nineteenth century. Electric washing machines appear to have been introduced as a product line in the 1940s. They were sourced from the Lovell Co. and were marketed under a joint Snowhite and M-H badge. The machines had an electric motor which powered a four-blade gyrator in the washing tub and a wringer above the tub. The exterior finish was enamel and chrome. The washing tub could be aluminium or enamel according to model. 145, 143 and 142 models are also known to have been offered.

MODEL A-142
High quality and low price make Model A-142 outstanding value. It has aluminum finish standard type tub, one-hand wringer control, four blade gyrator and "Slater" wringer. Attractive in appearance and outstanding in performance.

MODEL 143
The most popular model in modern design "Snowhite" washers is the 143. Dirt-trap tub gives fast, thorough, easy-action washing. Well-known "Lovell" wringer—convenient one-hand wringer control. This fine looking washer is a great labour saver—moderate in price, too.

MODEL 145
The extra features of Model 145 give latest advantages in a modern washer. Highly polished "Lovell" wringer. Finger-tip height control lever — one-hand wringer control. Dirt-trap tub. Lustrous porcelain tub with chrome band. Superior in design and finish.

▲ M-H water pressure systems. They may be powered by electric or gasoline motors, 1948-51.

WATER PRESSURE SYSTEMS

Complete water supply and delivery systems were marketed to service farms and homesteads. These were suited to deep-well (over 22 ft well lift) or shallow-well (less than 22 ft lift) applications. Twin-cylinder pumps were available for shallow wells to give higher output. The systems were described as being suitable for small and large homes, summer cottages, small and large farms. Maximum working depth for the deep well system was 75 ft with a 0.33 hp power supply. Power units could be gasoline or electric. Units based on shallow wells could deliver 166 or 300 Imperial gals/hr. Those based on deep wells could deliver between 79 and 215 gals/hr depending on the depth of the well.

The complete systems comprised a powered well pump of the vertical shaft, driven-piston type, which feeds water as required to a galvanised pressure tank with safety pressure gauge and control. The latter is pressurised by a second pump and this effects the delivery to house and farm.

WHEELBARROWS AND SACK TROLLEYS

A considerable range of these were made and some examples are shown here.

M-H wheelbarrows and bag trucks.

WINDMILLS

A wide range of windmills were sold for many years for both domestic and farm use. They were a long selling line, dating back to the nineteenth century.

▲ M-H Brantford Ideal Windmill. Develops 2-4 hp in 15-20 mph winds, 1895.

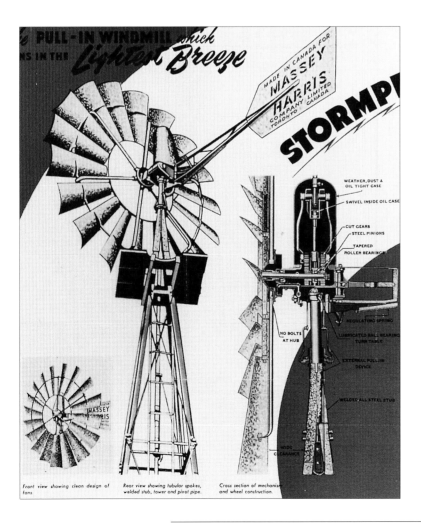

◄ M-H 'Pull-in Windmill', 1947.

DESKS AND FURNITURE

M-H-F acquired the Sunshine Waterloo Co. as part of the final and complete takeover of H. V. McKay in 1955. Out of the existing Waterloo product range, the office furniture range was favoured for development. In 1964 this was joined with the Art Woodwork Co. which was one of Canada's largest exporters of wood office furniture. The Waterloo plant made steel office furniture and the Art Woodwork plant, wooden furniture. The two were operated under the joint holding of Sunar Ltd. MF divested itself of its interests in office furniture in the late 1970s.

CHAPTER SIX

Landscape, Garden and Forestry Equipment

This chapter endeavours to review the range of equipment which has been marketed for landscape, garden and forestry purposes. For tractors, the distinctions between them which are made in this chapter may appear somewhat vague, but this is inevitable given that some are in fact derivatives of basic agricultural machines.

GARDEN TILLERS

A 1976 catalogue shows the following tillers being offered which could operate to a depth of 9 in.

MF 253/255/256 garden tillers, 1976. ▼

	Engine/hp	Tillage width in.
MF 253	Briggs and Stratton/3	14 or 24
MF 255	Briggs and Stratton/5	13 or 28
MF 256	Briggs and Stratton/5	14 or 28

'SMALL' TRACTORS

For convenience, this section reviews the small horsepower types of tractors which have been designated for use in the garden and landscape sectors—any distinction between the two is very blurred! Indeed, the division between industrials and these tractors has sometimes become confused, with turf and compact tractors appearing in industrial specifications brochures. An approximate definition is that tractors in this section do not exceed 35 hp and are generally of a 'compact' nature.

Massey Ferguson entered the small garden tractor market in about 1964. The first small tractor to have been produced appears to have been the MF 8 'Executive', which was targeted at people with large gardens, particularly those with large lawns. The range of implements offered for use with the MF 8 included a 10 in. mouldboard plough, two-gang disc harrow, one-row planter with fertiliser applicator, seven-shovel cultivator, snow thrower, grader snowplough and general purpose toolbar. At the same time the MF 22 and 26 rotary tillers were being offered which could pulverise soil down to 8 in. depth.

▲ **Introducing the MF Executive lawn tractor in the 1964 Farmers' Handy Catalogue.**

Specifications of the MF 8 Executive Tractor

Frame	0.25 in. steel; mounting points for mower, dozer blade, snow thrower, pull-behind implements and pick-up hitch point
Engine	heavy-duty, 8 hp Kohler with electric starter generator Single cylinder
Electrical system	12 V
Speeds	3F + 2R; forward speeds 2–6 mph
Clutch	belt driven
Brake	mechanical
Tyres	front 4.80 × 8 ribbed; rear 6 × 12 suburban tread
Shipping weight lb	510
Length/width in.	63/32

MF 12 garden tractor ▶

The demand for this type of tractor grew rapidly and the next generation—the MF 7, 10 and 12—were offered with a very wide range of small implements. These were 10 and 12 hp tractors, the latter with clutchless Hydra Speed. The engines were air-cooled Tecumsehs. There was also a wide range of accessories for the tractors including lights, deep lugged or flotation tyres, wheel weights, tyre chains, chrome

Implements for MF 10 and 12 Tractors

Implement		Implement	
Rotary mower	42 in. wide	Front loader	hydraulic
Reel mowers	3 or 5 gang (4–5 acre/hr)	Lawn roller	ballast to 550 lb with water
Rotary tiller	22 in. wide + 16 in. extension	Post-hole digger	to 30 in. deep. Five auger sizes
Tractor cab		Roller blade	for seeding, aerating
Rotary broom		Dump cart	MF 641
Front blade	MF 60	Trailer	1000 lb capacity
Flail mower	36 in. wide	Sweeper	for clippings, leaves
Sickle bar mower	48 in. wide	Rake	for smoothing etc.
Disc harrow	single or double row	Compressor	for spraying etc.
Lawn Aerator	for lawns	Fogger	for insecticides
Planter-Fertiliser	seeding/fertilising	Power caster	spreads anything
Spiker-Aerator	32 in. for water penetration	Spreaders	30 and 36 in. for seed and fertiliser
Carrier frame	hauling and grille guard	Vacuum	for leaves and debris
Tool bar	for cultivators	Mouldboard plow	10 in. × 6 in. deep

wheel covers, cigarette lighters and power lift hydraulics. Thus the garden market was soon demanding an implement and accessory range to match those of its agricultural and industrial counterparts! These tractors were styled similarly to the 100 agricultural tractor series. The 7, 10 and 12 range soon expanded to the MF 8, 10, 12, 14 and 16 models. Riding mowers were being offered in a 1976 North American catalogue as the MF 832 and 626 models which had 8 and 6 hp Tecumseh engines.

Currently the terms 'Garden', 'Lawn' and 'Riding Mower' tractors are used to designate a range of small tractors offered in North America with a power range of between 8.5 and 20 hp provided by Kohler or Briggs and Stratton engines, according to model. These tractors are variously able to take a range of attachments and accessories which include a turbo bagger, clean-sweep twin collector, mulcher, leaf shredder kit, dump cart, snow-dozer blade, snow throwers, snow cab, front-end loader, tyre chains and wheel weights, tyre options, tiller and three-point hitch.

In more recent years, the term 'Compact' tractors has been coined to describe some ranges of higher horse-power tractors for landscape work which have a compact design and profile. An early range of these was the 200 series, which had the 205, 210 and 220 models of 16, 21 and 26 pto hp respectively, and all with two-cylinder diesel engines. These were offered in 2 and 4WD versions and were styled similarly to the agricultural 200 series.

▲ **MF 205 compact tractor of 16 pto hp.**

▲ The Japanese-made MF 200 series of compact tractors came in 2 and 4WD models. They were powered by Toyosha 2-cylinder diesel engines of between 15 and 25 hp. The narrowest model was 1010 mm wide and weighed 617 kg in 2WD form, 1980.

Implements for the 1000 Series compact tractors. ▶

MF 205/206 Rear mounted cultivator

MF 38 Tiller

Some Specifications of the 200 Series Compact Tractors

	MF 205/205-4	MF 210/210-4	MF 220/220-4
Max. pto hp	16	21	26
Engine hp	20	25	31
Engine make/model	Toyosha S107	Toyosha P126	Toyosha S148
No. of cylinders	2	2	2
Gears	6F + 2R	12F + 3R	12F + 3R
Shipping weight lb	1687/2039	2216/2590	2557/3020
Front tyres, agricultural	4.00 × 12F2	5.00 × 15F2	5.00 × 15F2
Front tyres, turf	20 × 8.00–10G2	20 × 8.00–10G2	20 × 8.00–10G2
Front tyres, 4WD	6.00 × 14R1	6.00 × 14R1	7.00 × 16R1
Rear tyres, agricultural	8.375 × 24R1	11.2/10 × 24R1	12.4/11 × 24R1
Rear tyres, turf	13.6 × 16R3	13.6 × 16R3	13/6 × 16R3
Rear tyres, 4WD	8.375 × 24R1	11.2/10 × 24R1	12.4/11 × 24R1

MF 1075/76 Rear mounted rotary cultivator

Overall width mm (in)	1170 (46)	1400 (55)	1220
No. of blades	24	30	24
Weight, kg (lb)	160 (353)	176 (388)	240 (5
Offset, mm (in)	170 (7)	220 (9)	130 (5

▲ An MF 1035 tractor shown fitted with cab. It weighs 1590 kg, 1990.

A recent series is the 1200 compact series now on offer in North America and the 'Grass and Power Equipment' compact tractor range offered in the U.K. in 1990. A wide range of implements can be fitted to these, including backhoes capable of digging to 8 ft depth; hence such tractors have come to serve in an almost light industrial role in the landscape sector. Most are available in 2 or 4WD versions. In 1995, they were manufactured and distributed for MF by Simplicity Manufacturing Inc. of Wisconsin.

MF 37 Cultivator

MF 1070 Mid-mounted mower

MF 1071 Rear mounted mower

MF 1074 Front end loader

MF 1073 Backhoe

m versatility for maximum productivity

Tiller				MF 37 Cultivator			MF 1074 Front end loader		MF 1070 Mid-mounted mower		MF 1071 Rear mounted mower		MF 1073 Backhoe	
tines	5	7	9	No. of tines	15	19	Reach, mm (in)	1100 (43)	Weight, kg (lb)	101 (223)	Weight, kg (lb)	110 (243)	Reach, mm (in)	3280 (129)
width,	1700 (67)	2100 (83)	2200 (87)	Overall width, mm (in)	1800 (71)	2300 (91)	Lift height, mm (in)	2000 (79)	Overall width, mm (in)	1500 (59)	Overall width, mm (in)	1400 (55)	Digging depth, mm (in)	2500 (98)
(in)														
kg (lb)	180 (397)	240 (529)	280 (617)	Weight, kg (lb)	120 (265)	140 (309)	Weight, kg (lb)	188 (415)	Ground clearance m (in)	75 (3)	Cutting height, mm (in)	127 (5)	Weight, kg (lb)	360 (794)
th depth							*Fitted to MF 1010 – 4WD.		Discharge	Rear	Discharge	Rear	*Fitted to MF 1010 – 4WD	
ntrol wheels														

Brief Specifications of the 1990 Grass and Power Equipment Compact Tractor Series (all diesel engines)

	1010-4	1010-4HST★	1020-4	1020-4HST	1030-4	1035-4
Engine DIN hp	16	16	21	21	26	31
Capacity cc	865	865	1126	1126	1505	1505
Cylinders	3	3	3	3	3	3
No. gear ratios	6F 2R	2	12F 4R	3	12F 4R	12F 4R
Speed range kph	1–12.4	0–11.8	0.5–13	0–21	0.7–18.1	0.7–21
pto rpm	540/790	540/1000	540/790	540/900	540/1050	540/1050
Lift capacity kg	550	550	700	700	700	780
Weight lb ★★	641	650	830	960	1235	1235

★denotes hydrostatic clutch   ★★weight 4WD model w/o cab; cabs available on all but 1010 models.

Brief Specifications of MF Lawn Tractor Range 1990

	MF 10-10	MF 20-12	MF 30-13	MF 30-13 4-wheel steer	MF 30-15	MF 30-15 4-wheel steer	MF 30-17 4-wheel steer
Engine			All Briggs and Stratton				
hp	10	12.5	13	13	15	15	17
Engine type	industrial	industrial	V twin industrial	V twin industrial	V twin industrial	V twin industrial	V twin industrial
Transmission	mechanical	mechanical	hydrostatic	hydrostatic	hydrostatic	hydrostatic	hydrostatic
Cut width mm	812	914	1016	1016	1016	1016	1168
Turn radius mm	812	762	711	305	711	305	305
Weight kg	180	158	190	203	190	203	226

Overhead shot of MF 30-17 lawn tractor demonstrating four-wheel steer manoeuvrability. ▶

▲ MF 2818H garden tractor with 18 hp Kohler engine. The tractor is fitted with a 36 in. rotary tiller, tyre chains and wheel weights, 1995.

▲ The MF 2514 H ride-on mower is one of MF's latest lawn-type tractors. It is fitted with a 14 hp Briggs and Stratton engine with electric starter. It has a 38 in. cut.

Brief Specifications of Garden, Lawn and Riding Mower Tractors 1995

	Garden Tractors				Lawn Tractors				Riding Mowers	
	2920H	2918H	2818H	2718H	2616H	2614H	2514H	2512G	2413H	2409G
hp	20	18	18	18	16	14	14	12.5	13	8.5
Transmission	hydro	hydro	hydro	hydro	hydro	hydro	hydro	gear	hydro	gear
Engine	Kohler	B&S	Kohler	B&S	B&S	Kohler	B&S	B&S	Kohler	B&S
Cylinders	2	2	2	2	2	1	1	1	1	1
Fwd. speed mph	0–8	0–8	0–7	0–6.6	0–5.6	0–5.6	0–5.6	0–4.7	0–5.2	0–5.7
Rev. speed mph	0–4	0–4	0–4	0–3.1	0–3	0–3	0–3	0–1.4	0–2.9	0–2
Wheelbase in.	51	51	50.7	51.5	48	48	50.25	50.25	43	43
Weight lb	1051	1051	824	664	570	540	462	437	450	387
Mower cut in.	42/48	42/48	42/48	50	44	38	38	38	34	30

◄ **MF 1240 28 net hp tractor fitted with MF 1217 Quick-Attach backhoe and MF 1246 Quick-Attach loader. The loader will dig down to 8 ft, 1996.**

◄ **MF 1215 4WD 17 net engine hp tractor fitted with turf tyres, and mid and rear pto.**

Brief Specifications of the 1200 Compact Tractor Series (all diesel engines) 1996

	1210	1220	1230	1240	1250	1260
Net engine hp	17	20	25	25	30	35
pto hp	15	17.2	21.5	22.5	26.2	31
No. of cylinders	3	3	3	3	3	3
Gears	6/2 mechanical HT★	6/2 mechanical HT★	9/3 mechanical HT★	16/16 synchro shuttle	16/16 synchro shuttle	16/16 synchro shuttle
Forward speeds mph	0.93–11.2	1–13	1.2–13.4	0.3–14.7	0.3–15.5	0.3–16.2
Reverse speeds mph	1.2–5.6	1.4–6.5	1.2–6.8	0.26–14	0.27–14.7	0.29–15.3
Lift capacity lb ★★	1210	1210	1984	2866	2866	2866
Weight lb ★★★	1587	1653	1896	2645	2745	2855
Wheelbase in.	59.4	59.4	64.6	63.7	67	67

★HT = hydro transmission   ★★ at link ends   ★★★ 4WD model

▲ **MF 35 Turf Special with Dyna Balance mower. This mower can cut above and below ground level.**

'LANDSCAPE' TRACTORS

Like the previous section on 'small' tractors, this section is hard to define. However, some tractors were clearly too large for even large gardens and such tractors are the subject of this section.

One of the first tractors introduced to serve the large area landscape sector was the MF 35 'Turf Special'. This tractor was simply a derivative of the Ferguson TO-20 tractor in the form of the TO-35 given the MF 35 badge. The principal features were great stability on slopes, conferred by its wide flotation tyres (18.4/15 × 16 rears) or rear dual flotation tyres (8 × 24). It was offered with a four-cylinder 45.4 hp gasoline engine or a 47 hp three-cylinder diesel engine. A manual shuttle was offered as an option. This enabled changes from

Gang Reel Mowers

Available singly or in gangs. Cutting widths from 2′6″ to 21′. Self powered. Mechanical or hydraulic height adjustment.

Cutter Bar Mowers

Dyna-Balance Drive Mowers

MF135: Heavy duty highway mower: side mounted with 6′ or 7′ cutter bars.

MF31: Available with 6′, 7′ or 8′ cutter bars: 3 point hitch mounted.

MF51: Pull-type with 6′, 7′ or 8′ cutter bars.

Improved Pitman Drive Mowers

MF32: 3 point hitch mounted with 6′ or 7′ cutter bars.

MF52: 6′ or 7′ cutter bars — pull-type.

Hammer Knife Mowers

4′, 5′ or 6′ sizes; three point hitch with p.t.o. drive. Available in a 3-gang "hybrid" combination; one tractor powered 6′ unit and two self-powered 4′ units. Pull-type mowers, 5′ or 6′ cut, center or offset trailed, mechanical or hydraulic height adjustment.

Rotary Cutters — Pull-Type and Mounted

MF60: 60″ cut, pull-type and lift-type.

MF65: 66″ cut, pull-type and lift-type.

MF84: 84″ cut, pull-type.

Mowing equipment for MF 35 Turf Special tractors. ▶

forward to reverse to be made using a steering column lever in whatever gear had been selected in the main gearbox. MF implements offered for the tractor included gang-reel mowers, hammer-knife mowers, cutter-bar mowers and rotary mowers—all in various sizes. The 35 Turf Special was followed by an MF 135 version of the Turf Special which was labelled the MF 2135, and also the 2165 Turf Special which was based on the MF 165 tractor. Following these Turf Specials, a 20C Turf Special became available in the style of the 200 series agricultural tractors. The description of 'Turf tractor' has also been extended to certain optional models of the 1000 series Grass and Power equipment tractors noted earlier in this chapter.

▲ **MF 35 Turf Special tractor with salt/lime spreader.**

▲ **An MF 20 C turf tractor shown fitted with low pressure tyres, 1977.**

Specifications of the MF 20C Turf Special Tractor

Engine	Perkins 45 hp diesel or CMC 42 hp gasoline★
Operating weight lb	Diesel 3812; gasoline 3568
Standard tyres	Rear 18.4 × 16.1. Front 9.00 × 10 (4 ply)
Optional tyres	Rear 18.4 × 16.1. Front 9.00 × 10 (6 ply)
	21.5 × 16 9.50 × 10
	14.9 × 24 26 × 12
	13.6 × 28 7.50 × 16
	14.9 × 24 11 × 15
Standard transmission	Heavy duty, dual range, 8F + 2R
Optional transmission for gasoline engine only	Heavy duty, dual range, 6F + 2R
Steering	Hydrostatic with single booster cylinder
Forward speeds on 18.4 × 16.1 tyres mph	1.84–24.88
Ground contact pressure with 21.5 × 16 front and 21.5 × 16 front tyres, diesel	5.48 psi rear and 9.66 psi front

★the gasoline engine was later discontinued

In the Varity period in North America, a series of tractors which were actually called 'Landscapers' were marketed. These were targeted at the landscape market where duties were less arduous than for industrial situations. The recent 1100 series of tractors are designed for landscapers, building contractors, nureries, retired farmers and municipalities. They are reputedly very good for loader work in these situations, with their single lever shift for forward and reverse on the steering column. All are 4WD.

▲ **40E Turbo Landscaper tractor of 58 bhp, 1986.**

MF 1190 landscape type tractor with 60 hp turbo-charged diesel tractor. ▶

Some Specifications of Landscaper tractors 1986

	20 F	30 E	40 E Turbo
Engine, Perkins	D3.152	AD3.152	T3.152
bhp at 2250 rp	46	48	58
Transmission	Manual shuttle	Power shuttle	Power shuttle
Loader max. lift to full height lb	2923	3597	3597
Weight with standard bucket and tyres, fuel, ballast etc. lb	9257	9532	9576

Some Specifications of 1100 Series Tractors 1995 (U.S.A.)

	MF 1160	MF 1180	MF 1190
Engine★ hp	41	52	60
pto hp	37	46	53
Transmission	All 16/16 synchro shuttle		
Tractor weight kg	1745	1975	1985
Max. linkage lift kg	1400	2200	2200
Wheelbase in.	74.7	79.9	79.9

★all four-cylinder diesels

FORESTRY TRACTORS

As far as can be established, there were no purpose-built M-H forestry tractors. Ferguson tractors were adapted for forestry work with such accessories as half tracks and callipers for towing logs. Ferguson also marketed a winch for light duty work which was sold into the MF era (see chapter one).

In 1967, MF took a policy decision to move seriously into the forestry sector, which led to the introduction of the MF 220 Skidder in 1969. An MF 165 tractor was offered as the 'Kubik' and this also may be one of the products of this policy decision. This was a half-track adaptation with front winch and rear-mounted hydraulic log grab. The articulated 'Treever' tractor was a classic of its time with excellent manoeuvrability. This machine was offered before the 1967 policy decision. The Skidders only achieved relatively low sales but over 3500 Treevers were sold.

'Skidder' tractors were heavy-duty 4WD articulated machines with equal size wheels. They were fitted with a front blade and rear winch.

▲ Logging callipers on a Ferguson hitch.

▲ MF 165 'Kubik' logging in Australia.

▲ MF Treever.

▲ The introduction of the MF Treever marked MF's entry into the heavy forestry equipment field.

Specifications of the MF 2200 Treever★

Engine	Perkins A3.152 diesel, three cylinder
Hp, bare engine	43.5
Gears	6F + 2R
Steering	articulated frame, outside turning radius 208 in.
Drive	4WD
Differential locks	front manual; rear no spin
Carrier capacity	2 cords
Boom lift capacity	1500 lb
Tyres	16.9–26 10 ply
Overal width	88 in.
Overall length	162 in.
Weight	10,200 lb approx.

★ Originally produced as the MF 203 Forwarder

Specifications of the MF 320 Skidder 1977

Engine	Perkins 4-cylinder, 80 flywheel hp
Transmission	power shift; 4F + 4R with high and low ratio for each; also manual shuttle
Winch capacity lb	22,000
Turning circle ft	31 on standard tyres
Safety features	safety canopy, seat belts, grille and engine protection, enclosed dozer cylinders
Blade in.	75 wide, 20 high
Standard tyres	23.1 × 26 (optional 18.4 × 26, 18.4 × 34, 28.1 × 26)
Width in.	96–106 depending on tyres
Tread in.	77.25
Weight lb	16,000
Weight distribution lb	front 9,600, rear 6,400

▲ The MF 320 80 hp skidder fitted with winch and ROPS (Roll Over Protection Structure).

▲ 86 hp MF 390/4 forestry tractor.

Industrial tractors such as shovel loaders and fork lifts were also adapted for the forestry sector.

At present, the 390 4WD tractor of 80 DIN hp is being offered with others of the 300 range adapted for forestry use. The adaptation basically consists of extra engine guarding, a robust cage over the whole tractor, strong front guard, underbelly guarding, raised rear fenders to allow use of tyre chains or half tracks, flexible cab steps and strengthened frame across the back of the cab for mounting spool valves.

▲ MF 3366 dozer in Australia, clearing woodland.

▲ MF 204 fork lift with 48 in. log clamp and of 5000 lb capacity.

▲ MF 356 shovel loader equipped for log handling with 7000 lb capacity log grapple.

CORD AND PULPWOOD SAWS

Many models have been made through the years. They were a good selling line of equipment in the days of forest clearance for agriculture in Canada.

In the mid-1930s these types of saw were represented by M-H models Nos. 1A and 3A, which incorporated heavy flywheels. The saw pulley had a two-pin ratchet which allows the saw to run down after power is shut off. 24, 26, 28 or 30 in. saw blades were available. The saw units were mounted on skids with drag links.

▲ M-H No. 2 tilting frame wood saw, c.1917.

▲ M-H No. 5 pole saw mounted on truck with M-H engine for drive, c.1917.

M-H No. 1 tractor driving M-H wood saw. ▶

▲ The M-H No. 1A cordwood saw and No. 3A pulpwood saw, 1930s.

M–H 1A and 3A Saws

	Woodsaw	Pulp and Cordwood
No.	1A	3A
Weight lb★	400	560
rpm	1000–1500	1000–1500
hp required	3–4.5	3–4.5
M-H engine pulley in.	12 or 14	12 or 14
Saw pulley in.	6 × 6	6 × 6
Distance balance wheel to saw blade in.	39	51

★without blade

▲ M-H No. 3 cord and pulpwood saw requiring 4.5-6 hp.

M-H No. 4 pole saw on skids requiring 3-4.5 hp. ▶

◀ Sawyer & Massey portable saw mill, 1906.

Sawyer-Massey produced large lumber saws and an example is shown here. The Ferguson cordwood saw was a very widely sold simple implement for farm use. It was continued in the MF line for many years.

▲ The Australian-made MF 20 cordwood saw is a direct derivative of the Ferguson cordwood saw. The 30 in. diameter saw blade was recommended to turn at 120 rpm, 1970.

FERGUSON FORESTRY AND SUGAR CANE RAKE

This unique implement was first manufactured in 1957 for use on the Ferguson 35 tractor. It was essentially a heavy-duty version of a pto-driven hay side-rake, designed for use in swathing together forestry trimmings or sugar cane debris.

▲ **M-H marketed this grassland aerator in the U.K. It is thought to have been made by Stephenson of Newark.**

GRASSLAND AERATOR

The MF archives in Coventry turned up an example of a grassland aerator which had been marketed by M-H and may represent their first venture into the landscape sector!

THE BRIGHTON BEACH CLEANER

The MF Brighton Beach Cleaner must rate as one of the more unusual products in the company's long history.

◄ **MF 'Brighton' beach cleaner. Thought to have been made in Australia, 1971.**

Specification of the Brighton Beach Cleaner

Width of cut	48 in.
Normal cleaning depth	2-3 in.
Cleaning rate★	2 acres/hr
Amount of sand cleaned and sifted	800 cu. yd./hr
Rear refuse container	0.5 cu. yd
Screens available	0.5, 0.75 and 1 in.

★based on 1 in. screen and dry sand.

CHAPTER SEVEN

Stationary Engines

Stationary engines have been a product line since 1911 when Massey-Harris began marketing the Olds engines which were made by the Seager Engine Works in Lansing, Michigan. M-H have either manufactured them or bought them in as required for various purposes. They have been used to provide power in a wide range of situations, particularly before the wide-scale availability of electricity in the countryside, and were used for such tasks as:

- turning cream separators and milk churns
- powering milking machines
- driving barn machinery such as chaff choppers, grinders, mills, pulpers
- driving electricity generators and air compressors
- pumping water
- driving saw benches
- driving field machinery harvesting mechanisms such as combine harvesters, balers and potato diggers

Olds gasoline engine, 1913. ▼

OLDS ENGINES

These were marketed by M-H between 1911 and 1913. Olds engines had been in production for some 30 years by then, with both gas and gasoline type engines having been produced. They reputedly had the largest factory in the world devoted solely to engine production. It would appear that M-H sold the engines with the Olds badge but without any

M-H badge. Type 'A' and 'B' engines were sold by M-H.

The engines were generally mounted on sub-bases which contained the gasoline tank. A key feature of the engines was claimed to be that it had 40 per cent less wearing parts than any other high-class engine. They were fitted with four ring pistons, and water jackets were designed to give the pistons protection from freezing and cracking should water not be drained off. Type 'A' and 'B' engines used a jump spark ignition system (battery electric supply) and had hit and miss governors. Engine speeds could be adjusted by a thumb screw. The carburettor had no moving parts and could operate on gasoline, alcohol distillate and cold kerosene, as well as higher grades of crude oil. On the gas engines, a mixer was used with only one moving part. Magnetos were available as an option. A friction clutch pulley was also available.

Catalogues of the day showed the engines being sold on skids or trolleys. They were also sold mounted on spraying outfits and circular saw outfits. Olds offered a speed governor pulley for use with cream separators. Other unitary applications were direct connected, double-acting pumps and diaphragm pumps, driving electric light outfits, powering water supply systems and as contractors' hoists.

▲ Olds No. 4 type AH 6 hp engine.

▲ Olds type B engines. These were made in 20 and 40 hp (two cylinder) versions.

The Olds Engine Range Offered by M-H

Model	rpm	hp	Approx. shipping weight lb
No. 1. AH	600	1.5	350
No. 2. AH	500	3	725
No. 3. AH	450	4.5	1075
No. 4. AH	425	6	1550
	400	8	1750
	380	12	2700
	380	15	2900
Closed cooling jacket engines		3–15	
Gas engines		1.5–15	
Kerosene engines		3,4.5,6,8,12	
Type 8.B	400	20	4500
Type 10.B, 2-cylinder	400	40	7000

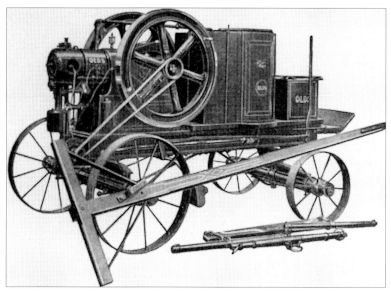

▲ **Trolley mounted Olds gasoline engine, 1913.**

Type 1, Old-style (OS) Engines

hp	rpm	Approx. shipping weight lb
1.5	500	320
3★	475	750
4.5	450	1150
6	425	1540
8	400	1750
12	380	2700
15	380	2850
20	380	3250

★a 3.5 hp model has also been found listed in one repair parts list

DEYO-MACEY ENGINES

In 1913 M-H purchased the Deyo-Macey Co. of New York to acquire a range of stationary engines after the demise of their relationship with Olds. There were several series of these engines, each with a range of engine sizes.

Type 1 old-style engines had battery and spark plug ignition and the timing gears were located outside of the crankcase. These engines were produced at the old Deyo-Macey works in New York between 1914 and 1916. All but the 1.5 hp engine were available with a closed water cooling jacket serviced by a separate tank or running water. All but the 20 hp engine could be had on skids. All were available on wooden or steel trucks according to size.

The next range of engines was the first to be produced at the M-H Toronto works. These were the Type 1 old-rating (OR) engines and the same power range was offered. These engines had the exhaust valve seated in the cylinder and the inlet valve still in a cage. The timing gears were placed inside the crankcase.

Then followed the new-rating (NR) Type 1 engines. These were generally offered with low tension and battery ignition but magneto options were available for export. Pistons had four rings. The engines had hit and miss governors and speed was claimed to be adjustable from about 275 rpm up to full speed. The carburettor had no moving parts and the suction of the piston drew petrol up from the tank. Friction clutch pulleys were available as an optional extra.

Sectional view of M-H 3-20 hp engines (the 1.5 hp engine was of somewhat different construction). ▶

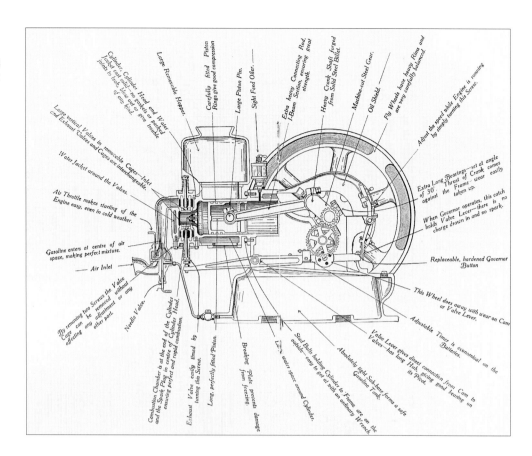

▲ **Final testing shed for M-H stationary engines at Weston Engine and Tractor Plant, c. 1921.**

Type 1 New Rating (NR) Engines

hp	rpm	Approx. shipping weight lb
2	500	460
3	475	750
4.5	450	1150
6	425	1540
8	400	1696
10	380	2700
12	380	2850
15	380	3250

▲ **M-H gasoline engine – 2-15 hp. Stationary, portable or semi-portable, c. 1917.**

▲ **End view of an M-H No. 2 engine.**

In 1923 a new-style Type 2 engine was introduced in four sizes to burn gasoline or kerosene. These engines were in production up to 1932 and incorporated design improvements over the previous series. Both valves were in the cylinder head. Ignition was by high tension magneto. Early engines had an open crank with splash guard which was later enclosed with an inspection cover on top. This facilitated greasing of the big end bearing.

Type 2 Engines

hp	rpm	Approx. shipping weight lb
1.5	650	268
3	600	430
4.5	550	540
6	550	820

A Type 3 engine was brought out in 1933 and came in three sizes. They were sold until 1935. The engines had throttling governors, burnt gasoline or kerosene, had a diaphragm type fuel pump, single flywheel and rotary high-tension magneto. The 6 hp model had provision for water injection into the combustion chamber—a feature of the Wallis style tractors. There is, however, some doubt that any 6 hp engines were ever built.

Type 3 Engines

hp	rpm
1.5	800–1100
3	750–1050
6	575

The 'new' M-H kerosene engine, 1924. ▶

▲ High tension wico magneto fitted to M-H engine.

▲ Overhead view of 'closed crank' M-H type 2 engine.

Fuel gauge fitted to an M-H 1.5 hp type 2 engine. ▶

JOHNSTON HARVESTER (MASSEY-HARRIS) ENGINES

An engine has been observed bearing an M-H Harvester Co. Inc., Batavia, N.Y. badge and manufactured at the Gas Engine works in Milwaukee. This suggests some link with the Johnston Harvester Company (which M-H took over in 1910), but this is not certain. Details of the engine design suggest themselves to be different from the normal M-H engines of the period.

Also, a copy of an instruction book (in English, French and German) for Johnston Harvester No. 2 Kerosene and Petroleum engines has been found, in which the illustrations and specifications are as for M-H Type 2 engines. Additionally, an engine is shown fitted with a fuel gauge as were some later M-H Type 2 engines.

Correspondence with MF personnel indicated that Johnston Harvester was a subsidiary of M-H—the particular instruction book referred to gave them an address in Paris. Hence there are possibly two different Johnston connections in M-H history.

▲ A rare 1.5 hp 600 rpm M-H Harvester Co. Inc. Batavia N.Y. engine. It was manufactured at the Gas Engine Works, Milwaukee, U.S.A.

SUNSHINE, SUNDEX AND SUNDIAL FARM ENGINES

A 1919 *Land, Transport and Sea* magazine shows an H. V. McKay advertisement for Sunshine engines. These were portable or stationary and available in 3, 5, 7 and 10 hp sizes.

A 1931 H. V. McKay Massey Harris Pty. Ltd catalogue offered 2 and 4 hp

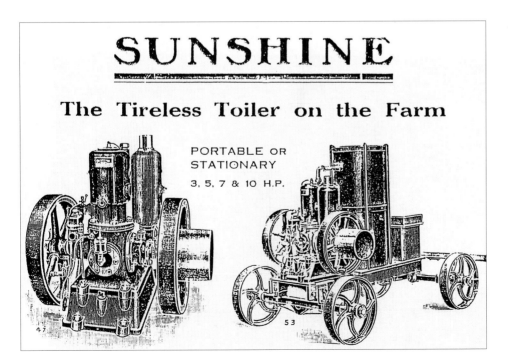

◄ Sunshine stationary and portable engines, 1919.

Sundex farm engines. These were badged Sundex and are presumed to be of Australian manufacture. These were single-cylinder horizontal engines with high-tension magnetos and renewable sleeve cylinders. Pistons had three rings; speed control was with a centrifugal governor. The 4 hp model had a mechanical lift pump for the fuel but the smaller model utilised suction. The engines were available on skids or trolleys.

Sundex Engines

Model	rpm	Weight
2 hp	550	4 cwt 0 qrs 7 lb
4 hp	400–500	8 cwt

▲ Sundex farm engines – sizes 2 hp and 4 hp, H. V. McKay Massey-Harris Pty. Ltd, Sunshine Harvester works, Sunshine, 1931.

A 2 hp Sundial petrol engine was offered in 1935 by Sunshine and M-H in Australia. It ran at 600 rpm, was fitted with a high-tension magneto, and had a cylinder bore of 4 × 4.5 in.

▲ Sundial 2 hp petrol engine, 1935.

CUSHMAN ENGINES

From 1936 to 1952 M-H sold Cushman engines of the vertical and horizontal type. Smaller engines were represented by the Cushman 'R' types. These were designed to burn gasoline, kerosene or natural gas, had flyball governors and high-tension magnetos. The 4 hp model had an extended water hopper.

Cushman 'R' Type Engines

Model	hp	rpm★	hp at 850 rpm★	Approx. shipping weight lb
R-14	2	400–800	3	225
R-20	3	400–850	3.7	265
R-30	4	450–900	4.5	285

★ Data from different brochures

Larger engines were represented by three Cushman vertical engines. These were referred to as 'LK' engines because they had an L-head cylinder. V-belt drive pulleys could be had to special order. Lubrication was by pump and splash which utilised a plunger type oil pump. Ignition was by high-tension magneto and the governor was a flyball type throttling the carburettor. All were designed for radiator or tank cooling.

Cushman Vertical Engines

Model	hp	rpm	No. of cylinders	Approx. shipping weight lb★
R-40	5–6	400–1400	1	270
E-35	8	500–1400	2	296
	10–12		2	

★ engine only without tanks or radiator
NB A C-34-U 6 hp vertical engine is referred to in a 1941 catalogue

▲ M-H single cylinder 5-6 hp vertical engine, 1938.

▲ M-H stationary engine of the Cushman type, 1936.

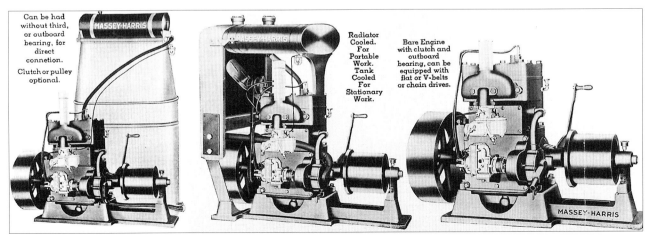

▲ M-H E35 twin cylinder engines of 10-12 hp, 1938.

CLARK ENGINE

During the Cushman era, M-H also went to the D. R. Clark Engine Co. of Toronto for their air-cooled gasoline engines. The model 'S' engine was sold by M-H from 1946–1951. M-H advertised these shown driving such machines as air compressors, cement mixers, water pumps, conveyors, electric generators and small two-wheel garden tractors. Clarks also made an 'SR' marine model and an 'SK' kerosene model. The 'S' model developed 1.4 to 2.7 hp depending on speed, which could be taken as high as 2400 rpm. The engines had flywheel magnetos and started on a rope pull. The carburettor was of a float-feed type and the engine was reputed to give its best performance on non-leaded, white gasoline. Lubrication was by splash and compression ratio was 5:1. Built-in, speed reduction gear drives were available to suit different applications. Many engine components were made of aluminium alloy.

1948 Model S driving milking machine vacuum pump. ▼

WEATHER KING ENGINE

It is uncertain who built this air-cooled engine which was marketed by M-H, then M-H-F, between 1951 and 1956. It appears to mark the end of the sale of gasoline engines by M-H. Like the Clark engines, they were a variable speed type. Two models were offered at 2–3 and 5 hp. Piston, crankcase, connecting rod and cylinder head were made of aluminium alloys. Ignition was magneto with impulse coupling and automatic spark advance. The 2–3 hp model could develop 5 hp at peak power rating but 3 hp was recommended for continuous operation.

M-H 25 ENGINES

The need for bigger stationary engines in the 1930s was met by utilising the Model 25 four-cylinder tractor engines. These were simply uprated Wallis design engines which had been developed for the Model 25 tractor. These had a power rating of 45 hp and ran at 1200 rpm. They had a 14 in. diameter pulley as standard and the engine bore was 4.375 in. × 5.75 in. The engines were offered in the green livery of the early 25 tractors, or the red livery of the later ones. Similarly, the different radiator chaff guard appropriate to each tractor model was fitted. The engines were offered as standard on skid bases and with integral hand-operated clutch unit with bare output shaft from the clutch. The engines were water-cooled by radiator and fan.

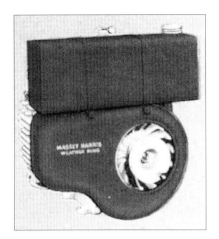

▲ M-H Weather King 2-3 hp engine, 1951.

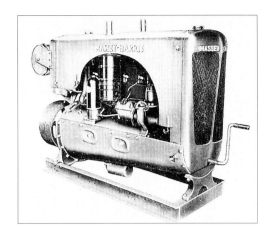

◄ M-H 'Model 25' stationery power unit, 1939.

A very rare surviving example of an M-H 25 stationary engine, serial No. 40104, 1939. ▼

▲ M-H 'Model 25' stationary power unit, 1937.

CONTINENTAL ENGINES

M-H was a big purchaser of Continental engines for its tractors, starting in 1938 with the 101 tractor series. Use of Continental engines in tractors continued through into the M-H-F period. They were also used on some of the early combine harvesters. For heavier load work 'Red Seal' Continental engines were sold by M-H, with M-H and Continental badging, as skid-mounted power units with integral and

◄ M-H Continental No. PF218 gasoline power unit of 37 hp, 1941.

**M-H Continental ▶
power units, 1941.**

▲ **Four cylinder, 24 HP at 1800 rpm.
PF 140 gasoline, PF 162 distillate.**

▲ **Six cylinder, 50 HP at 1800 rpm. PM 290
gasoline, PM 330 distillate.**

hand-operated clutch mechanism, and a bare output shaft from the clutch. Five models were offered, two of which were for distillate. The engines were water-cooled with fan and radiator.

Ignition was by magneto with impulse coupling; the governor was centrifugal and gear driven. Starting was by handle but starter motors were available as an option.

Continental Engine 'Power Units'

Model	Fuel	No. of cylinders	Displacement cu. in.	hp	Governed rpm	Approx. shipping weight lb
PF 140	Gasoline	4	140	24.8	1800	853
PF 162	Distillate	4	162	24	1800	870
PF 218	Gasoline	6	217.8	37	1800	1085
PM 290	Gasoline	6	289.9	50	1800	1525
PM 330	Distillate	6	329.8	50	1800	1550

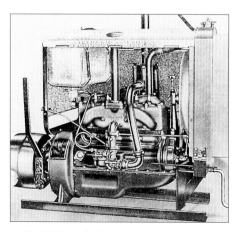

▲ **M-H 'Hercules' stationary power
unit, 1939. Shield has been removed
from side to show detail of unit.**

HERCULES ENGINES

A Hercules 25 hp engine is noted in a 1939 price list. This was sold as a skid-mounted unit equipped with a 14 in. diameter pulley. It ran at 1400 rpm and had a 4 × 4.5 in. bore. Apparently it was commonly used mounted on a truck with a hammer mill or grinder as a mobile outfit for going round farms giving contract services.

A six-cylinder, 40 hp Hercules engine was used to power the No. 14 reaper-thresher and a Hercules engine was used in some of the General Purpose 4WD tractors and the Cleveland tractor.

OTHER ENGINES OF THE PRE-MASSEY FERGUSON PERIOD

A 1944 catalogue offered a 1.75 hp 'B and S' engine of the single-cylinder air-cooled type and a 1948 catalogue offered a 1–1.5 Briggs and Stratton engine. Limited evidence suggests that this latter was possibly model 'N', 'NP' or 'NR'. Advertising reference was also found to a 0.75 hp engine and this may have been another Briggs and Stratton of the 'I' series for which there were ten variants.

On the first M-H baler, Armstrong Siddley diesel and Wisconsin petrol or petrol/tvo engines were used; these were replaced with Ferguson tractor (Standard) engines in the merger period.

The No. 1 M-H potato digger was offered with a New-Way air-cooled engine or a Novo engine.

In the U.K., where M-H had a marketing agreement with Blackstone for their implement range, M-H offered the Blackstone 'Fuelol' 5–7 bhp engine which operated on diesel fuel. This was a one-cylinder vertical engine marketed alongside the M-H No. 2 engine.

Also in the U.K., M-H offered an 'All Steel' elevator which could be had with 1.5 hp engines of Lister, Ruston Hornsby, Bamford or Petter manufacture.

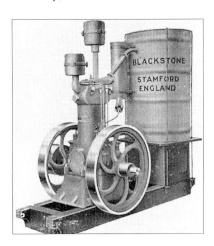

◄ A British-made 5-7 bhp Blackstone 'Fuelol' engine which was marketed by M-H. The engine ran on diesel fuel, 1930s.

POWERSTATIONS

Today MF produces 'Powerstations'. These are diesel engines close coupled to generators. In 1996 there were forty-four basic models to produce a power range of 22 kVA to 880 kVA of 415/240V, 50Hz or 380/220V, 60Hz. They are produced as skid-mounted, container or trailer units according to size and application.

Examples of two MF powerstations with and without canopies, 1994. ►

PUMP JACKS

Pump Jacks were used to transmit power from, typically, the older type one-cylinder stationary engines to pumps. They supplied power more uniformly to the application and eliminated the common twisting and wracking strains when power was supplied through a single gear.

▲ **M-H No. 4 (right 4 hp) and 5 (left 5 hp) pump jacks, 1937.**

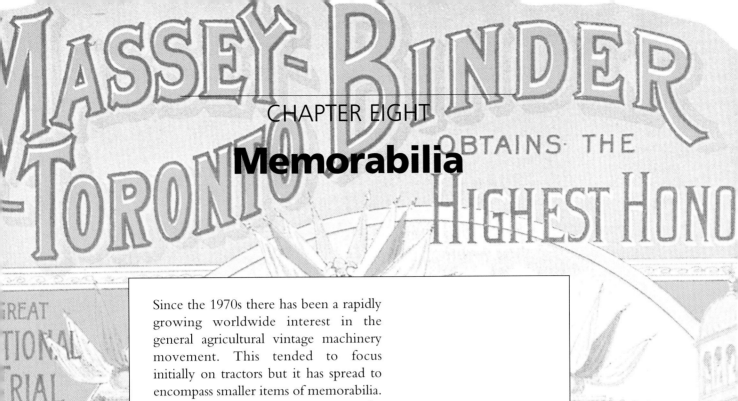

CHAPTER EIGHT

Memorabilia

Since the 1970s there has been a rapidly growing worldwide interest in the general agricultural vintage machinery movement. This tended to focus initially on tractors but it has spread to encompass smaller items of memorabilia. With the exception of literature, the M-H period was much richer in memorabilia than the Ferguson or MF periods. The following types of items have become quite treasured amongst present-day enthusiasts of Massey–Harris, Ferguson and Massey Ferguson.

▲ M-H combine harvester on 1996 Canadian postage stamp.

▲ **MF 165 tractor on Ethiopian 10 birr note. Ferguson brown tractor and portrait of Harry Ferguson on Northern Ireland £20 banknote.**

BANK NOTES AND STAMPS

An MF 165 tractor has been featured on an Ethiopian 10 Birr bank note, whilst the TE Ferguson tractor is currently featured on a Northern Ireland bank note.

In Canada, the famous M-H No. 21 self-propelled combine harvester has been featured in a set of postage stamps commemorating farm and frontier vehicles.

In Australia H.V. McKay and his stripper harvester have been featured on 30 and 15 cent stamps, respectively.

▲ **M-H seed drill box ends.** ▶

CAST-IRON DRILL ENDS

For many years, seed-drill boxes were made of timber but with cast-iron plates in the ends. These frequently had quite ornate manufacturer's badges.

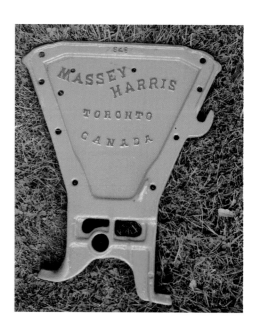

CAST-IRON MACHINERY BADGES

A less frequent type of cast-iron manufacturer's badges are wheel hubs and occasionally manufacturer's plates.

◄ A cast-iron name plate badge which was affixed to the earlier M-H Dickie 'V' model hay tedders.

▲ A sheet steel hub cap off a British-made fertiliser spreader.

▲ A heavy cast hub cap from an M-H 34 land-drive trailer mower.

▲ An M-H tractor rake badge which was fitted to British-made tractor rakes.

CLOCKS AND THERMOMETERS

In North America, a circular single-face office clock was available to dealers for $25. This had a 16 in. diameter face and 20 in. diameter aluminium casing in a baked pearl grey finish. In the case was an electric motor for the clock and three 25 watt bulbs to illuminate the face. The clock was available for 60 or 25 cycle current. The rear of the case was boxed in but with a door to access the bulbs. It was hung by a bead chain. A later type of North American clock had an octagonal-sided face.

In the U.K., a plainer version of the clock was offered. This was a simple 14 in. diameter glass face without case or illuminating bulbs. The electric motor was mounted on the rear in the centre. The clock was suspended by a chain with two attachment points drilled into the glass.

Circular thermometers were also offered to dealers in both the M-H and M-H-F era. Similar humidity meters are understood to also have been offered.

▲ M-H Dealers' clock with surround as issued in North America. The casing is 20 in. diameter and the clock face 16 in. The clock is illuminated by three 25 watt bulbs.

▲ M-H dealers' clock as issued in the U.K, 14 in. diameter face.

▲ Later type of octagonal shaped M-H dealers' clock.

▲ Examples of thermometers from the M-H and M-H-F era.

DEALERS' SIGNS

There were a large number of these. They could be of enamel, pressed tin, timber or neon in the M–H period. Research for this book found an M–H catalogue for dealers' signs. It is probably 1940s era.

▲ Two M-H North American dealers' signs. The base colour was blue, lettering white with orange outline for M-H, and the sign borders were orange.

▲ British dealers' sign. Paint on galvanized sheet steel, 72 in. x 36 in.

▲ A rare M-H engine advertising sign found in the U.K. It is of heavy gauge tin and measures 20 in. x 15 in. (Derek Hackett).

Dealers' Signs c. 1940s

Type	Price $	Description
Circular trade mark	8	enamel, 42 in. diameter
Flat wall sign	25	3-section enamel, mounted on timber, 17 ft long and 2 ft high
Neon sign gold	196.5	8 ft 10 in. long. with 8 in. × 5/8 in. orange neon tube
	(297★)	optional dealer name sign also separately illuminated
Block letter sign	5.75/letter	18 in. high, 4 in. face and 2.5 in. return; enamel on 18 gauge steel
Block letter sign	4.25/letter	9 in. high, 2 in. face and 1.25 in. return; enamel on 18 gauge steel
Double faced hanging sign	50.25 complete	5 ft × 3 ft and 6 in.thick; enamel; optional overhead electric light, pole and hanging equipment

★with extra dealer's name section

▲ British-made M-H dealers' sign. Tin sheet on hardboard with wood surround, 22 in. x 22 in.

▲ British dealers' sign. Hardboard on 2 in. timber frame. Raised lettering nailed to main body. 42 in. diameter.

▲ Old Canadian M-H dealers' sign.

▲ U.K. M-H dealers' sign, made of tin framed in wood and measuring 8 ft. x 20 in. Original colours, now fading, are red, white and blue.

▲ British M-H dealers' sign made of tin sheet and measuring 59 in. x 9 1/2 in., c. 1900.

▲ A double-faced hanging sign.

▲ M-H-F logo from front cover of 1955 M-H-F Farmers' Handy Catalogue.

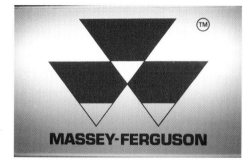

▲ A U.K. Massey-Ferguson dealers' sign from the days before the hyphen was dropped.

▲ Two British dealer's signs, enamelled. These are recent reproductions.

▲ A North American dealers' sign.

▲ A North American dealers' sign.

▲ A North American dealers' sign.

▲ A Ferguson system dealers' sign as distributed in the U.K.

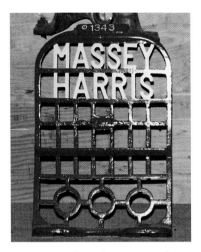

▲ An M-H footplate currently in a Canadian collection.

One of a pair of footplates from a British-made M-H S.A.M. rake. This rake was made by Steels Agricultural Machinery of Edinburgh, Scotland. ▶

FOOTPLATES

Some M-H horse-drawn machinery had distinctive footplates. Two examples are reproduced here, one being of U.K. origin and showing an M-H link to a supply manufacturer.

▲ Silver Ferguson cuff links.

▲ North American AGCO produced commemorative belt buckle.

LAPEL BADGES AND PERSONAL ITEMS

In the U.K. Ferguson, M-H-F and MF produced lapel badges for salesmen. They had a simple lug on the rear side which pressed through a lapel button-hole. Ferguson also made a simple badge which was widely given out to farmers and which was simply the tractor and plough as shown on the salesmen's badges. Silver Ferguson cuff links were given to long serving employees. In 1997 AGCO in North America had commemorative belt buckles made and put on general sale.

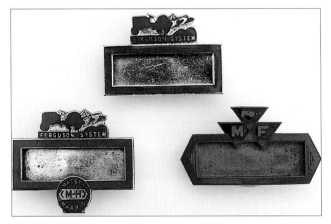

▲ Three salesmen's lapel badges which chart the change from Ferguson to M-H-F to MF.

LITERATURE

There is a wide variety of collectable literature from early days and generally the older the literature, the rarer it is. Such is the interest in literature that some enthusiasts now routinely collect new sale brochures as they are issued. For a long period, Massey, Harris and M-H had their own printing facilities. Early literature and posters were often very colourful, having been hand–designed and produced by their own staff.

Literature types include sales literature, operator's and workshop manuals, equipment parts lists, advertising literature and posters, diaries, calendars, farmer's catalogues, in–house newspapers, product information brochures, sales advice, service information advice leaflets, company notepaper, delivery tags, special celebration literature, correspondence and much, much more! A limited selection is reproduced here.

▲ The front cover of a 1972 48-page brochure produced by MF to celebrate the 125th anniversary of MF's history.

A U.K. dealer's advertisement for the M-H 21 combine. It is made of paper on cardboard, the wooden frame being recent. ▶

▲ A 1947 inspection tag which was attached to tractor Serial No. TE 2609 on delivery.

M-H 1950 calendar issued to North American dealers. ▶

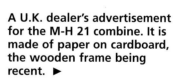

Top section of an M-H calendar found in the U.K. ▶

Farmers' 1944 Handy Catalogue. ▶

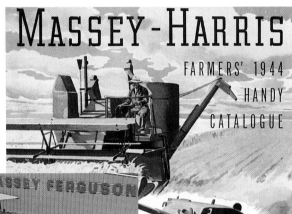

1976 Complete Farm Machinery Guide. ▶

▲ M-H Blackstone catalogue.

MF Buyer's Guide, 1977. ▶

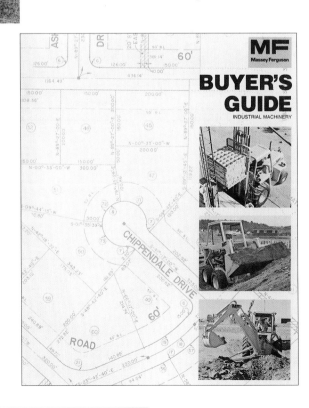

A British M-H plough sales leaflet. ▶

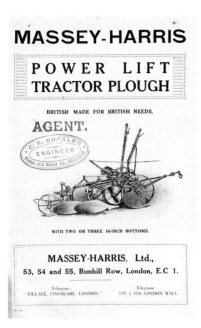

An M-H equipment delivery tag, U.K. ▼

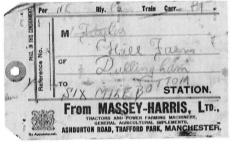

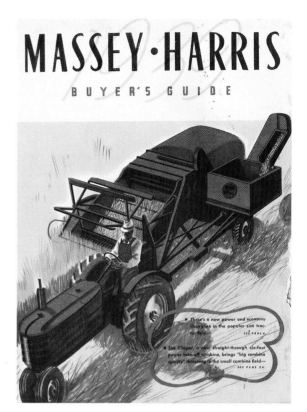

▲ **An M-H Buyer's Guide from the 1940s, U.S.A.**

Ferguson and Massey-Ferguson operator instruction books.

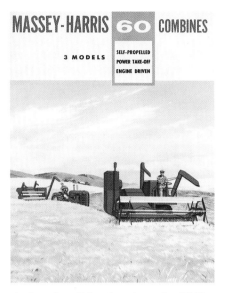

▲ An advertising brochure for M-H 60 combines, U.S.A.

▲ An advertising brochure for M-H 92 and 82 combines, U.S.A.

▲ M-H cultivator brochure, 1930s, Canada.

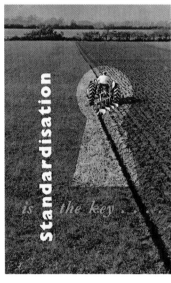

▲ MF advertising brochure, U.K., 1950s.

▲ Ferguson service manual, U.S.A.

▲ Ferguson implements parts list, U.K.

▲ MF 500 series tractor brochure, U.K.

▲ Brochure for Ferguson service tools, U.K.

▲ MF 85 tractor operator's manual, U.S.A.

▲ MF Dynashift brochure, 1993, U.S.A.

▼ M-H-F compliments slip, U.K.

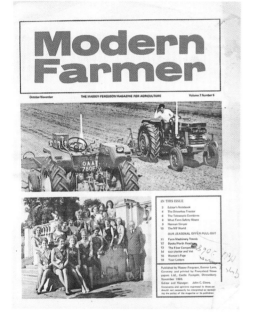

▲ An issue of the U.K. MF Modern Farmer magazine.

▲ MF industrial highway tractor brochure, 1991, U.K.

▲ Ferguson 35 tractor operator's manual, U.S.A.

AGCO Australia product catalogue, 1996. ▶

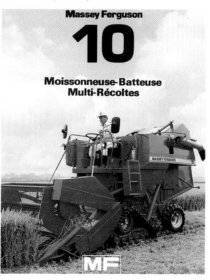

◀ 1986 French brochure for the MF 10 tracked rice combine harvester.

SEATS, CAST-IRON AND TIN

There is a considerable range of cast-iron seats from the 'Massey lineage', a few of which are very rare. Most are of North American origin, but two were cast in the U.K. These can be identified as being of 'Massey' origins by lettering or numbering. After the end of the cast-iron seat era, at about the turn of the century, tin or pressed steel seats became the fashion for economic reasons. Most M-H tin or pressed steel seats were plain with no recognisable M-H lettering or number. However, two were made identifiable, one with Massey-Harris impressed in the rim and the other with Massey-Harris cut out.

The Massey range of seats rightly includes those of manufacturers of equipment which Massey marketed, and also Sawyer Massey. These include Buckeye, the Rake and Akron. There are also Patterson and Wisner seats, but apparently no Harris seats.

Markings of seats of the Massey lineage:

Cast-iron

Akron Mower Newcastle
Buckeye
J.O. Wisner (plain seat, no lettering)
Massey
Massey Buckeye
Massey Mower
Mas ey Toronto (casting error)
Massey To onto (casting error)
Massey-Harris Canada Z 82
Massey-Harris Dickie
Massey Harris England
M. 208 (none known to exist)
P. W. &. Co.
P 287 (later tin version P 2871/2)
P 2516
Sawyer's
Sawyer's 30
Sawyer's W30
Sawyer's Canadian Harvester
  Hamilton. Ont
S.51 (hinged on cast tool box 182)
SU4 M-H
S 572 (solid bicycle style/size seats)
S 847
The Rake
The Rake Newcastle
The Rake Toronto
Toronto 3
Toronto 34
Wisners Royal
Z 82 M-H
Z 82
79 seats: 79, 7.9, 7'9, 7_9, 79 M-H

Tin or Pressed Steel

Massey-Harris (impressed in outer rim)
Massey-Harris (cut out of inner rim)
Unmarked plain types not readily identifiable as M-H

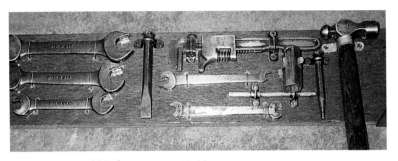

▲ Original tool kit for an M-H 12-20 tractor.

▲ A selection of implement spanners collected in Canada.

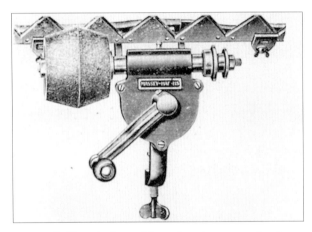

▲ M-H knife grinder, with optional emery wheel.

▲ Knife grinder.

SPANNERS AND TOOLS

Many M-H spanners were stamped M-H and/or numbered. M-H marketed a considerable range of tools, including a bench vice with a bold M-H cast into the lower jaw. Another bench tool was a hand-powered 'Handy Knife Grinder'. The classic Ferguson spanner, which was used for measuring plough furrow widths as well as adjusting two of the commonest sizes of nuts on implements and tractors, is now also valued by collectors.

▲ A selection of implement spanners collected in the U.K.

▲ Grease gun and spanners as issued with new Ferguson TE tractors. The upper spanner is marked in inches; the lower later one is marked in centimetres.

▲ M-H multi-purpose vice.

▲ M-H oil cans.

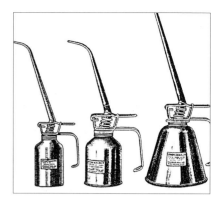

▲ M-H pump type Symons oil cans.

TOOLBOXES AND TOOLBOX LIDS, CAST-IRON AND TIN/PRESSED STEEL

Toolboxes and their lids have become highly collectable. The tin or pressed steel boxes with M-H or Massey–Harris pressed into the lid, although perhaps not as interesting, are quite scarce because most have rusted away.

Examples of M-H tool boxes and tool box lids

▲ A Ferguson dealers' demonstration model was used to demonstrate the advantage of the Ferguson three point linkage over a single point linkage system. The two models can be seen to be different – the lower is the older type of the Ford Ferguson era. ▼

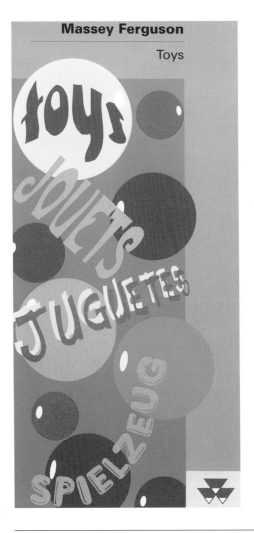

TOYS AND MODELS

Ferguson produced large, working, table-top models of his tractor plus plough to demonstrate the safety aspects of the three-point linkage. Most dealers were given one of these to demonstrate the Ferguson system to customers. Some of these are still in existence, including both the Ford Ferguson and Ferguson tractor designs.

Many external companies have made small model tractors and implements of the Massey-Harris, Ferguson and M-H-F tractor and implement ranges which have now become keenly sought after collector's items. At present, a range of companies manufacture varying standards of models from the old tractor ranges, often in limited editions.

MF itself has marketed a range of agricultural and industrial tractor models and implements for many years. Some of the models are of 'ride-on' size for children. In 1983, the U.K. Powerpart catalogue listed 18 types of models.

▲ British-made toys – M-H 744 tractor and manure spreader (made by Dinky), c.1950.

◄ 1996 U.K. MF toy catalogue.

Powerpart Model and Toy Range in the U.K. 1983

Toy or Model (scale)	Description	Price £
Remote control MF loader	battery operated remote control	14.33
MF 50D digger and loader	die-cast model, fully working	10.60
Deluxe farm set (1:16)	2805 tractor, 4-furrow plough, tandem disc harrow, steel flare box wagon, calf and cow, storage barn	33.86
MF loader construction kit	easy build model of die-cast parts	10.75
MF 760 combine harvester (1:32)	cast metal and plastic with some moving parts	7.05
MF 130 seed drill (1:32)	die-cast metal and plastic	1.46
Plough (1:16)	four-furrow with raise and lower function	6.48
Tandem disc harrow	with folding arms and adjustable wheel height	9.00
MF 760 combine	working model with rotating wheels, gear drive auger, swivel grain spout etc.	21.95
MF 2805 tractor (1:20)	rugged die-cast metal, dual wheels etc.	16.45
MF 275 tractor (1:16)	full steering action, roll over protection canopy, deep tread tyres	14.22
Gravity feed wagon (1:16)	opening and closing gate, hitches to 1:16 scale model tractors	9.06
Auger elevator (1:16)	Archimedes screw type with adjustable height	6.40
Barge wagon (1:16)	120 degree front axle turning and swing-up tail gate	5.38
Deluxe spreader (1:16)	belt driven beater	5.38
Pedal tractor	shatterproof plastic, chain drive	39.00
Trailer for pedal tractor	shatterproof plastic, two wheel	7.02
Pedal tractor with front loader	manually operated loader with lift and tip function	46.43

◄ **MF loader construction kit.**

**MF barge ►
wagon.**

**MF deluxe ►
spreader.**

◄ **MF 760 combine harvester and MF 130 seed drill.**

**MF pedal ►
tractor with
front loader.**

Some examples of the 1983 MF Powerpart toy range.

▲ MF presentation pack of penknives.

WRITING PENS, PENKINIVES, PLAYING CARDS AND STATIONARY

Both M-H and Ferguson gave away writing pens, often with a floating model incorporated. Ferguson also produced a penknife and M-H a set of playing cards.

▲ A Ferguson penknife and ball point pen with 'floating' tractor.

▲ M-H blotter.

Special sighting poles made by M-H for markng out fields for ploughing. ▶

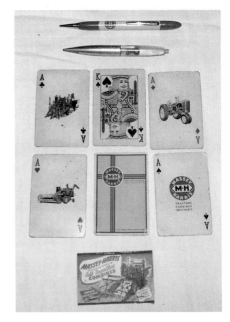

▲ M-H playing cards and biros.

▲ M-H even badged their own tyres.

AND OTHER ITEMS...

So much remains to be found...or has been, but is not widely known of. The diversity of possible items is very large and deserves careful preservation.

CHAPTER NINE

Trends, Innovations and the Present Status of Massey Ferguson

AUTOTRONIC

Autotronic is an automated control and information system fitted on certain MF tractors. It has 19 functions operating in five different areas of the tractor to monitor driver actions and eliminate the repetitive tasks of daily operation. It ensures that 4WD is engaged when needed and switches it off when it is not, all at speeds of 9 mph and over. It also engages differential lock when needed (after manual engagement) and disengages it when not. Similarly pto is controlled by engaging the pto clutch gradually and disengaging it when necessary, e.g. at engine start up or in overload situations. Autotronic also prevents inappropriate gear or range selections.

▲ Autotronic links functions and controls, automatically, 1995.

CELLULAR MANUFACTURING

At the Coventry U.K. tractor manufacturing plant, which has produced tractors continuously since the first TE-20 grey Ferguson rolled off the line in 1946, a revolution in factory organisation took place in 1995 with the advent of Cellular Manufacturing. This involved the relocation of almost all its 1400 machine tools. The aim was to enhance quality production. The cells are small teams of multi-skilled employees who essentially form their own mini factories within the large factory environment. Under a cell leader they produce families of completed components and minor sub-assemblies for the next cell in the production process. Each cell takes responsibility for its own quality, costs, lead times, inventory and scheduling. The essence of the scheme is the empowerment and involvement of employees in the total production process. Each cell also has its own cafeteria area. Complementary to cellular manufacturing has been the adoption of the disciplines of the International Standards Organisation System for Quality Management, ISO 9002.

1	Transaxle
2	Chassis Assembly & Paint
3	Engine & Front Axle Assembly
4	Bulkhead Assembly
5	G1 Final Assembly
6	H1 Final Assembly
7	G2 Final Assembly
8	H2 Final Assembly & Fender
9	Cab Preparation
10	Final Finish
11	Customer Tractor Validation
12	Paint Shop
13	CKD Packing
14	Wheel & Tyre
781	Transmission Assembly
782	Hydraulic Assembly & Test
783	Rear Axle Assembly

▲ Cellular assembly at the U.K. Coventry plant.

MF 390 coming off the production line at Coventry, England, U.K. in 1996. Note how the next tractor to come off the line will be an entirely different model and specification. Each tractor can now be manufactured to different specifications. ▶

DATATRONIC

Datatronic is an electronic monitoring and recording system for a tractor's functions. Besides monitoring and recording it can also optimise any activity, e.g. fuel consumption or wheel slip, in both physical and financial terms. The recorded activities in a particular field can be downloaded and transferred to the farm office information management system and the data can be used in field, crop and machinery budgeting and costing. The system has four programmable memories which can be identified as, for example, a different implement, driver or contractors' customers, etc. Field settings can be optimised by storing reference information which may be referred to.

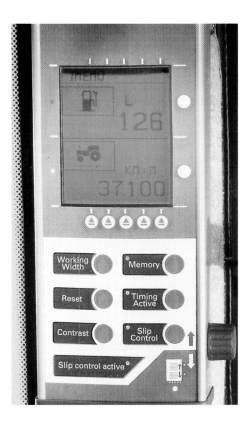

◄ The datatronic display panel in the tractor cab, 1995.

Datatronic II System Functions

Function	Display	Benefit
Engine	instantaneous rpm	control precise engine speed
pto	instantaneous rpm	maintain precise pto speed
Forward speed	true ground speed	ensure precise planting and sowing rates
Fuel/hr	current rate of consumption	select gear and engine speed for best economy
Acres/hr	rate whilst implement is in work position	set and operate implements for best productivity
Cost factor	index number incorporating the above items	compare the cost effect of various operation techniques
Wheelslip	instantaneous display of actual wheel slip	improve operating efficiency
Wheelslip limit	overrides 3-point hitch depth control to maintain pre-set wheelslip limit	automatically ensure best operating efficiency and prevent excess spin and wear
Acres worked	total area covered based on implement width and time the 3-point hitch is in work position	measure productivity and approximate field sizes
Fuel used	amount used since last reset	plan refuelling needs
Fuel reserve	time remaining based on fuel used and current consumption	avoid running out of fuel, schedule refuelling needs
Distance	distance travelled since last reset	measure distances
Counter	interacts with implement sensor to count events such as bales made	measure productivity, determine yields, and assesses transportation and storage needs
Next service	hours to next scheduled service	prevent breakdowns due to improper servicing
Time elapsed	time since last reset	determine operator productivity and schedule events
Date	current time and date	avoid missing important events
Temperature	air temperature outside the cab	respond when high or low temperatures require action

DYNASHIFT TRANSMISSION

Dynashift transmission is a powershift gearbox enabling on the move speed changes in small increments within each gear. It is in essence a sophisticated modern development of the old multi-power system of clutchless speed changes within a set gear. Dynashift is based on a simple design concept and is mechanically efficient enabling over 97 per cent of available power to be transmitted through the gearbox. It has no potentially unreliable rotating seals and is controlled by two electrovalves and two clutches. It can be operated in conjunction with a forward/reverse shuttle. The operator is free to change speeds by using the synchromesh main gear ranges and the dynashift ranges within each gear. There is full protection against inadvertent selection of a wrong range because the tractor's Autotronic control systems will prevent the change if the speed of the tractor is too great for the gears to be properly engaged.

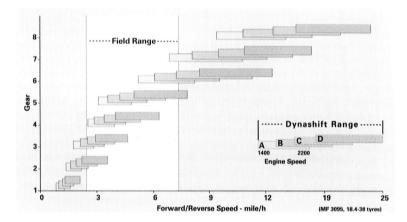

▲ **Dynashift speed ranges on an MF 3095 tractor, 1992.**

Cutaway diagram ▶ of a Dynashift gearbox.

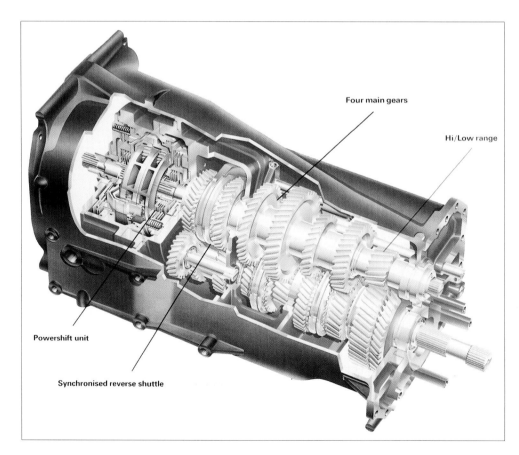

DYNATORQUE

Dynatorque is a Perkins engine development. It is based on a piston design which has a unique four-lobed combustion bowl which optimises and controls air motion in the cylinder. It enhances fuel and air mixing for more effective and efficient combustion than occurs with conventional direct injection systems. Because of this precise combustion control, the time between the start of fuel injection and the start of combustion is shorter. The rate of pressure rise in the cylinder is lower and less noise results. The main benefits are increased maximum torque, increase in torque backup and more power at all engine rpms.

The Quadram principle is incorporated in the new Perkins 1000 series engines. Two zones in engine response at different engine rpms have been identified. The upper zone (A) of between 1800 and 2200 rpm provides high torque and fast torque rise for heavy cultivation and heavy pto work, whilst the lower zone (B) of between 1400 and 1800 rpm for general applications and light pto work provides high torque but with less variations in load the torque rise is more progressive.

Quadram combustion characteristics, 1993. ▼

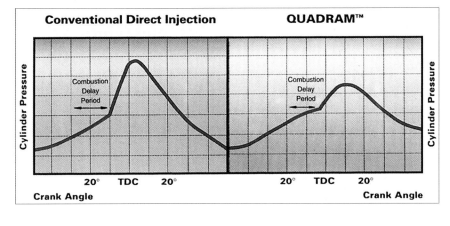

Dynatorque rpm zonal characteristics, 1993. ▼

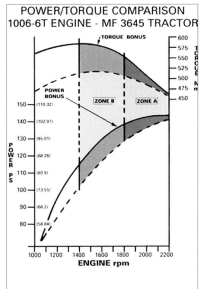

TRACTOR REBUILD OPERATIONS

In the past, Ferguson paraffin tractors could be rebuilt to high specifications. One such scheme was that offered in South Africa and called the 'Silver Star'. They were rebuilt to 'good as new' standard. Ferguson in the U.K. also rebuilt used tractors and they were turned out with red mudguards.

From the 1980s MF has been involved internationally in tractor rebuild projects. This is a service which is targeted at farm machinery graveyards which are not an

uncommon site in the developing areas of the world. Frequently these graveyards are created not by an inability of local people to repair machines, but rather by logistical difficulties of finance and supply of spare parts which frequently have their roots in inadequate government administrations. Such problems are beyond the resolution of local people and projects.

In 1992 MF estimated that there were 100,000 disabled and worn out tractors lying idle in Africa alone. After 10 years of operations, MF had rebuilt over 5000 tractors in 30 countries. Besides the rebuilding of tractors, MF try to ensure that necessary training is given to re-establish qualified and skilled labour as well as more effective operators, and establish a sustainable parts supply structure and technical support capability.

Advertisement for the South African Silver Star Ferguson tractor reconditioning service. ▶

'Rehab' programmes have attractive financial benefit for poor countries in that they can save on foreign exchange and often end up with three working tractors for the price of one new one. Two basic services are offered, namely rehabilitation and ROC (rehabilitation, overhaul and certification). ROC upgrades the machine to the latest specification and includes full warranty and a new registration, making it equivalent to a new tractor.

Recently, two new standards have been introduced to the ROC scheme. These are the ROC Gold and Silver standards. The gold standard offers a tractor that is new in everything but name whilst the silver standard puts the emphasis on providing a tractor in full working order and replacing or overhauling components which are unserviceable or in need of repair.

Typical replacement parts for an ROC Gold MF 290 tractor are:

- remanufactured engine
- new clutch assembly
- overhauled gearbox/hydraulics
- new steering
- new sheetmetal
- new tyres
- new battery
- new radiator

TRAINING

Both M-H and Ferguson have a history of training personnel and customers in the use of machinery and its maintenance, and in marketing. Ferguson developed world famous training centres in North America and the U.K. Initially these were for the practical aspects of machinery operation and maintenance. Ferguson recognised that the introduction of his mounted implements was a completely new concept for farmers to grasp and went to great lengths to ensure that his equipment was properly demonstrated—a task which he often took part in himself.

▲ **Classroom instruction at the original Ferguson training centre in Coventry.**

▲ **Workshop instruction during the 1950s at the Ferguson training centre in Coventry.**

▲ **Practical instruction at the MF training centre.**

Ferguson's original U.K. training centre near Coventry lives on to this day, albeit in modified form. It is now the Central Training Centre for MF worldwide. It has a diverse range of training activities which includes:

- training of all levels of dealer organisation staff, including managers, salesmen, parts specialists and workshop supervisors etc.
- training of machinery demonstrators, mechanics and machine operators
- training of trainers
- technical product training.

The centre undertakes its activities both at the U.K. centre and by overseas assignments. In 1996 the approximate personnel throughput at the centre was 1200 from the U.K. and 400 from overseas. About 1600 personnel were trained in overseas locations by Coventry training staff and it is estimated that resident trainers overseas train a further 5000.

The centre occupies a 20 ha site at Stoneleigh near Coventry and was established in 1953. Over 100,000 students have been trained at the centre. Besides the farm area, the centre has modern lecture rooms and state of the art workshops.

▲ **The MF training centre at Coventry, U.K, serves MF on a worldwide basis.**

▲ **A modern lecture room at the MF training centre in Coventry, 1996.**

▲ **Training in paddy field mechanisation and rice growing at the TAFE training centre near Madras in India.**

▲ **School children on a visit to 'J' farm.**

TAFE of India, which is one of MF's oldest associate companies, operates a training school at the village of Kelambakkam, some 30 km outside Madras. It is called the 'J' farm after the late chairman Shri S. Anantharamkrishnan who was known as 'J'. The farm site was identified by him and had been in operation since 1964. The 'J' farm is somewhat different to the MF training centre in Coventry in that it actively pursues crop production research and demonstration to farmers as well as dealing with training in machinery use and maintenance. The training centre also promotes integrated rural development programmes, including health care. The dissemination of crop production research results is mainly through TAFE's quarterly publication, *Farm Progress,* which is sent free to farmers, agricultural scientists, government officials, agricultural research institutes and universities.

In a lighter vein, MF in North America distributes *Farm Profit* which gives advice and product news to farmers, and MF marketing in the U.K. distributes *Voice International* which records MF activities around the world.

◄ **An example of the 'Farm Progress' magazine produced by TAFE of India.**

▲ 'Farm Profit', produced in North America, is published four times per year.

◀ The 'Voice International' magazine records MF activities around the world.

YIELD MONITORING

MF is involved with ongoing trials with scientists of different disciplines in the development of yield monitoring systems. This uses global positioning satellite (GPS) information and a yield monitor on a combine harvester to monitor yield on a field almost yard by yard. The system is also being developed for other crops, such as potatoes and sugar beet. MF combines equipped with this technology have been developing the system for several years. Combines are equipped with DATAVISION, which is a display system monitoring combine performance and output on an electronic display for the driver. Data across the field is cumulatively stored and transferred on a 'smart card' to a farm office computer. The output of the activity is a yield map of the field which shows where the low and high yielding areas occur. This data can be translated into financial aspects of crop productivity and even a map of gross margins for different areas of the field. Using the yield pattern established across the field, analysis of soils, weed growth etc. can indicate how inputs should be modified

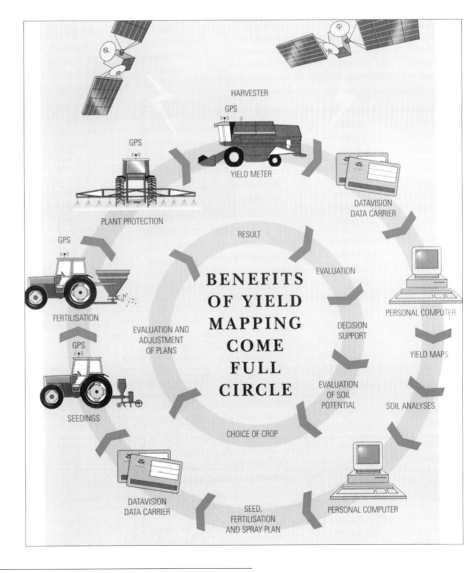

in different parts of the field to benefit the next crop. Initial indications are that cereal growing profitability can be increased by £20–£40/ha by using the yield monitoring data and adjustment of subsequent inputs.

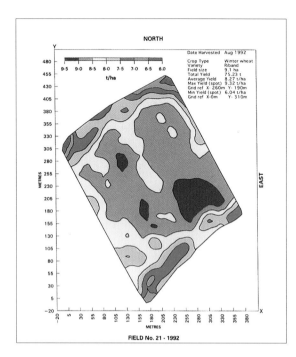

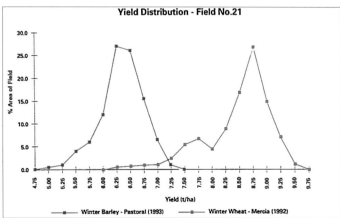

▲ Typical map and graphical data from the MF Yield Monitoring System, 1993.

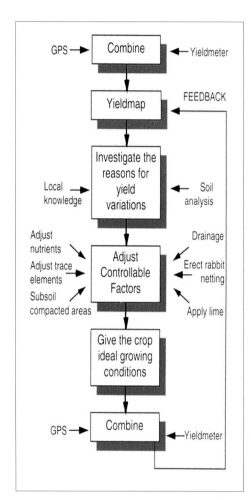

▲ Diagram illustrating how the yieldmap data from one crop is used to improve the yield of the next, 1995.

AGCO: THE MASSEY FERGUSON HOLDING COMPANY

AGCO was founded in 1990 and is based in Duluth, Georgia, U.S.A. The company started with the purchase of the Deutz Allis Corporation from KHD in Germany, and then went on to purchase other agricultural machinery companies, including Massey Ferguson. Since 1990 the company has come to have some 7000 dealers in 140 countries on six continents. Additionally it has relationships with other companies such as Mengele and Sohne, Ursus, Droninborg and Renault Agriculture.

In 1996 the French Beauvais and British Coventry tractor plants made about equal values of MF tractors, but they specialise in producing different series of tractors. It was reported in 1996 that MF accounted for about 64 per cent of AGCO's turnover.

AGCO Acquisitions from 1990 to 1996

Year	Acquisition
1990	Deutz-Allis from KHD
1991	Hesston Corporation
	White Tractors
1992	North American distribution rights for SAME Tractors
1993	50% of Agricredit Acceptance Corporation
	North American distribution rights for Massey Ferguson White-New Idea
1994	Massey Ferguson's worldwide holdings
	Remaining 50% of Agricredit Acceptance Corporation
	McConnell Tractors resulting in the AGCOSTAR articulated tractor range
	Black Machine (planter range)
1995	North American distribution rights for Landini Tractors
	Ag. Equipment Group (Glencoe, Tye, Farmhand)
1996	Agricultural equipment business of Iochpe-Maxion of Brazil

MF INDUSTRIAL

The only plant now remaining which makes 'MF' Industrial products is the FERMEC factory at Manchester in the U.K. This is based on the old M-H factory on Barton Dock Road, Stretford. The factory had originally been owned by the Ministry of Aircraft Production and operated by Ford to assemble and test Merlin engines. In 1944 M-H took over the site and started producing trailers for agricultural equipment and then proceeded to make parts for other MF factories in the U.K. before coming to specialise in industrial equipment.

The sales and marketing activities for MF Industrials were acquired by Case in late 1996 from FERMEC Holdings Ltd. At the time of this acquisition FERMEC

▲ The FERMEC MF industrial factory at Manchester, U.K, 1996.

Holdings had five principal investments for their operations as follows.

In early 1997 FERMEC dropped the MF badge name bringing to an end the era of 'MF' industrial equipment.

FERMEC Holding Principal Investments

Investment	Country	Principal activity
Fermec Manufacturing Ltd	England	manufacture of backhoe loaders and associated products
Fermec International Ltd	England	distribution of backhoe loaders and associated products
Fermec North America Ltd	England	marketing of backhoe loaders and associated products in North America
Fermec S.A.	France	distribution of backhoe loaders and associated products
Fermec Baumaschinen GmbH	Germany	distribution of backhoe loaders and associated products

Maintaining past links! At an exhibition in May 1997, FERMEC, after dropping the MF badge, display an MF 3305 industrial tractor which will be placed in their museum. ▼

THE PRESENT SIGNIFICANCE OF MF IN THE AGCO PORTFOLIO

In early 1997 AGCO announced that it had acquired Fendt and Deutz–Argentina. This has somewhat reduced the contribution that MF makes to total sales in the AGCO group to 49 per cent. However, MF still contributes by far the largest part of AGCO's sales.

Projected Contribution of Individual Companies to AGCO Sales in Early 1997

Company	Per cent contribution
Massey Ferguson	49
Fendt	20
Parts	15
Deutz–Argentina	4
Gleaner	3
Hesston	3
Allis	2
White–New Idea	2
White Tractor	1
Other	1

THE NEW 1997 MF TRACTOR SERIES

On Saturday, May 31st 1997 (the day on which it had been decided to finally close this book!) AGCO launched a new eight-model range of MF tractors. They are known as the 4200 series and replace the 300 series. They are being made at the U.K. Coventry plant. Although they are equipped with modern features, they are of a standard and conventional build in the 52-110 hp range, designed to meet the wide ranging demands of the complex variety of worldwide agricultural enterprises. Perkins engines are used in all models with the three-cylinder models using the 'green' 900 series Perkins engines. Commentators make the point that operators will find the most difference in the cabs, with some 16% or more space and better all-round visibility. Standard, LoProfile and HiVisibility models will be offered.

▲ 'Drive into the 21st century in the luxury of the cab of the 1997 MF 4255 tractor.'

Some Specifications of the New MF 4200 Series Tractors

	4215	4220	4225	4235	4245	4255	4260	4270
Engine BS hp	54.3	65	69	79	88	99	106	114
pto kW	32.9	38.4	42.4	49.7	55.7	63.8	68.7	72.9
Aspiration	Natural	Turbo	Natural	Natural	Turbo	Wastegate turbo	Natural	Natural
Cylinders	3	3	4	4	4	4	6	6
Capacity cu. in.	165	165	248	248	244	244	356	365
Transmissions	8-speed shuttle,12-speed synchro, 12-speed shuttle or 18-Speedshift according to model and options							
Max. lift capacity kg	2200	2200	2600	2600	3000	4000	4000	5000
Wt. 2WD kg ★	2385	2385	3146	3456	3509	3509	3871	3871
Wt. 4WD kg ★★	2635	2635	3396	3730	3730	3730	4105	4105

*With assistor rams   **Standard cab etc. and full fuel, oil, eater and standard wheels/tyres

A NEW BALER AND TELESCOPIC HANDLER FOR 1997

Two new products of 1997 announced in the U.K. are MF badged machines. The baler is produced by an MF sister company in the AGCO group, whilst the handler is produced in France. The 130SB series balers are 'centre line' balers producing conventional type bales. Whilst centre line balers are presently in vogue for large round and square balers, centre line types producing conventional size bales have been produced by various manufacturers, including MF, in the past. Three models will eventually be released and all are suitable for small power tractors. They are designed and built by Hesston.

▲ **A 13OSB series MF baler.**

Some Specifications of the MF 130SB Balers

	MF 135	MF 137	MF 139
Overall width in.	93	101	101
Overall length with chute in.	201	204	204
Weight Kg	1224	1383	1497
Bale cross section in.	14 × 18	14 × 18	14 × 18
Bale length in.	12 × 52	12 × 52	12 × 52
Density control	Spring loaded rail	Spring loaded rail	Rail or hydraulic
Pickup width in.	61.1	75.9	75.9
No. of tines	33 double	42 double	56 double
Plunger strokes/min.	92	100	100
Twine balls	4	4	6
Standard tyres	7.60 × 15	9.5 × 14	11L × 14
pto requirement hp	30	35	35
Optional equipment	Hydraulic pickup lift, hydraulic bale tension, bale chute extension, bale chute quarter turn, trailer hitch, lighting kit		

The launch of the MF 8937 Telescopic Handler alomst marks a turn back to industrial products! This machine brings back memories of the MF 24 Telescopic Handler of the 1980s. The MF 8937 appears to be targeted at the farm market against a perceived large growth area in the next few years for this type of product. It is being offered with a normal 57 kW and turbo 78 kW engine.

▲ **The French-made MF 8937 Telescopic Handler.**

Brief Specifications of the MF 8937 Telescopic Handler

Engine	Perkins 4-cylinder 1004-4 or 4T
Max. height capacity kg	3000
Max. reach capacity kg	1200
Max. reach m	4
Max. tear out force kg	5500
Transmission	2-speed hydrostatic
Tyres in.	24 or 20
Unladen weight kg	6500
Working speed range 24 or 20 in. tyres	0-8 km/hr or 0-7 km/hr
Road speed range 24 or 20 in. tyres	0-30 km/hr or 0-27 km/hr

OPTIONS AND ACCESSORIES FOR THE 21ST CENTURY

M-H, Ferguson and MF have, over the years, always offered various accessories for their tractors. AGCO now offer an extremely sophisticated range of accessories for the current MF tractor models in the MF 200, 300, 3000, 4200 and 8100 series. Perhaps the most significantly new and recent group of accessories are those of an electronic nature for tractor management. The driver of an MF tractor can now work in a variable environment of technical sophistication and comfort. The accessories are classified into groups as follows and are variously available for the different models of tractors.

Cab accessories

Air conditioning
Air suspension seats
Carbon filter
Passenger seat
Seat cover, washable
Safety seat belt

Tractor accessories

Belly weights
Front weights/frame
Front weight frame extension
Tow hitch weight
Wheel weights front and rear

Linkage and pto accessories

Active transport control to cushion shocks from heavy implements
Auxiliary fuel tank

Creeper gearbox
Dual control to enable adjustment from the cab of the implement in parallel motion
Economy pto for use with low power pto driven equipment
Engine air pre-cleaner for dusty conditions
External flow kit to provide oil feed and return for external hydraulic valves
Front linkage and pto
Hitches and drawbars for all applications
Linkage ropes for quick hitching without leaving the operator seat
Spool valves for hydraulically controlled implements
Toolbox – large capacity

Electric options

Clock – digital or analogue
Electric plug to provide 12v electrical supply for ancillary equipment
Worklights to extend the working day

See and be seen

Beacons
Front fenders
Locking fuel cap
Mirror extension
Rear hitch viewing mirror
Rear wiper
Telescopic mirror
Trailer brake valve

Tractor Management

Optional equipment	Principal monitoring and recording functions
Tractronic 1000	Forward speed, work rate, travel log, counter for bales etc. For all machines
Tractronic 1000 Mk. 2	For autotronic tractors – forward speed, pto speed, area worked, time elapsed
Tractronic 1200	Aids cost reduction and yield increases – litre/ha, travel log; time, unit rate, rpm; area, speed, time. For MF 200, 500, 600 and most other makes of machine
Tractronic 300	For information on spraying and fertilising with MF 300 tractors – ground speed, part/total area worked, pto shaft speed, litre/ha, litre left in tank stopwatch facility
Tractronic 3000	As for Tractronic 300 but for 3000 series autotronic tractors
Tractronic 6000	As for tractronic 3000 but for 6100 series tractors with addition of work rate and litres/min.
Datatronic	Top of the range monitor. Information at touch of a button. Speed/area/distance, work rate and engine rpm, counter pto/speed, wheel slip and limit facility, fuel used/ha and total, cost factor/service due
Datatronic electrical switch	Mechanical switch, magnet and reed switch, hydraulic switch kits

Other lines

Assistor rams
Audio equipment
Cigar lighter
Engine pre-heater
Exhaust conversion kits
Fender extensions
Hitches, drawbars and accessories
Horizonatal exhaust kit
Hydraulic couplers
Hydraulic lines for loaders
Interchangeable pto shafts for
540/1000 rpm
Linkage accessories
Lubricants and chemicals
Reverse bleeper
Safety frames and sunshades
Seat accesssories
Speed shift
Speedometer
Trailer tipping pipes
Tool box
Wheel wedges

▲ **The top of the range
14 hp 4WD MF 4270
tractor, 1997.**

APPENDIX ONE

Sales and Production

The following tables are reproduced from a selection of old data. There are some inconsistencies between data in individual tables, but unfortunately there is no way of reconciling them. Question marks indicate that the figures are uncear in the original documents.

M-H MACHINERY SALES
UK, 1892-1949

Machine	1892	1893	1894	1895	1896	1897	1898	1899	1900	1901	1902	1903	1904	1905	1906	1907	1908	1909
1 Tractors																		
2 Ploughs																	36	11
3 Grub Breakers																		
4 One Way Disc																		
5 Disc Harrows																	4	9
6 T.D. Harrows																		
7 S.T. Harrows							28								36	36	54	69
8 Cultivators	10	109	1085	1867	1633	1844	1531	1396	1085	1162	894	842	820	510	445	313	354	316
9 Drills			5		21	39	31	22	85	55	62	70	68	42	48	66	120	119
10 Sowers																		
11 Scufflers																	???	??
12 Mowers	51	45	119	103	72	151	408	461	453	398	604	646	524	383	461	632	???	???
13 Tedders			50		40		36	106	189	112	186	272	321	118	93	128	???	140
14 Horse Rakes	71	33	91	68	55	84	153	121	127	140	154	186	189	123	156	175	???	143
15 Hay Loaders																		
16 Binders	1170	741	1112	789	1026	1691	2568	3523	2975	1961	2046	1856	1479	1284	1565	1763	1656	1753
17 Combines																		
18 Steel Threshers																		
19 Straw Trussers															33	51	85	77
20 Ensilage Cutters																		
21 Elevator Diggers																		
22 Manure Spreaders																		
23 Hammer Mills																		
24 Cream Separators																	52	52
25 Reapers	1	2	3	1	1		8	4	2	1	7	23	22	25	15	8	19	27
26 Side Rakes																		70
27 Grinders																		
28 Spike Tooth Harrows																		
29 Engines																		
30 Pulverators																		
31 Sprayers																		
32 Toolbars																		
Yearly Total	1303	930	2465	2828	2848	3809	4763	5635	4870	3829	4953	3895	3423	2485	2852	3172	3609	3387

Machine	1910	1911	1912	1913	1914	1915	1916	1917	1918	1919	1920	1921	1922	1923	1924	1925	1926	1927
1 Tractors																		1
2 Ploughs					2		130	248	810	1596	1353	130	68	58	37	191	127	142
3 Grub Breakers																		
4 One Way Disc																		
5 Disc Harrows	8	9	12	21	30	53	92	80	697	253	232	81	40	42	13	106	70	70
6 T.D. Harrows																		
7 S.T. Harrows	113	130	268	350	496	601	642	576	1216	1319	1010	357	387	705	682	980	895	820
8 Cultivators	381	309	268	303	273	290	310	450	559	223	220	62	65	65	48	70	64	53
9 Drills	175	152	147	288	365	931	953	1811	3161	1335	1627	190	173	197	227	283	235	193
10 Sowers																		
11 Scufflers	73	100	142	108	229	260	267	420	332	22	947	295	387	347	277	338	486	361
12 Mowers	667	610	608	781	671	813	1068	1863	1106	889	886	250	289	539	671	571	633	558
13 Tedders	173	108	108	149	145	114	125	125	68	34	41	22	16	7	32	44	54	8
14 Horse Rakes	178	195	216	228	216	236	299	349	127	199	187	93	140	203	294	239	191	156
15 Hay Loaders					13	97	69	776	567	356	535	110	73	131	163	224	187	168
16 Binders	1569	1224	1308	1461	1579	2399	2465	3143	3946	1512	1645	349	740	653	951	880	749	492
17 Combines																		
18 Steel Threshers																		
19 Straw Trussers	86	65	79	49	50	116	106	131	391	246	173	87	50	32	53	34	32	30
20 Ensilage Cutters										3	70	21	45	52	40	12	10	4
21 Elevator Diggers																		
22 Manure Spreaders		1									2		1		1	1		
23 Hammer Mills																		
24 Cream Separators	9	9										1	1	51	125	137	223	229
25 Reapers	23	5	7	6	9	5	20	29		21	8	2	3			6	1	1
26 Side Rakes	158	70	43	83	61	48	78	27	39	13	3					1		
27 Grinders												1	15	4				
28 Spike Tooth Harrows													2					
29 Engines														46	31	27	50	56
30 Pulverators																		
31 Sprayers																		
32 Toolbars																		
Yearly Total	3613	2987	3206	3827	4139	5963	6624	10028	13019	8021	8919	2051	2495	3132	3651	4144	4007	3352

Machine	1928	1929	1930	1931	1932	1933	1934	1935	1936	1937	1938	1939	1940	1941	1942	1943	1944	1945
1 Tractors	11	72	102	140	106	102	115	136	184	298	208	310	411	496	646	270	615	173
2 Ploughs	67	31	60	74	52	70	93	144	174	318	187	551	2739	4124	3365	2280	1260	1084
3 Grub Breakers														54	66	274	31	
4 One Way Disc							2	3	2	5	4	4	?	30	1			
5 Disc Harrows	83	59	75	47	55	33	36½	26	20	34	31	39	37	??				
6 T.D. Harrows								41	106	260½	283½	479	????	????	1605½	527	15	4
7 S.T. Harrows	909	820	632	733	543	466	499	705½	1061	1594	831	1675	30??	2800	606	273½	9	8
8 Cultivators	66	62	43	45	24	25	42	34	34	68	49	67	80	82	2			
9 Drills	211	202	161	88	91	98	159	234	361	388	326	900	2076	2689	2483	3186	1292	1453
10 Sowers								23	53	112	157	294	298	370	413	88	415	6
11 Scufflers	285	283	462	400	329	333	516	576	578	631	559	714	720	363	2	1		
12 Mowers	463	441	580	394	224	110	286	423	362	615	614	653	771	663	290	250	29	173
13 Tedders	4	21	50	64	42	32	28	39	56	100	44	25	64	21				
14 Horse Rakes	159	306	312	218	89	73	138	27	29	30	104	142	88	59				
15 Hay Loaders	220	220	322	274	78	73	119	223	266	274	145	286	248	33				
16 Binders	437	403	393	289	221	249	412	739	946	976	682	837	3088	3367	2417	3342	1028	2609
17 Combines	1		1	1	1	3	7	2		5	5	14	23	40	145	300	475	305
18 Steel Threshers													12	9	14			
19 Straw Trussers	35	24	22	14	19	16	31	50	47	21	71	41	193	352	483	222	225	
20 Ensilage Cutters	7	6	4	6	3	1	3	5	3		2	2			10	30		59
21 Elevator Diggers								5		5	7		5			231	141	100
22 Manure Spreaders	26	30	21	10	9	6	22	24	37	55	32	68	122	61		100		389
23 Hammer Mills			2	6	2		4	25	27	23	18	25	59	62	225		1012	158
24 Cream Separators								8	1			1						
25 Reapers		2			2	1		1										
26 Side Rakes																		
27 Grinders								1										
28 Spike Tooth Harrows								22	19	30	23	33	25	16				
29 Engines	51	51	48	28	16	33	25	7										
30 Pulverators								2	3	2	3	3						
31 Sprayers									?	10								
32 Toolbars											8	4						
33 Tractor Rakes																		1
34 Swathers																		4
Yearly Total	3035	3033	3290	2834	1906	1724	2537	3546½	4403	5822½	4512½	7184	5058	18156	12773½	11374½	6547	6726

Machine	1946	1947	1948	1949
1 Tractors		38	73	345
2 Ploughs	915	139	596	3
3 Grub Breakers				
4 One Way Disc				
5 Disc Harrows				
6 T.D. Harrows	502	388	$1914\frac{1}{2}$	$101\frac{1}{2}$
7 S.T. Harrows	763	1827	2324	365
8 Cultivators	10			
9 Drills	2215	666	642	1182
10 Sowers	1470	2538	4358	2303
11 Scufflers		261	640	
12 Mowers	930	2587	2581	2524
13 Tedders		96	88	109
14 Horse Rakes	225	643	238	143
15 Hay Loaders			149	143
16 Binders	832	259	270	540
17 Combines	301	402	873	2422
18 Steel Threshers				
19 Straw Trussers				
20 Ensilage Cutters	11	2		
21 Elevator Diggers	24	1		
22 Manure Spreaders	135	376	2084	758
23 Hammer Mills	520	134	1002	336
24 Cream Separators				
25 Reapers				
26 Rakes CMA		386	110	4
27 Grinders				
28 Spike Tooth Harrows				
29 Engines				
30 Pulverators				
31 Sprayers				
32 Toolbars				
33 Tractor Rakes		453	123	304
34 Swathers	11	22	29	55
35 Side Rakes				918
36 Pick-up Attachments				555
37 Pick-up Reels				576
38 Swath Turner	903	1877		2284
39 Elevators	854	607	594	505
Yearly Total	10621	13701	$18688\frac{1}{2}$	$16495\frac{1}{2}$

Source: OAM collection

M-H BRANCH SALES
UK, 1935-1945

M-H LINE	1939	1940	1941	1942	1943	1944	1945	TOTAL
Disc Harrows	518	1894	2812	1632	1526	1851	788	11,021
Hammer Mills	25	59	62	225	—	1009	146	1,526
Manure Spreaders	68	122	61	—	100	1	389	741
P.T.O. Diggers	—	5	—	—	231	136	107	479
Reaper-Threshers	14	17	39	145	300	479	370	1,364
Binders	837	3122	3360	2417	3344	1027	2808	16,915
Mowers	653	771	655	290	250	29	187	2,835
Hay Loaders	286	248	33	—	—	—	—	567
Hay Rakes	142	120	58	—	—	—	—	320
Drills & Sowers	1194	2377	3054	3601	6086	3774	3059	23,145
Plows	541	2739	4178	3426	2546	1273	1102	15,805
Tractors	310	413	435	647	281	587	188	2,861
Threshers	—	12	—	14	—	—	—	26
Trussers	41	193	352	505	222	225	—	1,538
Sundry Other Lines	2528	3884	3054	622	304	9	63	10,464
TOTAL	7157	15,976	18,153	13,524	15,190	10,400	9,207	89,607

BLACKSTONE LINE

	1939	1940	1941	1942	1943	1944	1945	TOTAL
Haymakers	219	231	174	175	66	100	—	965
Side Rakes	323	375	341	450	334	—	2	1,825
Horse Rakes	412	507	555	953	1049	399	605	4,480
Swath Turner	522	446	312	394	301	150	1	2,126
Elevators	192	239	255	313	449	649	980	3,077
Potato Diggers	357	1185	1236	4135	5961	3444	2043	18,361
Tractor Rakes	—	—	—	—	—	615	958	1,573
TOTAL	2,025	2,983	2,873	6,420	8,160	5,357	4,589	32,407
Add Total M-H LINE	7,157	15,976	18,153	13,524	15,190	10,400	9,207	89,607
GRAND TOTAL	9,182	18,959	21,026	19,944	23,350	15,757	13,796	122,014

Source: OAM collection

M-H MACHINERY SALES
UK, 1945 and 1946

(N.B. Inconsistencies in totals are noted between this and the previous table)

1945			**1946**	
Combines No. 21-12 ft. w/GT	187		Ensilage cutters No. 8	11
12 ft. w/B	158		Manure spreaders No. 9	16
No. 15-8 ft. w/B	3		No. 11	95
8 ft. w/GT.	17		Combines No. 15/6 ft.	10
Blackstone machinery 16 B	821		No. 15/8 ft.	40
16 C	768		No. 21/12 ft.	199
TD.H	784		No. 21/10 ft.	51
Swathers 4/12 ft.	2		Clipper combine	1
5/16 ft.	2		Swather, 12 ft.	11
Horse rakes No. 2 SAM	3		Blackstone machinery MD 16B	749
No. 3 SAM	602		16C	850
Tractor rakes	959		TDH	768
Swathturners 2 HG	1		FACTORY GOODS★★	
No. 16 Binder 5 ft. Std.	140		Hammer mill 21A	487
6 ft. Spec	1048		Manure distributor 16B	745
7 ft. Spec	628		16C	736
No. 18 Binder 6 ft.	324		Tandem disc harrow 28/18	500
7 ft.	387		No 11 Manure spreader	6
8 ft.	81		Spring tooth harrow	763
Drills No. 5/13	328		Mowers 345 5 ft.	744
No. 20/13	98		6 ft.	173
No. 20/15	726		Binders No. 16 5 ft.	50
No. 20/20	96		6 ft. sp	523
No. 30/16	1		7 ft. sp	132
306/16	100		No. 18 6 ft.	32
306/20	75		7 ft.	72
30/24	3		8 ft.	30
30/28	10		Drills 5/13	643
306/24	27		20/13	100
Hammer mills No.21A★	76		20/15	658
No. 31A	72		20/20	151
Ploughs No. 26 27w/25	357		306/16	407
27 w/20C	460		306/20	154
37 w/25	136		306/24	73
37 w/20C	133		Ploughs No. 26 2/25	324
No. 28 57 w/20	15		2/200	217
Spring tooth harrow No. 14 14/17	2		3/25	135
14/26	4		3/200	157
Mower No. 33	57		No. 78 57/200	79
34	117		Mowers No. 33	39
Ensilage cutter No. 8	59		No. 34	8
Manure spreader No. 9	335		Potato diggers No. 2	25
No. 11	54		ABC No. 1	432
Tractors 102 Jr RC	28		No. 1 SL	314
102 Sr RC	2		Dickie Machinery swath turner w/shafts	916
102 Jr Std	1		w/TH	284
102 Sr Std	56		6 ft.	9
203	101		Steels Machinery Elevator 30 ft.	199
Potato diggers ABC No. 1	28		28 ft.	399
No. 2	107		Tractor rakes	2
No. 1SL	1004		No. 3 S.A.M	224
No. 4	126		Twose Machinery:	
No. 4 SL	115		Self lift tractor cultivator 7 tine	17
PTO digger	19		9 tine	53
C.M.A.s	2		11 tine	1
Elevators 28 ft.	500			
30 ft.	481			

★ the original text suggests that some were made in the factory   ★★ the original text seems to suggest that the next five items were made in the factory

N.B. There was also an entry for Nicholson swath turners but no sales recorded

Source: Old M-H Factory records

HARRY FERGUSON INCORPORATED SALES, 1939-1947

	Tractors*	Implements
1939	10,233	9,730
1940	35,742	47,774
1941	42,910	85,219
1942	16,478	48,896
1943	21,062	56,393
1944	43,443	174,176
1945	28,749	176,022
1946	59,773	238,142
1947	47,682	169,367

*Based on Units produced

HARRY FERGUSON INCORPORATED PRODUCTION, SALES, 1946-1953

	Assembly of tractors at Detroit (Units)
1946	—
1947	—
1948	1,800
1949	12,859
1950	24,503
1951	33,517
1952	35,965
1953	17,314*

*Ten months

HARRY FERGUSON LIMITED PRODUCTION, 1946-1953

	Production of tractors at Banner Lane (Units)
1946	316
1947	20,578
1948	56,678
1949	38,689
1950	51,381
1951	73,623
1952	69,567
1953*	48,060

*Ten months

Source: OAM collection

MASSEY-HARRIS COMBINE PRODUCTION, 1946-1954

| | Production Year (Aug. 31) | | | | | | | Fiscal Year (Oct. 31) | |
	1946	1947	1948	1949	1950	1951	1952	1953	1954
SELF-PROPELLED									
TORONTO, Canada									
21 & 21A	4,601	4,678	9,139	10,279					
222		610							
26			2,792	5,311	4,616	5,209	5,797		
27				25	8,166	10,470	10,945		
60								200	795
70								1,499	
80							287	4,590	2,766
90								8,145	6,924
BATAVIA, United States									
S.P. Clipper	750	750	1,000	1,000	875	635	670	196	
MANCHESTER, England									
722			395						
KILMARNOCK, Scotland									
726				1,321	4,100	5,000	4,636	1,150	
780								2,362	3,855
MARQUETTE, France									
890 Petrol								99	910
TOTAL SELF-PROPELLED	5,351	6,038	13,326	17,936	17,757	21,314	22,335	18,241	15,250
PULL TYPE									
TORONTO, Canada									
15 & 17	950	1,012	1,000	1,975	926	780	953	700	
30, 32, 33									
60								100	985
50									
BATAVIA, United States									
P.T. Clipper	4,000	3,340	7,585	10,909	13,041	12,426	3,558		
50						100	850	3,670	3,912
KILMARNOCK, Scotland									
750								385	546
TOTAL PULL TYPE	4,950	4,352	8,585	12,884	13,967	13,306	5,361	4,855	5,443
Grand Total	10,301	10,390	21,911	30,820	31,724	34,620	27,696	23,096	20,693

MASSEY-HARRIS AND FERGUSON TRACTOR PRODUCTION, 1946-1954

	1946	1947	1948	1949	1950	1951	1952	1953	1954
MASSEY-HARRIS									
RACINE, United States									
101 Sr.		537							
203		40							
20		4,367	3,564						
22			886	5,387	3,917	4,797	2,194	14	
23							257	3,088	207
21							100	1,569	
30		3,888	5,868	6,114	7,072	6,376	3,094	4	
33							1	5,614	2,605
44		4,147	10,442	16,364	16,955	19,942	12,534	4,404	6,894
55		1,293	2,627	3,235	2,968	2,999	3,454	2,390	1,787
TOTAL Racine	N/A	14,272	23,387	31,100	30,912	34,114	21,634	17,083	11,493
WOODSTOCK, Canada									
11 Pony		1,314	9,073	5,106	2,834	4,543	4,087	962	705
14						33	17	24	
16 Pacer								164	1,444
MANCHESTER, England									
744			16						
KILMARNOCK, Scotland									
744				1,054	2,783	4,660	5,547	2,546	
745									2,952
MARQUETTE, France									
811 Pony						1,813	10		
812 Pony						587	5,800	8,133	8,758
TOTAL Massey-Harris	N/A	15,586	32,476	37,260	36,529	45,750	37,095	28,912	25,352
FERGUSON									
Ford	59,773	47,682							
Detroit			1,800	12,859	24,503	33,517	35,965	17,314	14,047
United Kingdom	316	20,578	56,878	38,689	51,381	73,623	69,567	48,060	62,483
France								2,007	4,496
TOTAL Ferguson	60,089	68,260	58,678	51,548	75,884	107,140	105,532	67,381	81,026

Source: OAM collection

MASSEY-FERGUSON LTD TRACTOR PRODUCTION, 1955-1966

	1955	1956	1957	1958	1959	1960	1961	1962	1963	1964	1965	1966
NORTH AMERICA												
WOODSTOCK, Canada												
16 Pacer	1,159											
Pony			122									
ST. THOMAS, Canada												
MF-470 Tractor Loader										49	282	350
RACINE, United States												
22		220	60									
33	3,359											
333		2,644	100									
44	3,616											
244	2	273	427									
444		3,961	1,889	394								
404		50	68									
55	1,038	140										
555		1,087	893	854								
303			76	156	796							
TOTAL Racine	8,235	8,291	3,533	2,044								
DETROIT, United States												
TO-35	27,623	3,659	5,951	9,839	14,670	6,471						
MF-35							1,204	13,258	13,386	12,526	10,094	
MF-135										1,904	12,958	9,843
F-40		5,038	4,059									
MH-50		9,250	4,658									
MF-50			292	6,183	7,307	256	1,402	3,602	2,892	1,705		
MF-150										246	3,281	2,021
MF-65				10,269	9,986	8,528	6,584	7,670	9,630	8,260	108	
MF-85					4,350	3,400	813					
MF-88					1,450	700	345					
MF-90								4,035	4,452	4,315	1,776	
MF-95★				450	650	700	700	525				
MF-97★								600	1,756	1,439	305	
MF-98★					25	475						
MF-165											6,105	8,687
MF-175											1,198	1,852
MF-180											2,042	2,714
MF-202			837	1,920	1,624	1,527	757	1,055	1,271	869	1,009	974
MF-203							680	659	370	291	566	533
MF-204					1,100	790	645	555	614	530	715	854
MF-205							375	310	230	186	312	230
MF-244G			427									
MF-356							125	380	481	356	308	460
MF-406					436							
1001					500							
MF-302									95	314	433	428
MF-304									66	311	398	460
MF-1100/1130										4	867	6,170
MF-2135										82	1,702	1,785
MF-2500												327
MF-3165											946	1,496
TOTAL Detroit	27,623	17,947	16,224	28,661	42,098	24,051	25,684	32,777	34,383	30,906	35,029	38,834
TOTAL	37,017	26,238	19,879	30,705	42,098	24,051	25,684	32,777	34,383	30,955	35,311	39,184

★Tractors purchased from suppliers

	1955	1956	1957	1958	1959	1960	1961	1962	1963	1964	1965	1966
UNITED KINGDOM												
KILMARNOCK, Scotland												
745	2,965	3,126	1,245	889								
COVENTRY, England												
TE-20	64,342	41,049										
FE-35			65,219	51,379	48,862	53,900	49,656	43,081	47,215	44,469	582	
MF-203							402	1,382	1,111	1,189	1,074	976
MF-205							200	567	606	695	844	792
MF-702					63	1,167	1,370					
MF-765				8,585	9,887	12,700	17,321	20,329	23,288	25,554	2,861	
MF-135											33,802	44,246
MF-165											13,148	20,640
MF-175											5,651	8,658
MF-2135											707	701
MF-3165											1,136	2,365
MF-3303/5												175
TOTAL Coventry	64,342	41,049	65,219	59,964	58,812	67,767	68,949	65,359	72,220	71,907	59,805	78,553
TOTAL U.K.	67,307	44,175	66,464	60,853	58,812	67,767	68,949	65,359	72,220	71,907	59,805	78,553
FRANCE												
MARQUETTE												
812		11,536	13,101	1,894								
820				11,953	14,297	4,033	948	46				
821						4,036	5,004	355				
20-25-8									810	645	25	
TOTAL Marquette		11,536	13,101	13,847	14,297	8,069	5,952	401	810	645	25	
BEAUVAIS												
MF-825 & 30-8							10,171	12,725	9,341	9,037	707	
MF-35-8 & 35x						10,702	6,178	4,473	1,481	1,426	316	
MF-35-8 & 37-8								4	3,363	5,980	987	
MF-42-8								3,161	3,210	3,195	370	
MF-802						200	300	120				
MF-865						2,104	2,673	1,729	643			
MF-65-8 MK II									1,292	3,154	739	
MF-122											590	590
MF-130											8,439	7,510
MF-2130											175	47
MF-135											2,115	3,575
MF-140											5,898	8,459
MF-145											2,230	3,300
MF-165											4,742	5,686
TOTAL Beauvais						13,006	19,322	22,212	19,330	23,152	27,308	29,167
ST. DENIS												
TO-20	7,910	9,286	3,145									
TEF-20	3,985	6,545										
FE-30			15,622	13,953								
MF-835				3,408	19,453							
MF-802					62							
TOTAL St. Denis	11,895	15,831	18,767	17,361	19,515							
TOTAL FRANCE	23,431	28,932	32,614	31,658	27,584	18,958	19,723	22,212	20,140	23,797	27,333	29,167
BRAZIL												
MF-11-50								1,175	2,982	4,209	2,859	3,631
MF-11-65											79	420
TOTAL BRAZIL								1,175	2,982	4,209	2,938	4,051

	1955	1956	1957	1958	1959	1960	1961	1962	1963	1964	1965	1966
ITALY												
FABBRICO												
L-25	1,650	1,410	240									
C-25, R-25		50	950	947	853							
L-30			600	860	274							
C-35					367	688	615	438				
C-1-35							59					
L-35	501	502			325							
MF-44										5	140	186	247
L-45	165		30	30	21							
L-55B & L-55	200	200	10	26	116							
R-50 & DT-50					215	915	347					
R-50J							404	955	446	665	400	
MF-244									248	289	536	768
R-3000						2	493	828	879	759	1,009	835
C-4000								296	1,105	341	355	813
C-4500										788	121	
C-1-4000								78	306	169	113	
DT-4500										190	54	
R-4000						1,184	1,907	1,574	1,429			
R-4500										1,161	551	
R-6000							454	950	1			
R-7000									995	1,216	662	266
DT-7000										270	248	46
C-1-8000										14	79	12
MF-3366											5	97
C-1-5000												162
C-5000											857	713
DT-5000											166	235
R-5000											885	1,285
DT-8000												26
R-8000												499
TOTAL Fabbrico	2,516	2,162	1,830	1,866	2,171	2,789	4,279	5,119	5,414	6,002	6,227	6,004
COMO												
L-35/8						141	30					
L-44/M			182	290	115	36	68					
TOTAL Como			182	290	115	177	98					
TOTAL ITALY	2,516	2,162	2,012	2,156	2,286	2,966	4,377	5,119	5,414	6,002	6,227	6,004

Source: OAM collection

F. PERKINS LIMITED
PRODUCTION, 1933-1958

	Engines produced (Units)
1933	N/A
1934	N/A
1935	N/A
1936	N/A
1937	N/A
1938	N/A
1939	N/A
1940	N/A
1941	1,486
1942	1,896
1943	1,746
1944	1,695
1945	2,278
1946	3,625
1947	3,895
1948	6,895
1949	15,093
1950	25,218
1951	34,961
1952	38,154
1953	46,168
1954	61,956
1955	68,875
1956	74,838
1957	56,388
1958	77,018

Source: OAM collection

MASSEY-HARRIS, SUNSHINE FERGUSON, AUSTRALIA 1948-1955

| | TRACTORS | | | COMBINE HARVESTERS | | |
	Massey–Harris (Imported)[1]	Ferguson (Imported)[2]	Total	Massey–Harris S.P. (Imported)[1]	H. V. McKay P.T. (Local Prod.)[1]	Total
1948	674	1482	2156		1639	1639
1949	772	3768	4540		1567	1567
1950	655	5852	6507		1349	1349
1951	1493	8213	9706		1485	1485
1952	1347	7851	9198	299	1579	1878
1953	1304	7257	8561	200	2022	2222
1954	792	6445	7237	101	2291	2392
1955	315	6538	6853	102	2642	2744

[1] Sold by H. V. McKay–Massey Harris Proprietary Limited

[2] Sold by Ferguson Distributors

Source: OAM collection

LANDINI TRACTOR PRODUCTION, 1945-1966

	Semi–Diesel	Diesel	Crawler Diesel	Total
1945	171	—	—	171
1946	444	—	—	444
1947	586	—	—	586
1948	520	—	—	520
1949	662	—	—	662
1950	749	—	—	749
1951	1174	—	—	1174
1952	1630	—	—	1630
1953	2308	—	—	2308
1954	2500	—	—	2500
1955	2516	—	—	2516
1956	2112	50	—	2162
1957	1062	950	—	2012
1958	1209	947	—	2156
1959	851	1435	—	2286
1960★	177	2789	—	2966
1961	98	3605	674	4377
1962	—	4307	812	5119
1963	—	3750	1664	5414
1964	—	4261	1741	6002
1965	—	3975	2252	6227
1966	—	3192	2812	6004

★ Acquired by MF in 1960

Source: OAM collection

AUSTRALIAN TRACTOR SALES 1948-1959

	1948	1949	1950	1951	1952	1953	1954	1955	1956	1957	1958	1959
20K	183	22		1								
55K	84	213	216	162	194	251	189	78	36	125		
44K	169	375	209	214	94	61	16	31	14	59		
44K rc	38	28	22	21	8	9						
30K	191	77	42	68	35	8						
30K rc	8	57	11	16	3	2						
11 Pony	1											
TEA	1482	3591	4202		5104	4952	4953	4240	3359			
TED		175	1622		2741	1850	1143	934	956			
TEK		2	18		2	10	21	19	15			
744D			216	917	967	913	429	271	29	7		
744D rc			7	94	46	59	39	25	4	5		
TEF					4	446	1328	1345	1767			
745						1		75	838	1512	518	81
55D							119		90	80	37	103
55								85				
555D											36	
35 petrol										2580	1861	1466
35 kero										577	400	180
35 diesel										3275	2711	2687
65											350	1318

Source: MF Commonwealth Training Dept. Summary

MASSEY FERGUSON LIMITED
COMBINE PRODUCTION
1955-1966

	1955	1956	1957	1958	1959	1960	1961	1962	1963	1964	1965	1966
SELF-PROPELLED												
TORONTO, Canada												
60	1,365	1,116	1,014	694								
35				404	3,919	2,222		475	550	600		
72					1,375	1,193	282	300	500	407	53	
80	2,293	2,728										
82			2,179	4,297	2,369	1,349	1,667	1,360	205			
90	4,231	3,722										
92			3,438	4,503	6,033							
92 (Super)						4,104	4,304	3,810	3,706	180		
92 (Super) Hillside							110					
MF-300								50	2,707	3,338	2,517	3,609
MF-410										4,200	4,140	3,410
MF-510										900	2,858	2,270
MF-205												201
TOTAL	7,889	7,566	6,631	9,898	13,696	8,868	6,363	5,995	7,668	9,625	9,568	9,490
KILMARNOCK, Scotland												
780	4,227	3,662	4,495	3,505	2,727	1,709	1,903	348				
500-7								1,296	932	1,659	1,224	570
400-7									1,017	1,356	1,614	956
788									1,126	820	792	361
735		50	1,915	1,155	1,211	83	386					
410-7												441
510-7												570
TOTAL	4,227	3,712	6,410	4,660	3,938	1,792	2,289	1,644	3,075	3,835	3,650	2,898
MARQUETTE, France												
830				796	1,397	757	810	404	302	381	300	
890	1,200	1,201	1,527	1,900	1,297	50						
892					100	1,448	1,568	788	572	847		
99-8										5	806	558
510												672
TOTAL	1,200	1,201	1,527	2,696	2,794	2,255	2,378	1,192	874	1,233	1,106	1,230
ESCHWEGE, Germany												
630	850	3,910	5,185	4,498	2,749	2,537	3,011	2,014				
685			9	353	1,375	1,096	2,460	2,235	616			
31-6								982	785	1,581	1,636	1,620
86-6								148	851	800	960	1,020
30-6									1,000	781	980	1,080
87-6									275	1,424	1,845	1,905
95-6										10		
TOTAL	850	3,910	5,194	4,851	4,124	3,633	5,471	5,379	3,527	4,596	5,421	5,625
MELBOURNE, Australia												
585 (Total)			11	190	336	342	392	337	451	543	496	475

	1955	1956	1957	1958	1959	1960	1961	1962	1963	1964	1965	1966
PULL TYPE												
TORONTO, Canada												
60	1,310	1,202	881	1,145								
50				1,807	418							
35					300	1,201	375	450		100		
72					1,000	200	300		300	160		
405												485
TOTAL	1,310	1,202	881	2,952	1,718	1,401	675	450	300	260		485
BATAVIA, United States												
50	3,000	2,221	1,293	256								
KILMARNOCK, Scotland												
750	250											
MELBOURNE, Australia												
6	991	459										
506			333	426	201	176	175	300	160		110	
508	1,286	525	474	386	718	250						
585					1	786	1,140	1,020	949	1,010	977	905
TOTAL	2,277	984	807	812	920	1,212	1,315	1,320	1,109	1,010	1,087	905
TOTAL PULL-TYPE	6,837	4,407	2,981	4,020	2,638	2,613	1,990	1,770	1,409	1,270	1,087	1,390
Grand Total	21,003	20,796	22,754	26,315	27,526	19,503	18,883	16,317	17,004	21,102	21,328	21,108

Source: OAM collection

MASSEY FERGUSON MACHINE/TRACTOR SUITABILITY GUIDE, 1976

PLANTING			2 Wheel Drive						4 Wheel Drive					
Model No.	Description	Source	> 50 hp	50-62 hp	62-75 hp	75-92 hp	92-110 hp	110+ hp	> 70 hp	70-80 hp	80-95 hp	95-110 hp	110-180 hp	180+ hp
	Seed Drills													
33	13 Row	N. America		X										
	15 Row	N. America		X	X									
	17 Row	N. America		X	X				X					
43	16 Row	N. America		X	X				X					
	22 Row	N. America			X	X			X	X				
	26 Row	N. America			X	X			X	X				
63	14 Row	N. America		X	X				X					
	16 Row	N. America		X	X	X			X	X				
	24 Row	N. America			X	X	X		X	X	X			
55	12 Row	Australia	X	X	X				X					
	16 Row	Australia		X	X	X			X	X				
56	20 Row	Australia			X	X			X	X	X			
	24 Row	Australia			X	X			X	X	X			
30	13 Row	U.K.	X	X										
	15 Row	U.K.	X	X	X				X					
	20 Row	U.K.		X	X	X			X	X				
34	15 Row	Brazil	X	X	X									
1003	9 Row	India	X											
	Planters													
37	2 Row Mounted	N. America	X	X										
	4 Row Mounted	N. America		X	X				X					
39	2 Row Mounted	N. America	X	X										
	4 Row Mounted	N. America		X	X									
41	2 Row Mounted	N. America	X	X										
	4 Row Mounted	N. America		X	X				X	X				
	Over 4 Row Mounted	N. America		X	X				X					
48	2 Row Mounted	S. Africa	X	X										
	4 Row Trailed	S. Africa		X	X				X	X				
468	4 Row Trailed	N. America		X	X				X					
	6 Row Trailed	N. America		X	X	X			X	X				
	8 Row Trailed	N. America			X	X	X			X				
20	1 Row Cane	Australia		X	X				X					
24	1 Row Cane	Australia		X	X				X					
	2 Row Mounted	S. Africa	X	X										
71	4 Row Mounted	S. Africa		X	X									
	PLOUGHS													
	Mouldboard Ploughs													
43	Fixed Mounted	N. America	2, 3F	2, 3F	3F				3F					
82	Fixed Mounted	N. America		3F	3, 4F	4, 5, 6F	4, 5, 6F	6F	3F	3, 4F	4, 5, 6F	5, 6F	6F	
66	Fixed Mounted	Australia	1, 2, 3F	2, 3, 4F	4F									
49	Fixed Mounted	S. Africa	2F	2, 3, 4F	2, 3, 4F	4F			3, 4F	3, 4F	4F			
74	Fixed Mounted	Argentina	3F	3, 4F	3, 4, 5F	4, 5, 6F	5, 6F	6F	3, 4F	4, 5, 6F	5, 6F			
43	Fixed Mounted	India	2, 3F	3, 4F	3, 4F				3, 4F	4F				
150	Fixed Mounted	International	2, 3F	2, 3F	3F									
160	Fixed Mounted	International	2, 3F	2, 3, 4F	3, 4, 5F	4, 5F	5F		3, 4F	4, 5F	5F	5F		
88	Semi Mounted	N. America		4F	4, 5F	4, 5, 6F	5, 6F	6, 7, 8F	4, 5F	4, 5F	4, 5, 6F	5, 6, 7F	6, 7, 8F	7, 8F
180	Semi Mounted	International				6F	6, 7F	6, 7F			6F	6, 7F	7F	
880	Semi Mounted	N. America		4F	4, 5F	4, 5, 6F	5, 6F	6, 7, 8F	4, 5F	4, 5F	4, 5, 6F	5, 6, 7F	6, 7, 8F	7, 8F
84	Semi Mounted	Argentina			3F	3F	3, 4F	4F	3F	3F	3, 4F			
57	Reversible Mounted	N. America			3F	3, 4F	4F	4F	3F	3F	3, 4F	4F		
260	Reversible Mounted	International	1, 2F	1, 2, 3F	2, 3F	3, 4F	3, 4F	4F	2, 3F	3, 4F	3, 4F			
270	Reversible Mounted	International			3F	3, 4F	4F	4, 5F	3F	3, 4F	4F	4F	4, 5F	
	Disc Ploughs													
65	Fixed Mounted	Australia	2, 3F	2, 3, 4F	3, 4F				4F	4F				
90	Fixed Mounted	Australia	2, 3F	2, 3, 4F	3, 4, 5F	4, 5, 6F	5, 6F		4F	4, 5F	4, 5, 6F	5, 6F		
91	Fixed Mounted	Australia	2, 3F	2, 3, 4F	3, 4F				4F	4F				
765	Fixed Mounted	U.K.	2, 3F	2, 3, 4F	3, 4F				4F	4F				

X = Suitable   m = metres   F = Furrows

PLOUGHS (Cont.)			2 Wheel Drive						4 Wheel Drive					
Model No.	Description	Source	> 50 hp	50-62 hp	62-75 hp	75-92 hp	92-110 hp	110+ hp	> 70 hp	70-80 hp	80-95 hp	95-110 hp	110-180 hp	180+ hp
80	Fixed Mounted	S. Africa	2, 3F	2, 3, 4F	3, 4, 5F	4, 5, 6F	6F		3, 4F	4, 5F	4, 5, 6F	5, 6F		
81	Fixed Mounted	S. Africa	2F	2, 3F	3, 4F	4F			3, 4F	3, 4F	4F			
62/64	Fixed Mounted	Brazil	2, 3F	2, 3, 4F	3, 4F				3, 4F	4F				
66	Fixed Mounted	Brazil			4F	4, 5F	5F			4, 5F	5F			
68	Fixed Mounted	Brazil	2F	2, 3F	3F				3F	3F				
70	Fixed Mounted	Brazil		3F	3, 4F	4F			3, 4F	3, 4F	4F			
65	Fixed Mounted	International	2, 3F	2, 3, 4F	3, 4F				3, 4F	4F				
17	Fixed Mounted	Mexico	2, 3F	2, 3, 4F	3, 4F	4F			3, 4F	4F				
61	Fixed Mounted	India	2, 3F	2, 3, 4F	3, 4F	4F			3, 4F	4F				
76	Reversible Mounted	Mexico	3F	3, 4F	4F				3, 4F	4F				
	Chisel Ploughs													
24	Mounted	U.K.	2m	2m,2.4m 3m	2.4m	3m,4.3m	4.3m	4.3m	2.4m,3m	2.4m,3m	3m,4.3m	4.3m	4.3m	
25	Mounted	U.K.				3.66m	3.66m				3.6m	3.6m		
126	Mounted	N. America	1.5m	1.5m	3.4m	3.4m			1.5m	3.4m				
127	Mounted	N. America		3.3m	3.3m	3.9m 4.5m	4.5m 5.1m	5.1m 5.7m	3.3m	3.9m	4.5m 5.1m	5.1m 5.7m	5.7m	
126	Mounted	Brazil	1.86m	1.86m	3.1m	3.1m			1.86m	3.1m				
128	Trailed	N. America					9.5m	12.5m				9.5m	9.5m	12.5m
	TILLAGE													
	Offset Disc Harrow													
34	Mounted	Australia	1.3m 1.8m	1.8m 2.1m	2.1m				2.1m	2.1m				
34	Mounted	S. Africa	1.4m	2.1m	2.1m 2.5m	2.5m			2.1m 2.5m	2.5m				
81	Mounted	Australia	1.1m 1.7m	1.7m										
35	Mounted	Mexico	1.8m	1.8m 2.3m	2.3m				1.8m 2.3m	2.3m				
30	Mounted	Brazil		2.1m	2.1m 3.5m	3.5m 3.7m	3.7m		2.1m	3.5m 3.7m	3.7m			
65	Mounted	India	1.6m 2.2m	1.6m 2.2m										
134	Mounted	France	1.4m 1.6m	1.6m 1.82m										
136	Semi-Mounted	France	1.7m	1.9m 2.2m	2.2m 2.3m				1.9m 2.2m	2.2m				
30	Trailed	N. America			2.8m 3.2m	2.8m 3.2m 3.7m	3.7m		2.8m 3.2m	2.8m 3.2m	2.8m 3.2m 3.7m	3.7m		
40	Trailed	N. America				3.7m	4.3m	4.3m		3.7m	3.7m 4.3m	4.3m	4.3m	
40	Trailed	Mexico		2.3m 2.7m	2.7m 3.2m	3.2m 3.7m			2.7m 3.2m	3.2m 3.7m	3.7m			
140	Trailed	France			3.1m	3.3m 3.6m					3.3m 3.6m			
42	Trailed	Mexico		2.3m 2.7m	2.7m 3.2m	3.2m			3.2m					
	Tandem Disc Harrows													
21	Mounted	N. America	1.9m	1.9m 2.1m 2.3m	2.3m				2.3m					
25	Mounted	N. America	2.0m 2.4m	2.4m 2.7m	2.7m				2.7m					
39	Mounted	N. America	2.4m	2.4m 2.7m	2.7m 3.1m				2.7m 3.1m					
914	Mounted	S. Africa	1.7m	1.7m 2.1m	2.4m 2.1m 2.4m				2.4m					
39	Mounted	S. Africa	2.4m	2.4m 3.4m	3.4m 3.8m				3.4m 3.8m	3.8m				
22	Mounted	Brazil	X	X										
23	Mounted	Brazil	2.1m	2.4m	2.4m 3.1m				2.4m 3.1m	3.1m				
28	Mounted	U.K.	2.3m	2.8m 3.2m	3.2m 3.7m				2.8m 3.2m	3.2m 3.7m				

X = Suitable   m = metres   F = Furrows

Model No.	Description	Source	>50 hp	50-62 hp	62-75 hp	75-92 hp	92-110 hp	110+ hp	>70 hp	70-80 hp	80-95 hp	95-110 hp	110-180 hp	180+ hp
TILLAGE (Cont)			**2 Wheel Drive**						**4 Wheel Drive**					
25	Mounted	Brazil			3.65m				3.65m	3.65m				
1007	Mounted Paddy	India	X	X										
520	Trailed	N. America		3.1m 3.7m	3.1m 3.7m 4.3m	4.3m 5.5m	5.5m 6.4m	5.5m 6.4m	3.1m 3.7m	3.7m 4.3m	4.3m 5.5m	5.5m 6.4m	6.4m	6.4m
620	Trailed	N. America		3.65m	3.65m 4.25m	4.25m 4.87m	4.87m 5.78m	7.01m	3.65m	3.65m 4.25m	4.25m 4.87m	5.78m 7.01m	7.01m	7.01m
52	Trailed	Argentina		3.25m	3.25m									
	Tillers and Cultivators													
37	Spring Tine Cultivator	International	2.6m 3.0m	3.0m 3.5m	4.7m 5.6m	4.7m 5.6m 7.2m	7.2m		4.7m	5.6m 7.2m	5.6m 7.2m	7.2m		
39	Spring Tine Cultivator	International	2.4m 3.0m	2.4m 3.0m 4.6m	4.6m	5.5m	5.5m		4.6m	4.6m 5.5m	5.5m	5.5m		
67	Row Crop Cultivator	Brazil	2.8m	2.8m					2.8m	2.8m				
428	Row Crop Cultivator	N. America	4.3m	4.3m 4.8m	4.8m 6.3m	6.3m	6.3m 8.3m	8.3m	4.3m	4.8m 6.3m	6.3m	6.3m 8.3m	8.3m	
221	Row Crop Cultivator	N. America	2.4m	2.4m										
160	Field Cultivator	N. America		3.2m 5.6m	3.2m 5.6m	5.6m 7.5m	7.5m 8.1m 8.7m	8.7m 11.2m	3.2m 5.6m	3.2m 5.6m	5.6m 7.5m 8.1m	7.5m 8.1m 8.7m	8.7m 11.2m	11.2m
23	Field Cultivator	U.K.	3m	3m 3.5m	3.5m 4.5m	4.5m	4.5m 6m	6m	3m 3.5m	3.5m 4.5m	4.5m	6m	6m	
21	Cultivator	Mexico	2.1m	2.1m										
227	Cultivator	France	2.5m	2.5m 3.6m	3.6m 4.2m				3.6m 4.7m					
236	Cultivator	France	1.4m	2.3m 3.2m	4.2m				3.2m 4.2m					
237	Cultivator	France	1.7m	2.6m 3.4m	3.4m				3.4m					
238	Cultivator	France	1.4m	2.6m										
138	Tiller	N. America	2.1m	2.1m										
38	Tiller	Australia	2.1m	2.1m 2.6m 2.8m	2.8m				2.6m 2.8m	2.8m				
938	Tiller	S. Africa	1.6m 2.2m	1.6m 2.2m	2.2m				2.2m					
38	Tiller	India	2.1m	2.1m										
38	Tiller	France	2.1m	2.1m 2.6m	2.8m									
120	Scarifier	Australia	2.6m 3.2m	2.6m 3.2m 3.8m	3.8m 4.4m	4.4m			3.8m 4.4m	3.8m 4.4m	4.4m			
500	Covering Harrow	Australia	2.1m 2.8m	2.8m 3.5m 4.2m	4.2m				4.2m					
585	Stump Jump Harrow	Australia	2.6m 3.5m	2.6m 3.5m 4.3m 5.2m	4.3m 5.2m 6.9m	8.7m 10.4m	10.4m		4.3m 5.2m 6.9m	8.7m 10.4m	10.4m			
586	Diamond Harrow	Australia	3.0m 4.0m	3.0m 4.0m 5.0m 6.0m	5.0m 6.0m				5.0m 6.0m					
38	Tiller	International	2.1m	2.1m 2.6m 2.8m	2.8m									
	One Way Discs													
36	Wide Level	N. America		2.7m 3.7m 4.6m	2.7m 3.7m	4.6m 5.5m	4.6m 5.5m		2.7m 3.7m 4.6m	2.7m 3.7m 4.6m	4.6m 5.5m			
63	Sundercut	Australia		2.1m 2.7m	2.1m 2.7m				2.1m 2.7m	2.1m 2.7m				
67	Sundercut	Australia		3.0m	3.0m 3.7m	3.0m 3.7m			3.0m	3.0m 3.7m	3.0m			
60	One Way Disc	S. Africa	1.4m	1.4m 1.9m	1.9m				1.9m					

X = Suitable   m = metres   F = Furrows

TILLAGE (Cont)			2 Wheel Drive						4 Wheel Drive					
Model No.	Description	Source	>50 hp	50-62 hp	62-75 hp	75-92 hp	92-110 hp	110+ hp	>70 hp	70-80 hp	80-95 hp	95-110 hp	110-180 hp	180+ hp
Subsoilers														
27	Depth 500mm	N. America	X	X										
35	Depth 800mm	N. America		X	X				X	X				
27	Depth 500mm	Australia	X	X	X				X					
35	Depth 700mm	S. Africa		X	X				X	X				
36	Depth 635mm	Mexico	X	X										
201	Depth 600mm	France	X	X					X					
202	Depth 600mm	France		X	X	X				X	X			
203	Depth 600mm	France			X	X	X			X	X	X		
27	Depth 500mm	India	X	X										
MISCELLANEOUS														
Transport and Trailers														
12	Transporter – 432kg	Australia	X	X										
122	Transporter – 500kg	Brazil	X	X										
2	Transporter – 964kg	India	X	X										
5	Running Gear 3600kg	N. America	X	X										
65	Running Gear 4550kg	N. America	X	X	X				X					
6	Running Gear 5450kg	N. America	X	X	X				X					
7	Running Gear 7260kg	N. America			X	X				X				
8	Running Gear 9080kg	N. America				X	X			X	X			
20	Trailer 3050kg	U.K.	X	X										
21	Trailer 3556kg	U.K.	X	X										
22	Trailer 4572kg	U.K.	X	X	X				X					
23	Trailer 4500kg	U.K.	X	X	X				X					
24	Trailer 6096kg	U.K.		X	X	X			X	X				
25	Trailer 7000kg	U.K.			X	X				X	X			
26	Trailer 10,000kg	U.K.				X	X			X	X	X		
27	Trailer 3000kg	India	X	X	X									
28	Trailer 5000kg	India	X	X	X									
47L	Trailer 4000kg	France	X	X										
47S	Trailer 4700kg	France	X	X										
105	Trailer 5000kg	France	X	X	X									
106	Trailer 6000kg	France		X	X				X	X				
107	Trailer 7000kg	France		X	X	X			X	X				
108	Trailer 8000kg	France		X	X	X				X				
108SE	Trailer 8000kg	France		X	X	X				X	X			
110	Trailer 10000kg	France		X	X	X					X	X		
210	Trailer 10000kg	France			X	X	X				X	X		
212	Trailer 12000kg	France				X	X	X			X	X	X	
215	Trailer 15000kg	France				X	X	X			X	X	X	
50	4 Wheel Trailer 5000kg	International	X	X					X					
55	4 Wheel Trailer 5000kg	International	X	X					X	X				
60	4 Wheel Trailer 6000kg	International		X	X					X				
80	4 Wheel Trailer 8000kg	International		X	X					X	X			
100	4 Wheel Trailer 10000kg	International			X	X				X	X			
19	Trailer 3048kg	Brazil	X	X	X									
Blades and Soil Scoops														
1	Soil Scoop	N. America	X											
15	Soil Scoop	S. Africa	X	X										
905	Soil Scoop	S. Africa	X	X										
16	Utility Blade	Mexico	X	X										
17	Utility Blade	Mexico	X	X										
18	Utility Blade	Brazil	X	X										
17	Utility Blade	India	X	X										
21	Utility Blade	Australia		X	X				X					
921	Utility Blade	S. Africa	X	X										
63	Grader	S. Africa		X	X				X					
338	Drag Scraper	Australia	X	X	X	X			X	X	X			
17	Bulldozer Blade	S. Africa	X	X	X									
Rotary Cutters														
58	Rotary Cutter	N. America	X	X					X					
61	Rotary Cutter	N. America	X	X					X					
68	Rotary Cutter	N. America		X	X				X	X				
71	Rotary Cutter	N. America		X	X				X	X				
145	Rotary Cutter	Australia	X	X										
150	Rotary Cutter	Australia	X	X	X				X					

X = Suitable   m = metres   F = Furrows

MISCELLANEOUS (Cont)			2 Wheel Drive						4 Wheel Drive					
Model No.	Description	Source	> 50 hp	50-62 hp	62-75 hp	75-92 hp	92-110 hp	110+ hp	> 70 hp	70-80 hp	80-95 hp	95-110 hp	110-180 hp	180+ hp
155	Rotary Cutter	Australia	X	X	X				X					
156	Rotary Cutter	Australia		X	X				X					
160	Rotary Cutter	Australia		X	X	X			X	X				
166	Rotary Cutter	Australia		X	X	X			X	X				
88	Rotary Cutter	Brazil	X	X	X				X					
77	Rotary Cutter	S. Africa	X	X	X				X					
61	Rotary Cutter	France	X	X	X									
62	Rotary Cutter	France	X	X	X									
64	Rotary Cutter	France			X	X	X			X	X			
66	Rotary Cutter	France			X	X				X				
	Loaders and Cranes													
14	Jib Crane	Australia	X	X										
14	Jib Crane	Brazil	X	X										
12	Jib Crane	India	X	X										
35	Loader	International	X	X	X									
40	Loader	U.K./Australia	X	X	X									
40	Power Loader	U.K.	X	X	X									
172	Loader	France	X	X	X									
174	Loader	France	X	X	X									
176	Loader	France	X	X	X									
178	Loader	France	X	X	X									
225	Loader	N. America	X	X	X									
235	Loader	N. America		X	X	X								
245	Loader	N. America				X	X	X						
	Spreading and Fertilising													
110	Manure Spreader	N. America	X	X										
160	Manure Spreader	N. America		X	X				X	X				
205	Manure Spreader	N. America			X	X				X	X			
13	Manure Spreader	Germany	X	X										
19	Manure Spreader	U.K.	X	X	X				X					
11	Spinner Broadcaster	International	X	X	X									
17	Slurry Tanker 3410 litre	U.K.	X	X										
17	Slurry Tanker 4318 litre	U.K.		X	X									
17	Slurry Tanker 5841 litre	U.K.			X	X								
17	Slurry Tanker 8124 litre	U.K.				X	X							

X = Suitable   m = metres   F = Furrows

Source: MF Worldwide Catalogue, 1976

MASSEY FERGUSON MACHINE/TRACTOR SUITABILITY GUIDE, 1980

Model No.	Description	Source	2WD >50 hp	2WD 50-62 hp	2WD 62-75 hp	2WD 75-92 hp	2WD 92-110 hp	2WD 110-140 hp	2WD 140-190 hp	4WD >70 hp	4WD 70-80 hp	4WD 80-95 hp	4WD 95-110 hp	4WD 110-180 hp	4WD 180-270 hp	4WD 270+ hp
	Seed Drills															
80	20 Row	Australia				X	X			X	X					
	24 Row	Australia				X	X			X	X					
	28 Row	Australia					X	X			X	X				
7000	Air Seeder	Australia					X	X					X	X		
33	13 Row	N. America		X	X					X	X					
	15 Row	N. America		X	X	X				X	X					
	17 Row	N. America		X	X	X				X	X					
43	16 Row	N. America		X	X					X						
	22 Row	N. America			X	X				X	X					
	26 Row	N. America			X	X				X	X					
63	14 Row	N. America		X	X					X						
	16 Row	N. America		X	X	X				X	X					
	24 Row	N. America			X	X	X			X	X	X				
1003	9 Row	India	X							X						
62-10	10 Row	S. Africa				X	X				X	X				
62-20	20 Row	S. Africa						X	X				X	X	X	
30	13 Row	U.K.	X	X						X						
	15 Row	U.K.	X	X	X					X	X					
	20 Row	U.K.		X	X	X				X	X	X				
	23 Row	U.K.					X	X				X	X	X		
	30 Row	U.K.					X	X	X					X	X	X
130	15 Row	U.K.				X	X				X	X				
	Planters															
401	2 Row Mounted	Brazil	X	X						X						
	4 Row Mounted	Brazil		X	X					X	X					
37	2 Row Mounted	N. America	X	X						X						
	4 Row Mounted	N. America		X	X					X	X					
39	2 Row Mounted	N. America	X	X						X						
	4 Row Mounted	N. America		X	X					X	X					
468	4 Row Trailed	N. America		X	X					X						
	6 Row Trailed	N. America		X	X	X				X	X	X				
	8 Row Trailed	N. America			X	X	X				X	X	X			
48	2, 3, 4 Row Mounted	S. Africa		X	X	X				X	X	X				
	2, 3, 4, 6 Row Trailed	S. Africa			X	X	X	X		X	X	X	X			
71	2 Row Mounted	S. Africa	X	X						X						
	4 Row Mounted	S. Africa		X	X					X	X					
	PLOUGHS															
	Mouldboard Ploughs															
74	Fixed Mounted	Argentina	3F	3-4F	3, 4, 5F	4, 5, 6F	5, 6F	6F		3, 4F	4, 5, 6F	4, 5, 6F	5, 6F			
66	Fixed Mounted	Australia	3F	3-4F	4F					3-4F	4F					
150	Fixed Mounted	France	2-3F	2-3F	3F					2-3F	3F					
160	Fixed Mounted	France	2-3F	2, 3, 4F	3, 4, 5F	4-5F	5F			3-4F	4-5F	5F	5F			
180	Semi Mounted	France				6F	6-7F	6-7F					6F	6-7F	7F	
260	Reversible Mounted	France	2F	2-3F	2-3F	3-4F	3-4F	4F		2-3F	3-4F	3-4F				
265	Reversible Mounted	France	2F	2-3F	2-3F	3-4F	3-4F	4F		2-3F	3-4F	3-4F	5F			
270	Reversible Mounted	France			3F	3-4F	5F	5F		3F	3-4F	4-5F				
43	Fixed Mounted	India	2-3F	3-4F	3-4F					3-4F	4F					
43	Fixed Mounted	N. America	2-3F	2-3F	3F					3F						
82	Fixed Mounted	N. America		3F	3-4F	4, 5, 6F	4, 5, 6F	6F		3F	3, 4F	4, 5, 6F	5-6F	6F		
57	Reversible Mounted	N. America			3F	3-4F	4F	4F		3F	3F	3-4F	4F			
345	Fixed Mounted	N. America	3F	3-4F	4-5F	4-5F				3-4F	4-5F	4-5F				
570	Reversible Mounted	N. America			3F	3-4F	4F	4F		3F	3F	3-4F	4F			
880	Semi Mounted	N. America		4F	4-5F	4, 5, 6F	5-6F	6, 7, 8F		4-5F	4-5F	4, 5, 6F	5, 6, 7F	6, 7, 8F	7-8F	
49	Fixed Mounted	S. Africa	2F	2, 3, 4F	2, 3, 4F	4F				3-4F	4F					
58	Reversible Mounted	S. Africa	1-2F	2-3F	3F					2-3F	3F	3F				
345	Fixed Mounted	S. Africa	3F	3-4F	4-5F	4-5F				3-4F	4-5F	4-5F				

X = Suitable   m = metres   F = Furrows

PLOUGHS (Cont.)			2 Wheel Drive							4 Wheel Drive						
Model No.	Description	Source	>50 hp	50-62 hp	62-75 hp	75-92 hp	92-110 hp	110-140 hp	140-190 hp	>70 hp	70-80 hp	80-95 hp	95-110 hp	110-180 hp	180-270 hp	270+ hp
Disc Ploughs																
90	Fixed Mounted	Australia	2-3F	2, 3, 4F	3, 4, 5F	4, 5, 6F	5-6F			4F	4-5F	4, 5, 6F	5-6F			
91	Fixed Mounted	Australia	2-3F	2, 3, 4F	3-4F					4F	4F					
202/204	Fixed Mounted	Brazil	2-3F	2, 3, 4F	3-4F					4F	4F					
203	Fixed Mounted	Brazil	2-3F	2-3F						2-3F						
205	Fixed Mounted	Brazil	3F	4F						3-4F						
206	Fixed Mounted	Brazil	2-3F	2, 3, 4F	3-4F					4F	4F					
212	Reversible Mounted	Brazil		X						X						
61	Fixed Mounted	India	2-3F	2, 3, 4F	3-4F	4F				3-4F	4F					
17	Fixed Mounted	Mexico	2-3F	2, 3, 4F	3-4F	4F				3-4F	4F					
76	Reversible Mounted	Mexico	3F	3-4F	4F					3-4F	4F					
78	Reversible Mounted	Mexico		X						X						
Chisel Ploughs																
226	Chisel Plough	Brazil		2m	3m	3m				2m	3m	3m				
129	Chisel Plough	N. America	1m	3m	3m	3m	5m	5m		1-3m	3m	5m	5m	5m		
24	Mounted	U.K.	2m	2-3m	2-3m	3m				2-3m	2-3m	3m				
25	Mounted	U.K.				3m	3m	4m	6m			3m	3m	4m	6m	
MISCELLANEOUS																
Transport and Trailers																
12	Transporter	Australia	X	X												
802	Trailer	Brazil	X	X												
812	Transporter	Brazil	X	X												
2	Transporter	India	X	X												
27	Trailer – 3 tonne	India	X	X	X											
27	Trailer – 4 tonne	India	X	X	X											
28	Trailer – 5 tonne	India	X	X	X											
55	4 Wheel Trailer – 5,5 tonne	International		X	X					X						
200	Trailer – 3t. Low Loader	U.K.	X	X												
	Trailer – 4t; 4,5t Tipping	U.K.	X	X	X					X						
	Trailer – 4,5t Hi Level	U.K.	X	X	X					X						
	Trailer – 5t; 6,5t Tipping	U.K.		X	X	X				X	X					
	Trailer – 7t; 8,5t Tipping	U.K.			X	X					X	X				
	Trailer – 10t. Tipping	U.K.				X	X				X	X	X			
Blades and Soilscoops																
21	Utility Blade	Australia		X	X					X						
818	Blade	Brazil	X	X												
17	Utility Blade	India	X	X												
17	Utility Blade	Mexico	X	X												
226/7	Blade	N. America	X	X												
63	Grader	S. Africa		X	X					X						
125	Scoop	S. Africa	X	X												
Loaders and Cranes																
14	Job Crane	Australia	X	X												
800	Jib	Brazil	X	X												
12	Jib Crane	India	X	X												
216/236	Loader	N. America	X	X	X											
246	Loader	N. America				X	X	X	X			X	X	X	X	
200	Loader	S. Africa	X	X	X											
80	Loader	U.K.	X	X	X	X				X	X	X				
Spreading and Fertilising																
110	Manure Spreader	N. America	X	X												
160	Manure Spreader	N. America		X	X					X	X					
205	Manure Spreader	N. America			X	X					X	X				
19	Manure Spreader	U.K.	X	X	X					X						
100	Slurry Tanker	U.K.	X	X	X	X	X			X	X	X	X			
General																
1	Post Hole Digger	Australia	X	X												
338	Drag Scraper	Australia				X	X	X				X	X	X		
420	Tru Line Post Driver	Australia	X	X	X											
23	Culti-Wheel	India	X													
1007	Paddy Disc	India	X													

X = Suitable   m = metres   F = Furrows

Model No.	Description	Source	>50 hp	50-62 hp	62-75 hp	75-92 hp	92-110 hp	110-140 hp	140-190 hp	>70 hp	70-80 hp	80-95 hp	95-110 hp	110-180 hp	180-270 hp	270+ hp
TILLAGE			**2 Wheel Drive**							**4 Wheel Drive**						
	Offset Disc Harrows															
34	Mounted	Australia	1m	1-2m	2m					1-2m	2m					
81	Mounted	Australia	1m	1m						1m						
130	Trailed	Brazil			2m	2m	3m				2m	2m	3m			
65	Mounted	India	1-2m	1-2m						1-2m						
35	Mounted	Mexico	1m	1-2m	2m					1-2m	2m					
40	Trailed	Mexico	2m	2m	3m					2m	3m	3m				
42	Trailed	Mexico		2m	2-3m	3m				3m						
34	Mounted	India	1m	1m	2m	2m				2m	2m					
730	Trailed	N. America				3m				3m	3m					
34	Mounted	S. Africa	1m	2m	2m	2m				2m	2m					
20/21	Mounted	S. Africa	1m	1m						1m						
730	Trailed	S. Africa				3m	3-4m	4m	5m		3m	3-4m	4m	5m		
	Tandem Disc Harrows															
122	Mounted	Brazil	1-2m	1,2,3m	3m					1-3m	3m					
123	Mounted	Brazil	2m	2-3m	3m					2-3m	3m					
21	Mounted	N. America	1m	1-2m	2m					2m						
120/220	Mounted	N. America	2m	2-3m	3m					2-3m	3m					
39	Mounted	S. Africa	2m	2m						2m						
28	Mounted	U.K.	2m	2-3m	3m					2-3m	3m					
520	Trailed	N. America		3m	3m	4-5m	5-6m	5-6m		3m	3-4m	4-5m	5-6m	6m		
620	Trailed	N. America		3m	3-4m	4m	4-5m	7m		3m	3-4m	4m	5-6m	7m	7m	
720	Trailed	N. America			3m	3-4m	4m	4-5m	7m		3m	3-4m	4m	5-7m	7m	
820	Trailed	N. America						7m	7m				7m	7m		
	Tillers and Cultivators															
38	Tiller, Mounted	Australia	2m	2m	2m	3m				2m	3m					
120	Scarifier	Australia	3m	3m	3m	4m	4m	4m		3-4m	3-4m	4m				
259	Cultivator	Australia			8m	9m	10m	11m	12m	8m	9m	10m	11m	12m		
500	Covering Harrow	Australia	2m	2-3m	4m	5m	6m	8m	10m	4m	5m	6m	8m	10m		
585	Stump Jump Harrow	Australia	2-3m	3-5m	4-6m	8-10m	10m			4-6m	8-10m	10m				
38	Ridger	International	3m							3m						
38	Tiller, Mounted	International	2m	2m	2-3m					2-3m	2-3m					
567	Cultivator	International	X	X						X						
38	Seedbox	International	X	X	X					X						
39	Spring Tine Cultivator	International	3m		3m	4m	5m	5m		4m	4-5m	5m	5m			
137	Spring Tine Cultivator	International		2m	3m	3-4m	5m	6m		3m	3-4m	5m	6m	6m		
21	Cultivator	Mexico	X	X						X						
38	Tiller, Mounted	India	X	X						X						
259	Cultivator	N. America			8m	9m	10m	11m	12m		8m	9m	10m	11m	12m	
938	Tiller, Mounted	S. Africa	1-2m	1-2m	2m					2m						
23	Field Cultivator	U.K.	3m	3m	3-4m	4m	4-6m	6m		3m	3-4m	4m	6m	6m		
27	Subsoiler	Australia	X	X	X					X						
37	Subsoiler	Australia	X	X	X					X						
63	Sundercut Discs	Australia		X	X					X	X					
67	Sundercut Discs	Australia		2m	3m	3-4m				2m	2-3m	4m				
7300	Sweep Plough	Australia				5m	9-11m	12m			5m	9-11m	12m	12m		
586	Diamond Harrow	Australia	3-4m	3-4m	5-6m					5-6m						
27	Subsoiler	India	X	X						X						
36	Subsoiler	Mexico	X	X						X						
360	Wide Level Disc Harrow	N. America		2-3m	2-3m	4-5m	4-5m			2-3m	2-3m	4-5m				
12	Ripper	S. Africa	X	X						X						
30	One Way Disc	S. Africa	X	X												
112	Ripper Plough	S. Africa				X	X	X		X	X	X	X			
35	Subsoiler	S. Africa			X	X				X	X					
24	Subsoiler	U.K.						X						X		
25	Subsoiler	U.K.						X						X		

X = Suitable   m = metres   F = Furrows

Source: MF Worldwide Catalogue, 1980

MASSEY FERGUSON TRACTOR / HORSEPOWER / IMPLEMENTS COMPATABILITY CHARTS, 1989

MASSEY-FERGUSON TRACTOR MODELS / HORSEPOWER	Model	<40	230 / 40	240 / 47	350 / 52	355 / 58	360 / 63	365 / 68	375·3050 / 78	390·3060 / 86	3065 / 92	398·3070 / 100	399·3080 / 110	3090 / 116	3610 / 122	3630 / 142	3650 / 158	3680 / 190	>200
PLOUGHS																			
f = furrows									5,6f	5,6f	5,6,7f	5,6,7f	6,7,8f	7,8f	8f				
sm = semi-mounted									sm	sm	sm	sm	sm	sm	sm				
FIXED MOULDBOARD		2,3f	2,3f	2,3f	2,3,4f	2,3,4f	3,4f	3,4,5f	3,4,5f	4,5f	5f								
REVERSIBLE MOULDBOARD								2f	2,3f	2,3f	2,3,4f	3,4f	3,4,5f	3,4,5f	4,5f				
DISC	M-F 765		2,3f	2,3f	2,3f	2,3,4f	2,3,4f	3,4f	4f	4f									
	M-F 900				2,3f	2,3f	3f	3f	3,4f	3,4,5f	3,4,5f	4,5f	4,5,6f	5,6f	5,6f	6f	6f	6f	
	M-F 202			2,3f	2,3f	2,3f	3f	3f	3f										
	M-F 204			3f	3,4f	3,4f	3,4f	4f	4f	4f									
	M-F 206				4f	4f	4,5f	4,5f	4,5f	4,5f	5f	5f							
DISC HARROWS																			
TANDEM	M-F 280			2.3m	2.3m	2.3m	2.3m	2.7m	2.7m	3.2m	3.2m	3.7m	3.7m						
							2.7m	3.2m	3.2m	3.7m	3.7m								
	M-F 520				3.05m	3.05m	3.05m	3.66m	3.66m	4.27m	4.27m	5.47m	5.47m	5.47m	6.4m	6.4m			
							3.66m		4.27m				5.47m	6.4m					
OFFSET	M-F 222			1.8m	1.8m	1.8m	1.8m	1.8m											
								2.3m	2.3m	2.3m	2.3m								
	M-F 140						2.7	3.15	3.6	4.05	4.5	4.60	4.95	5.3	5.4	5.6	6.1	6.1	
CULTIVATORS																			
CHISEL	M-F 325 - M. DUTY								2.5m	2.5m	2.5m	2.5m	2.5m	2.5m					
	M-F 325 - H. DUTY											2.5m	2.5m	2.5m	2.5m	3.0m	3.0m		
														3.0m	4.2m	4.2m	4.2m	4.2m
	M-F 750			2.0m	2.0m	2.0m	2.0m	2.0m	2.5m	3.0m	3.0m	3.5m	3.5m	4.0m	4.0m				
				2.5m	2.5m	2.5m	2.5m	3.0m	3.5m	3.5m	4.0m	4.0m	4.0m						
							3.0m	3.0m	3.5m	4.0m	4.0m								
SPRING TINE	M-F 305			2.0m	2.0m	2.0m	2.0m	2.0m	3.5m	3.5m	3.5m	3.5m	3.5m	3.5m	4.5m	4.5m			
												4.5m	4.5m	4.5m	6.0m	6.0m	6.0m	6.0m	
												6.0m	6.0m						
	M-F 315	2.0m	2.0m	2.0m	2.0m	3.0m	3.0m	3.5m	3.5m	3.5m	4.5m	4.5m	4.5m	4.5m	4.5m	6.0m	6.0m		
				3.0m	3.0m	3.5m	3.5m	4.5m	4.5m	4.5m	6.0m	6.0m	6.0m	6.0m	6.0m				
					3.5m														
	M-F 754				3.0m	3.0m	3.0m	3.0m	3.5m	3.5m	4.5m	4.5m	4.5m	5.0m					
							3.5m	3.5m	4.5m	4.5m	5.0m	5.0m	5.0m	6.0m	6.0m	6.0m			
	M-F 755						3.5m	3.5m	3.5m	3.5m	3.5m	4.5m	4.5m	6.0m	6.0m				
								4.5m	4.5m	4.5m	4.5m	4.5m	6.0m	6.0m	6.5m	6.5m	6.5m	6.5m	6.5m
												6.0m	6.5m	6.5m					
RIGID TINE	M-F 738	1.15m	1.7m	1.88m	1.88m	2.34m	2.34m	2.79m	2.79m	2.79m	2.79m	3.23m	3.23m						
		1.7m	1.88m	2.34m	2.34m	2.79m	2.79m	3.23m	3.23m	3.23m	3.23m								
					2.79m	3.23m													
TOOLBAR	M-F 352	2.25m	2.25m	2.25m	2.25m	2.25m	2.25m	ALL	ALL	3.3m	3.7m	3.7m	3.7m						
							2.9m			3.7m										
	M-F 355							X	X	X	X	X	X						
RIDGERS	M-F 80	X	X	X	X	X	X	X	X	X	X								
	M-F 738	30 MIN	X	X	X	X	X	X	X	X	X								
BUNDFORMER	M-F 732			X	X	X	X	X	X	X	X	X							
DITCHER/SUBSOILER	M-F 731			X	X	X	X	X	X	X	X	X							
ROTARY CULTIVATORS	M-F 762	35 MIN	X	X	X	X	X	X	X										
PLANTING																			
DRILL, END WHEEL	M-F 30			2.4m	2.4m	2.4m	2.4m	2.4m	2.4m	2.4m		6.0m	6.0m	6.0m	6.0m	6.0m			
	M-F 500				3m	3m	3m	3m	3m	3m	3m	3m							
								4m	4m	4m	4m	4m	4m	4m					
PNEUMATIC	M-F 510										4.0m	4.0m	4.0m	6.0m	6.6m	6.6m			
												6.0m	6.6m	8.0m	8.0m				
												6.6m	8.0m						
PRECISION PLANTER	M-F 501					X	X	X	X	X	X	X	X						

MASSEY-FERGUSON TRACTOR MODELS			230	240	350	355	360	365	375 3050	390 3060	3065	398 3070	399 3080	3090	3610	3630	3650	3680	
HORSEPOWER		<40	40	47	52	58	63	68	78	86	92	100	110	116	122	142	158	190	>200
PLANTING - CONTINUED																			
TILLER/SEEDER	M-F 738			X	X	X	X	X	X											
WIDE LEVEL DISC SEEDER	M-F 360									X S	X S	X S	X S	X S	X S	X S	M XX	M XX	M XX	M XXX
M = Multiple S = Single																			
DUAL HITCH	M-F 450																X	X	X	X
FERTILIZER SPREADER	M-F 566			X	X	X	X	X	X	X										
	M-F 568					X	X	X	X	X	X	X								
	M-F 570							X	X	X	X	X								
HAY & FORAGE																				
DISC MOWERS	M-F 123		1.65m	1.65m	1.65m	1.65m	1.65m	1.65m	1.65m	1.65m										
	M-F 125			2.16m	2.16m	2.16m	2.16m	2.16m	2.16m	2.16m	2.16m	2.16m								
	M-F 127					2.4m	2.4m	2.4m	2.4m	2.4m	2.4m	2.4m	2.4m	2.4m						
DRUM MOWERS	M-F 122		1.65m	1.65m	1.65m	1.65m	1.65m	1.65m	1.65m	1.65m										
	M-F 124			1.85m	1.85m	1.85m	1.85m	1.85m	1.85m	1.85m	1.85m	1.85m								
	M-F 126					2.1m	2.1m	2.1m	2.1m	2.1m	2.1m	2.1m	2.1m	2.1m						
MOWERS/CONDITIONERS	M-F 164/165								2.75m	2.75m	2.75m	2.75m	2.75m	2.75m						
	M-F 166/167								3.2m	3.2m	3.2m	3.2m	3.2m	3.2m						
SLASHERS	M-F 672	12 MIN	X	X	X	X	X	X	X	X	X	X	X	X	X	X				
FORAGE HARVESTERS	M-F 610										X	X	X	X	X	X				
	M-F 620			X	X	X	X	X	X	X	X	X	X							
RAKES AND TEDDERS	M-F 35/36/38/40		X	X	X	X	X	X	X	X	X	X								
	M-F 62/64/72			X	X	X	X	X	X	X	X	X	X							
	M-F 104				X	X	X	X	X	X	X	X	X	X						
BALERS/CONVENTIONAL	M-F 1/2/3/4	30-35 min	1	1	1,2	1,2	1,2 3	1,2 3	1,2 3,4	2 3,4	2 3,4	2 3,4	3,4	3,4						
BALERS ROUND	M-F 822/828				822 min	822	822 828 min	822 828	822 828	822 828	822 828	822 828	828	828						
BALERS LARGE SQUARE	M-F 5										X	X	X	X	X	X	X	X		
MATERIAL HANDLING																				
LOADERS	M-F 875		X	X	X	X	X													
	M-F 880							X	X	X	X	X								
	M-F 885									X	X	X	X	X						
	M-F 890, 20 series			1020 1220	1020 1220	1020 1220	1020 1220 1420	ALL	1220 1420 1620	1420 1620	1620	1620	1620							
	M-F 890, 30 series			930	930	930 1430	930 1430	930 1430	1430											
	M-F 890, 40 series							1640	1640	1640	1640 1840	1640 1840	1640 1840	1640 1840	1840	1840	1840		
TRAILERS M-F 700, W/o power brakes - TONS		1/2.5	5	5	5	5	5	6	6	6	6	8	8	8	8	8	8	8	
M-F 700, W power brakes - TONS			6	6	6	6	6	8	8	8	8	10	10	10	10	10	10	10	
BLADES																				
FRONT	M-F 830							X	X	X	X	X								
REAR	M-F 685 - M. Duty		1.84 2.5m	1.84 2.5m	1.84 2.5m	1.84 2.5m													
	M-F 685 - H. Duty							2.5m	2.5m	2.5m	2.5m	2.5m	2.5m						
	M-F 721		X	X	X	X	X	X	X	X	X	X							
POSTHOLE DIGGER	M-F 1	25 MIN	X	X	X	X	X	X	X	X	X	X	X						

Source: MF Implements Guide, 1989

MASSEY-HARRIS, FERGUSON AND MF TRACTORS IMPORTED INTO FRANCE OR MADE IN FRANCE WITH NUMBERS AS KNOWN UP TO 1994

Model	No. imported to France	Imported from	No. made in France
M-H 102 junior	275	USA	
M-H 101 senior	399	USA	
M-H 101 junior	799	USA	
M-H 81 rowcrop	400	USA	
M-H 20K	717	USA	
M-H 30 gas and kerosene	1017	USA	
M-H 44 KS	415	USA	
M-H 744	656	UK	
Ferguson TE 20 including FF30	81449	UK	
M-H 11 pony	2406	Canada	
M-H 226	85	USA	
MF 811 Pony			1709
MF 812 Pony			42973
MF 745	469	UK	
MF 765	218	UK	
MF 835			43819
MF 865			6678
MF 821			9268
MF super 90	718	USA	
MF 42/8			10134
MF 825			25287
MF 37/8			10273
MF20/25			1472
MF 65 Mk II			6003
MF 30/8			16152
MF 7000	5566	Italy	
MF 4500	639	Italy	
MF 1100	191	USA	
MF 165 HX 211			13866
MF 145 HX 210			17965
MF 140 HX 208/209			57396
MF 135 HX 218			15183
MF 130			27527
MF 122			1888
MF 175/7DX 65	1938	UK	
MF 1080	284	USA	
MF 133 HX 218			13685
MF 163 Mk III			21636
MF 178/8			8993
MF 178/7	130	UK	
MF 1080/8			7032
MF 155			11597
MF 140 diesel	15148	Italy	
MF 1500	3	USA	
MF 185			5313

Model	No. imported to France	Imported from	No. made in France
MF 188			20092
MF 165 diesel			7396
MF 168			19144
MF 155 diesel			3440
MF 158 diesel			21722
MF 158 Mk III			2070
MF 152 diesel			8358
MF 148			4834
MF 133 diesel			5613
MF 135 diesel			2919
MF 1200	873	UK	
MF 1135	233	USA	
MF 1105	168	USA	
MF 132	104	Germany	
MF 1800	1	USA	
MF 595			22716
MF 1805	7	USA	
MF 1505	13	USA	
MF 590			13483
MF 285			7452
MF 575			6461
MF 275			7843
MF 260			5344
MF 560			1046
MF 245			3977
MF 148 Mk III			323
MF 235			3164
MF 133 Mk III			319
MF 135 Mk III			2936
MF 1132	220	Germany	
MF 1102	383	Germany	
MF 168 Mk III			1391
MF 255			3468
MF 592			1248
MF 274	1059	Italy	
MF 254	649	Italy	
MF 250			122
MF 2680			2952
MF 1250	49	UK	
MF 2640			6213
MF 2620			3305
MF 290			6849
MF 145 Mk III			1059
MF 184 F	115	Italy	
MF 174 F	261	Italy	
MF 168 F			443
MF 168 S			421
MF 158 F			799
MF 158 V			763
MF 154 F	121	Italy	
MF 152			945
MF 152 V			330
MF 152 S			410

Model	No. imported to France	Imported from	No. made in France
MF 145 V/S			1269
MF 135.8-V			?
MF 2720			2537
MF 698 T			5578
MF 690			12245
MF 298			1290
MF 675			9058
MF 230	73	UK	
MF 184 S	129	Italy	
MF 174 S	567	Italy	
MF 154 S	147	Italy	
MF 290	357	UK	
MF 275	300	UK	
MF 265	713	UK	
MF 250	582	UK	
MF 2725			883
MF 2645			779
MF 2625			511
MF 699			5454
MF 284	118	Italy	
MF 264	164	Italy	
MF 194 S	46	Italy	
MF 174 V	111	Italy	
MF 164 S	82	Italy	
MF 164 F	67	Italy	
MF 164 V	180	Italy	
MF 154 V	162	Italy	
MF 3090			3527
MF 3080			10872
MF 3070			6341
MF 3060			?
MF 3050			?
MF 3680			1181
MF 3650			1858
MF 3630			1182
MF 3610			353
MF 3065			?
MF 3655			?
MF 3645			?
MF 3125			?
MF 3115			1799
MF 3095			?
MF 3690			?
MF 3670			?
MF 3635			?
MF 3085			?
MF 3120			?
MF 3075			?
MF 3065 S Visioporteur			?
MF 3065 Visioporteur			?
MF 3060 Visioporteur			?
MF 3050 Visioporteur			?

Source. Recherches conception et production: Marketing FDC Massey Ferguson. 1994. Wall chart.

Product Lists

M-F WORLDWIDE 1970

TRACTORS

Machine No.	Type	Origin
7	Tractor	North America
10	Tractor	North America
12	Tractor	North America
130	Tractor	France
135	Tractor	United Kingdom
135	Tractor	North America
135	Tractor	France
140	Tractor	France
145	Tractor	France
150	Tractor	North America
155	Tractor	France
165	Tractor	United Kingdom
165	Tractor	France
165	Tractor	North America
175	Tractor	North America
175S	Tractor	United Kingdom
178	Tractor	United Kingdom
180	Tractor	North America
1080	Tractor	France
1080	Tractor	North America
1100	Tractor	North America
1130	Tractor	North America
1150	Tractor	North America
101C	Tractor	Italy
124C	Tractor	Italy
144C	Tractor	Italy
164C	Tractor	Italy
	Pressure Control	United Kingdom

GRAIN HARVESTING

Machine No.	Type	Origin
30	Combine	Germany
31	Combine	Germany
39	Combine	Germany
186	Combine	Germany
187	Combine	Germany
205	Combine	North America
300	Combine (inc. rice version)	North America
400	Combine Rice	United Kingdom
400	Bagger Combine	United Kingdom
405	Combine	North America
410	Combine (rice included)	North America
410/5	Combine	United Kingdom
487	Combine	France
510	Rice Combine	North America
510	Combine	France
510/5	Combinc	Unitcd Kingdom
585	Pto Header Combine	Australia
587	Self-Propelled Header Combine	Australia
	Cornheads	North America
	Quick Attach Tables	North America

HAY HARVESTING

Machine No.	Type	Origin
8	Pick-up Press	Germany
9	Baler	North America
12	Baler	North America
14	Baler	France
15	Baler	France
19	Dump Rake	South Africa
20	Baler	France
22	Bale Thrower	North America
25	Side Rake	North America
25	Side Rake	Australia
29	Mounted Wheel Rake	North America
30	Swather	North America
31	Rear Mower	Australia
32	Mower	Australia
32	Mower	United Kingdom
33	Mower	International
36	Side Rake	Australia
36	Swather	North America
37	Rake	North America
40	Hay Conditioner	North America
41/42	Mowers	North America
51	Rotary Mower	International
52	Mower	Australia
81	Hay-tender	North America
91	Rake	France
156	Mounted Haymaker	Australia
173	Mower	International
173	Trailed Bale Loader	Australia
829	Mower	France

TILLAGE

Machine No.	Type	Origin
9	Implement Carrier	North America
10	Offset Trailed Disc Harrows	Mexico
16	Hitch	North America
18	Scarifier	North America
19	Spring Tooth Harrow	North America
21	Disc Harrow	North America
22	Tandem Disc Harrow	Brazil
25	Disc Harrow	North America
27	Subsoiler	North America
30/40	Offset Disc Harrow	North America
33	Disc Harrow	North America
34	Mounted Offset Disc Harrow	Mexico
34	Disc Harrow	South Africa
34	Disc Harrow	Australia
35	Subsoiler	North America
36	Wide Level Disc Harrow	North America
37	Cultivator	International
38	Tiller	Australia
39	Cultivator	International
39	Harrow	South Africa
39	Disc Harrow	North America
50	Tool Carrier	Mexico
50-100	Tool Carriers	North America
52	Disc Harrow	North America
60	Harrow	South Africa
63	Trailed Sundercut	Australia
67	Sundercut	Australia
67	Harrow	North America
67	Row Crop Cultivator	Brazil
72	Disc Harrow	North America
80	Tool Carrier	Mexico
81	Disc Harrow	Australia
120	Scarifier	Australia
129/149	Row Crop Cultivators	North America
130	Cultivator	Australia
138	Tiller	North America
140	Cultivator	North America
140	Cultivator	South Africa
144/146	Cultivator	North America
220/221	Cultivator	North America
500/585/586	Harrows	Australia
560	Cultivator	Australia
728	Ridger	United Kingdom
738	Tiller	United Kingdom
765	Offset Disc Harrow	United Kingdom
825	Disc Harrow	France
838	Tiller	France
914	Disc Harrow	South Africa
920	Cultivator	South Africa
920/930	Poly Discs	South Africa
938	Tiller	South Africa
943	Toolbar Attachments	South Africa
965	Disc Harrow	South Africa
	Running Gear	North America
	Heavy-duty Wheel Hitch	North America

PLOUGHS

Machine No.	Type	Origin
10-13	Single Furrow Reversible Ploughs	International
24	Chisel Plough	United Kingdom
30-33	3 Furrow Reversible Ploughs	International
43	Mounted Mouldboard Plough	North America
44-50	Two Furrow Reversible Ploughs	International
49	Mouldboard Plough	South Africa
55	Reversible Plough	North America
55	Reversible Mouldboard Plough	South Africa
56	Reversible Disc Plough	Mexico
57	Reversible Plough	North America
59	Reversible Plough	North America
62	Plough	North America
64	Disc Plough	Brazil
65	Disc Plough	Australia
66	Plough	North America
66	Plough	Australia
68	Disc Plough	South Africa
68	Disc Plough	Brazil
74	Plough	Australia
74	Plough	North America
82	Mounted Plough	North America
84	Trailed Plough	North America
88	Plough	North America
124/126	Chisel Plough	North America
125	Chisel Plough	North America
127	Chisel Plough	North America
127	Chisel Plough	France
228	Chisel Plough	Australia
765	Disc Plough	United Kingdom
867/868	Vineyard Ploughs	France
880	Plough	North America
964	Disc Plough	South Africa
966	Plough	South Africa

UTILITY TOOLS

Machine No.	Type	Origin
NA 1	Reversible Soil Scoop	North America
12	Rear Jib Crane	Brazil
12	Transporter	Brazil
12	Transporter/Crane	Australia
16	Utility Blade	North America
17	Terracer Blade	North America
17	Rear Mounted Blade	Brazil
19	Trailer	Brazil
20	Trailer	United Kingdom
21	Blade	North America
21	Trailer	United Kingdom
21	Blade	Australia
22	Trailer	United Kingdom
23	Trailer	United Kingdom
24	Trailer	United Kingdom
25	Trailer	United Kingdom
35	Loader	United Kingdom
36	Loader	United Kingdom
38	Loader	North America
59	Rotary Cutter	North America
60	Rotary Cutter	North America
63	Grader	South Africa
65	Rotary Cutter	North America
75	Rotary Cutter	North America
77	Rotary Cutter	Brazil
95	Loader	North America
160	Mounted and Trailed Slashers	Australia
145	Mounted Slasher	Australia
150	Mounted and Trailed Slasher	Australia
164	Rotary Cutter	North America
180	Flail Stalk Shreader	North America
702	Transporter	United Kingdom
721	Multi-purpose Blade	United Kingdom
905	Soil Scoop	South Africa
921	Blade	South Africa

PLANTING

Machine No.	Type	Origin
25	Seed Drill	International
29	Grain and Fertiliser Drill	United Kingdom
33	Grain Drill	North America
34	Multi-purpose Drill	United Kingdom
37	Runner Planter	North America
37	Planter	Brazil
39	Planter	North America
41	Unit Planter	North America
43	Combined Drill	North America
55	Drill	Australia
63	Drill	North America
78	Planter	North America
468	Planter	North America
904	Planter	South Africa

MISCELLANEOUS

Machine No.	Type	Origin
1	Post Hole Digger	Australia
10	Spinner Broadcaster	United Kingdom
13	Manure Spreader	Germany
15	Grinder Mixer	North America
16	Dozer	South Africa
19	Manure Spreader	United Kingdom
20	Cordwood Saw	Australia
22	Broadcaster	Australia
22/24	Rotary Hoes	North America
26	Rotary Hoe	North America
45	Hammer Mill	South Africa
82	Side Mounted Forage Harvester	Australia
98	Forage Blower	North America
110	Manure Spreader	North America
160	Manure Spreader	North America
205	Manure Spreader	North America

Source: M-F Worldwide Catalogue, 1970

M-F WORLDWIDE 1976

TRACTORS

Model		Source
MF 235	Tractor	N. America
MF 235	Orchard Tractor	N. America
MF 255	Tractor	N. America
MF 265	Tractor	N. America
MF 275	Tractor	N. America
MF 285	Tractor	N. America
MF 1085	Tractor	N. America
MF 1105	Tractor	N. America
MF 1135	Tractor	N. America
MF 1155	Tractor	N. America
MF 1505	4WD Tractor	N. America
MF 1805	4WD Tractor	N. America
MF 154	Tractor	Italy
MF 174	Tractor	Italy
MF 184	Tractor	Italy
MF 194	Tractor	Italy
MF 154-4	4WD Tractor	Italy
MF 174-4	4WD Tractor	Italy
MF 184-4	4WD Tractor	Italy
MF 194-4	4WD Tractor	Italy
MF 134C	Agricultural Crawler	Italy
MF 154C	Agricultural Crawler	Italy
MF 174C	Agricultural Crawler	Italy
MF D300B	Agricultural Crawler	Italy
MF D400B	Agricultural Crawler	Italy
MF 150	Tractor	Mexico
MF 165	Tractor	Mexico
MF 185	Tractor	Mexico
MF 1105	Tractor	Mexico
MF 135	Tractor	U.K.
MF 148	Tractor	U.K.
MF 165	Tractor	U.K.
MF 168	Tractor	U.K.
MF 185	Tractor	U.K.
MF 188	Tractor	U.K.
MF 1200	4WD Tractor	U.K.
MF 133	Tractor	France
MF 135	Tractor	France
MF 148	Tractor	France
MF 152	Tractor	France
MF 155	Tractor	France
MF 158	Tractor	France
MF 165	Tractor	France
MF 168	Tractor	France
MF 185	Tractor	France
MF 188	Tractor	France
MF 595	Tractor	France

Model		Source
MF 168	4WD Tractor	France
MF 188	4WD Tractor	France
MF 595	4WD Tractor	France
MF 235	Tractor	Brazil
MF 250	Tractor	Brazil
MF 265	Tractor	Brazil
MF 275	Tractor	Brazil
MF 285	Tractor	Brazil
MF 290	Tractor	Brazil
MF 95X	Tractor	Brazil
MF 65R	Tractor	Brazil
MF 150	Vineyard Tractor	Argentina
MF 155	Tractor	Argentina
MF 165	Tractor	Argentina
MF 1078	Tractor	Argentina
MF 1088	Tractor	Argentina
MF 1098	Tractor	Argentina
MF 135	Tractor	International
MF 165	Tractor	International
MF 185	Tractor	International
MF 132	Narrow Tractor	International
MF 142	Narrow Tractor	International

COMBINES

Model		Source
MF 300	Combine	N. America
MF 510	Combine	N. America
MF 750	Combine	N. America
MF 760	Combine	N. America
Quick Attach Table		N. America
Universal Pick-up Reel		N. America
MF 61	Apron Pick-up	N. America
MF 542	Combine	Australia
MF 587	Combine	Australia
MF 587	PTO Combine	Australia
MF 520/525	Combine	U.K.
MF 620/625	Combine	U.K.
MF 206	Combine	France
MF 307	Combine	France
MF 506	Combine	France
MF 507	Combine	France
MF 520/525	Combine	France
MF 220	Combine	Brazil
MF 310	Combine	Brazil
MF 227	Combine	International
MF 52	Rotary Recleaner	South Africa

CORNHEADS

Model	Source
MF 24 to 83 Cornheads	N. America
MF 33/43/53/63c Cornheads	International

CANE HARVESTERS

MF 102 Cane Harvester	Australia
MF 201 Cane Harvester	Australia

OTHER HARVESTING

MF 129 Peanut Sheller	South Africa
MF 139 Thresher	South Africa
MF 149 Peanut Picker	South Africa
MF 159 Pto Maize Combine	South Africa

BALERS

MF 12	Baler	N. America
MF 124/126 Balers		N. America
MF 22	Bale Thrower	N. America
MF 560	Giant Round Baler	N. America
MF 14	Baler	France
MF 15	Baler	France
MF 20	Baler	France

MOWERS

MF 41/42 Mowers	N. America
MF 41 Mower	Australia
MF 42 Mower	Australia
MF 32 Mower	U.K.
MF 60 Mower	U.K.
MF 70 Mower	U.K.
MF 80 Mower	France
MF 82 Mower	France
MF 32 Mower	International
MF 173/273 Mowers	International

SEED DRILLS

MF 25	Side Delivery Rake	N. America
MF 29	Mounted Wheel Rake	N. America
MF 37	Side Delivery Rake	N. America
MF 35	Pull Type Swather	N. America
MF 655	Hydro Swather	N. America
MF 81	Hay Tender	N. America
MF 200	Forage Harvester	N. America
MF 260	Forage Harvester	N. America
MF 25	Side Delivery Rake	Australia
MF 85	Gyro Swather	France
MF 19	Dump Rake	South Africa

OTHER HAY AND FORAGE

Model		Source
MF 33	Seed Drill	N. America
MF 43	Seed Drill	N. America
MF 63	Seed Drill	N. America
MF 55	Seed Drill	Australia
MF 56	Seed Drill	Australia
MF 30	Seed Drill	U.K.
MF 1003	Seeding Attachment	India
MF 34	Seed Drill	Brazil

PLANTERS

MF 37	Planter	N. America
MF 39	Planter	N. America
MF 41	Planter	N. America
MF 468	Planter	N. America
MF 20	Cane Planter	Australia
MF 48	Planter	South Africa
MF 71	Planter	South Africa
MF 40	Planter	Brazil

MOULDBOARD PLOUGHS

MF 57	Mouldboard Plough	N. America
MF 43	Mouldboard Plough	N. America
MF 82	Mouldboard Plough	N. America
MF 88	Mouldboard Plough	N. America
MF 880	Mouldboard Plough	N. America
MF 66	Mouldboard Plough	Australia
MF 49	Mouldboard Plough	S. Africa
MF 43	Mouldboard Plough	India
MF 74	Mouldboard Plough	Argentina
MF 84	Mouldboard Plough	Argentina
MF 260	Mouldboard Plough	International
MF 250	Mouldboard Plough	International
MF 260	Mouldboard Plough	International
MF 260	Mouldboard Plough	International
MF 260	Mouldboard Plough	International
MF 150	Mouldboard Plough	International
MF 160	Mouldboard Plough	International
MF 180	Mouldboard Plough	International
MF 270	Diamond Plough	International

DISC PLOUGHS

Model		Source
MF 76	Disc Plough	Mexico
MF 17	Disc Plough	Mexico
MF 65	Disc Plough	Australia
MF 90/91	Disc Ploughs	Australia
MF 765	Disc Plough	U.K.
MF 80	Disc Plough	South Africa
MF 81	Disc Plough	South Africa
MF 61	Disc Plough	India
MF 62/64	Disc Ploughs	Brazil
MF 66	Disc Plough	Brazil
MF 68	Disc Plough	Brazil
MF 70	Disc Plough	Brazil
MF 65	Disc Plough	International

CHISEL PLOUGHS

MF 126/127/		
128	Chisel Ploughs	N. America
MF 24	Chisel Plough	U.K.
MF 25	Chisel Plough	U.K.
MF 126	Chisel Plough	Brazil

OFFSET DISC HARROWS

MF 40	Offset Disc Harrow	N. America
MF 35	Offset Disc Harrow	Mexico
MF 40	Offset Disc Harrow	Mexico
MF 42-3	Offset Disc Harrow	Mexico
MF 34	Offset Disc Harrow	Australia
MF 81	Offset Disc Harrow	Australia
MF 134/136/ 140	Offset Disc Harrows	France
MF 34	Offset Disc Harrow	S. Africa
MF 65	Offset Disc Harrow	India
MF 30	Offset Disc Harrow	Brazil

TANDEM DISC HARROWS

Model		Source
MF 520	Tandem Disc Harrow	N. America
MF 620	Tandem Disc Harrow	N. America
MF 21	Tandem Disc Harrow	N. America
MF 25	Tandem Disc Harrow	N. America
MF 39	Tandem Disc Harrow	N. America
MF 28	Tandem Disc Harrow	U.K.
MF 39	Tandem Disc Harrow	S. Africa
MF 914	Reversible Disc Harrow	S. Africa
MF 1007	Paddy Disc Harrow	India
MF 22	Tandem Disc Harrow	Brazil
MF 23	Tandem Disc Harrow	Brazil
MF 25	Tandem Disc Harrow	Brazil
MF 52	Tandem Disc Harrow	Argentine

TILLERS AND CULTIVATORS

MF 428	Row Crop Cultivator	N. America
MF 221	Row Crop Cultivator	N. America
MF 160	Field Cultivator	N. America
MF 138	Tiller	N. America
MF 21	Cultivator	Mexico
MF 120	Scarifier	Australia
MF 38	Tiller	Australia
MF 500/585/ 586	Harrows	Australia
MF 23	Cultivator	U.K.
MF 37	Cultivator	International
MF 39	Cultivator	International
MF 38	Tiller	International
MF 227/236/ 237/238	Cultivators	France
MF 38	Tiller	France
MF 938	Tiller	S. Africa
MF 38	Tiller	India
MF 67	Row Crop Cultivator	Brazil

ONE WAY DISC HARROWS

Model		Source
MF 36	Wide Level Disc Harrow	N. America
MF 63	Sundercut	Australia
MF 67	Sundercut	Australia
MF 60	One Way Disc Harrow	S. Africa
MF 930	Poly Disc Tiller	S. Africa

TOOL CARRIERS

Model		Source
MF 80/100	Tool Carriers	N. America
MF 50/80/100	Tool Carriers	Mexico
MF 110	Tool Carrier	Australia
MF 351/352	Tool Carriers	Australia
MF 75	Tool Carrier	S. Africa

SUBSOILERS

Model		Source
MF 27	Subsoiler	N. America
MF 35	Subsoiler	N. America
MF 36	Subsoiler	Mexico
MF 27	Subsoiler	Australia
MF 201/202/203	Subsoilers	France
MF 35	Subsoiler	S. Africa
MF 27-10	Subsoiler	India

TRANSPORT AND TRAILERS

Model		Source
MF 5/6/7/8/65	Running Gear	N. America
MF 12	Transporter	Australia
MF 20	Trailer	U.K.
MF 21	Trailer	U.K.
MF 22	Trailer	U.K.
MF 22	Hi-Level Trailer	U.K.
MF 23	Trailer	U.K.
MF 24	Trailer	U.K.
MF 25	Trailer	U.K.
MF 26	Trailer	U.K.
MF 47L/47S	Trailers	France
MF 105/106/107/108/108SE/110	Trailers	France
MF 210/212/215	Trailers	France
MF 2	Transporter	India
MF 27	Trailer	India
MF 28	Trailer	India
MF 122	Transporter	Brazil
MF 19	Trailer	Brazil
MF 50/55/60/80/100	Trailers	International

BLADES AND SOIL SCOOPS

Model		Source
MF 1	Soil Scoop	N. America
MF 16	Utility Blade	Mexico
MF 17	Utility Blade	Mexico
MF 21	Utility Blade	Australia
MF 338	Drag Scraper	Australia
MF 15	Soil Scoop	S. Africa
MF 905	Soil Scoop	S. Africa
MF 921	Utility Blade	S. Africa
MF 17	Bulldozer Attachment	S. Africa
MF 63	Grader	S. Africa
MF 17	Utility Blade	India
MF 18	Utility Blade	Brazil

ROTARY CUTTERS

Model		Source
MF 58/68	Rotary Cutters	N. America
MF 61/71	Rotary Cutters	N. America
MF 145	Rotary Cutter	Australia
MF 150/155	Rotary Cutter	Australia
MF 156/166	Rotary Cutter	Australia
MF 160	Rotary Cutter	Australia
MF 61/62/64/66	Rotary Cutters	France
MF 77	Rotary Cutter	S. Africa
MF 88	Rotary Cutter	Brazil

LOADERS AND CRANES

Model		Source
MF 225/235/245	Loaders	N. America
MF 14	Jib Crane	Australia
MF 40	Loader	Australia
MF 40	Loader	U.K.
MF 172/174/176/178	Loaders	France
MF 14	Jib Crane	Brazil
MF 35	Loader	International
MF 12-10	Jib Crane	India

SPREADING AND FERTILISING

Model		Source
MF 110	Manure Spreader	N. America
MF 160	Manure Spreader	N. America
MF 205	Manure Spreader	N. America
MF 13	Manure Spreader	Germany
MF 19	Manure Spreader	U.K.
MF 17	Slurry Tanker	U.K.
MF 11	Spinner Broadcaster	International

OTHERS

Model		Source
MF 1	Post Hole Digger	N. America
MF 15	Grinder-Mixer	N. America
MF 1	Post Hole Digger	Australia
MF 450	Tandem Implement Carrier	France
MF 45	Hammer Mill	S. Africa
MF 23	Wetland Cultiwheel	India

Source: M-F Worldwide Catalogue, 1976

M-F WORLDWIDE 1980

TRACTORS

Model		Source
MF 250	Tractor	Argentina
MF 255	Tractor	Argentina
MF 265	Tractor	Argentina
MF 1175	Tractor	Argentina
MF 1185	Tractor	Argentina
MF 1195	Tractor	Argentina
MF 1215	Tractor	Argentina
MF 8500	Tractor	Argentina
MF 9500	Tractor	Argentina
MF 235	Tractor	Brazil
MF 250	Tractor	Brazil
MF 265	Tractor	Brazil
MF 270	Tractor	Brazil
MF 275	Tractor	Brazil
MF 285	Tractor	Brazil
MF 290	Tractor	Brazil
MF 296	Tractor	Brazil
MF 95X	Tractor	Brazil
MF 65R	Tractor	Brazil
MF 135	Vineyard Tractor	France
MF 152	Vineyard Tractor	France
MF 152	Wide Vineyard Tractor	France
MF 152	Orchard Tractor	France
MF 158	Wide Vineyard Tractor	France
MF 158	Orchard Tractor	France
MF 168	Wide Vineyard/ Orchard Tractor	France
MF 235	Tractor	France

Model		Source
MF 245	Tractor	France
MF 255	Tractor	France
MF 260	Tractor	France
MF 265	Tractor	France
MF 275	Tractor	France
MF 285	Tractor	France
MF 290	Tractor	France
MF 560	Tractor	France
MF 575	Tractor	France
MF 590	Tractor	France
MF 595	Tractor	France
MF 2640	Tractor	France
MF 2680	Tractor	France
MF 132/132A Tractor		Germany
MF 139/139A Tractor		Germany
MF 142/142A Tractor		Germany
MF 154	Tractor	Italy
MF 174	Tractor	Italy
MF 184	Tractor	Italy
MF 194	Tractor	Italy
MF 154-4	4WD Tractor	Italy
MF 174-4	4WD Tractor	Italy
MF 184-4	4WD Tractor	Italy
MF 194-4	4WD Tractor	Italy
MF 254	4WD Tractor	Italy
MF 274	4WD Tractor	Italy
MF 1104	Tractor	Italy
MF 1114	Tractor	Italy
MF 1134	Tractor	Italy
MF 134C	Tractor	Italy
MF 154C	Tractor	Italy
MF 174C	Tractor	Italy
MF 184C	Tractor	Italy
MF 1114C Tractor		Italy
MF 1124C Tractor		Italy
MF 200	Tractor	Japan
MF 205	Tractor	Japan
MF 210	Tractor	Japan
MF 215	Tractor	Japan
MF 220	Tractor	Japan
MF 265	Tractor	Mexico
MF 285	Tractor	Mexico
MF 1105	Tractor	Mexico
MF 230	Tractor	N. America
MF 245	Tractor	N. America
MF 245	Orchard Tractor	N. America
MF 255	Tractor	N. America
MF 265	Tractor	N. America
MF 275	Tractor	N. America
MF 285	Tractor	N. America
MF 1085	Tractor	N. America
MF 2675	Tractor	N. America
MF 2705	Tractor	N. America
MF 2745	Tractor	N. America

Model		Source
MF 2775	Tractor	N. America
MF 2805	Tractor	N. America
MF 4840	Tractor	N. America
MF 4880	Tractor	N. America
MF 135	Narrow/Vineyard Tractor	Spain
MF 147	Vineyard Tractor	Spain
MF 245	Tractor	Spain
MF 275	Tractor	Spain
MF 285	Tractor	Spain
MF 297	Tractor	Spain
MF 240	Tractor	U.K.
MF 265	Tractor	U.K.
MF 275	Tractor	U.K.
MF 290	Tractor	U.K.
MF 550	Tractor	U.K.
MF 565	Tractor	U.K.
MF 575	Tractor	U.K.
MF 590	Tractor	U.K.
MF 1250	Tractor	U.K.

COMBINES

MF 587	Combine	Australia
MF 587	PTO Combine	Australia
MF 3342	Combine	Australia
MF 3342	PTO Combine	Australia
MF 220	Combine	Brazil
MF 3640	Combine	Brazil
MF 5650	Combine	Brazil
MF 240	Combine	France
MF 440	Combine	France
MF 520	Combine	France
MF 540	Combine	N.America
MF 550	Combine	N. America
MF 750	Combine	N. America
MF 760	Combine	N. America
MF 751	PT Combine	N. America
Rice Combines		N. America
Tables		N. America
Pick-ups		N. America
MF520/525 Super II Combine		U.K.
MF620/625 Super II Combine		U.K.

CORNHEADS

MF 1143-1183	Cornheads	N. America
MF 333-363C	Cornheads	Spain

CANE HARVESTERS

Model		Source
MF 105	Cane Harvester	Australia
MF 205	Cane Harvester	Australia

BALERS

MF 14	Baler	France
MF 120	Baler	France
MF 124/126	Baler	France
MF 128/130	Baler	France
MF 120	Baler	N. America
MF 124	Baler	N. America
MF 128/130	Baler	N. America
MF 450	Round Baler	N. America
MF 1560	Round Baler	N. America
MF 22	Bale Thrower	N. America
MF 122	Baler	Spain
MF 124 E/P	Baler	Spain
MF 124/126	Baler	Spain

MOWERS

MF 41	Mower	Australia
MF 42	Mower	Australia
MF 41	Mower	N. America
MF 42	Mower	N. America
MF 60	Mower	U.K.
MF 70	Mower	U.K.

OTHER HAY AND FORAGE

MF 29/39	Wheel Rake	N. America
MF 725/925	Haytender	N. America
MF 25	Rake	N. America
MF 37	Rake	N. America
MF 775	Swather	N. America
MF 35	P.T. Swather	N. America
MF 54	Forage Blower	N. America
MF 200	Forager	N. America
MF 260	Forager	N. America

SEED DRILLS

Model		Source
MF 80	Drill	Australia
MF 7000	Air Seeder	Australia
MF 1003	Seeding Attachment	India
MF 33	Seed Drill	N. America
MF 43	Seed Drill	N. America
MF 63	Seed Drill	N. America
MF 62-10	Seed Drill	S. Africa
MF 62-20	Seed Drill	S. Africa
MF 30	Drill	U.K.
MF 130	Direct Drill	U.K.

PLANTERS

Model		Source
MF 401	Planter	Brazil
MF 37	Planter	N. America
MF 39	Planter	N. America
MF 468	Planter	N. America
MF 48	Planter	S. Africa
MF 71	Planter	S. Africa

MOULDBOARD PLOUGHS

Model		Source
MF 66	Mouldboard Plough	Australia
MF 150	Mouldboard Plough	France
MF 160	Mouldboard Plough	France
MF 180	Mouldboard Plough	France
MF 260	Mouldboard Plough	France
MF 265	Mouldboard Plough (2/3F)	France
MF 265	Mouldboard Plough (4F)	France
MF 270	Mouldboard Plough	France
MF 43-10	Mouldboard Plough	India
MF 43	Mouldboard Plough	N. America
MF 57	Mouldboard Plough	N. America
MF 82	Mouldboard Plough	N. America
MF 345	Mouldboard Plough	N. America
MF 570	Mouldboard Plough	N. America
MF 880	Mouldboard Plough	N. America
MF 49	Mouldboard Plough	S. Africa
MF 58	Mouldboard Plough	S. Africa
MF 345	Mouldboard Plough	S. Africa
MF 880	Mouldboard Plough	S. Africa

DISC PLOUGHS

Model		Source
MF 90/91	Disc Plough	Australia
MF 202/204	Disc Plough	Brazil
MF 203	Disc Plough	Brazil
MF 205	Disc Plough	Brazil
MF 206	Disc Plough	Brazil
MF 212	Disc Plough	Brazil
MF 61-10	Disc Plough	India
MF 17	Disc Plough	Mexico
MF 76	Disc Plough	Mexico
MF 78	Disc Plough	Mexico

CHISEL PLOUGHS

MF 226	Chisel Plough	Brazil
MF 129	Chisel Plough	N. America
MF 24	Chisel Plough	U.K.
MF 25	Chisel Plough	U.K.

OFFSET DISC HARROWS

MF 34	Offset Disc Harrow	Australia
MF 81	Offset Disc Harrow	Australia
MF 130	Offset Disc Harrow	Brazil
MF 34	Offset Disc Harrow	India
MF 65-10	Offset Disc Harrow	India
MF 35	Offset Disc Harrow	Mexico
MF 40	Offset Disc Harrow	Mexico
MF 42-3	Offset Disc Harrow	Mexico
MF 730	Offset Disc Harrow	N. America
MF 20/21	Offset Disc Harrow	S. Africa
MF 34	Offset Disc Harrow	S. Africa
MF 730	Offset Disc Harrow	S. Africa

TANDEM DISC HARROWS

Model		Source
MF 122	Tandem Disc Harrow	Brazil
MF 123	Tandem Disc Harrow	Brazil
MF 520	Tandem Disc Harrow	N. America
MF 620	Tandem Disc Harrow	N. America
MF 720	Tandem Disc Harrow	N. America
MF 820	Tandem Disc Harrow	N. America
MF 39	Tandem Disc Harrow	S. Africa
MF 28	Tandem Disc Harrow	U.K.

TILLERS AND CULTIVATORS

Model		Source
MF 38	Tiller	Australia
MF 120	Scarifier	Australia
MF 259	Cultivator	Australia
MF 500/585/586 Harrow		Australia
MF 7000 Sweep Plough		Australia
MF 38-10 Tiller		India
MF 38	Seeder Attachment	International
MF 38	Ridger	International
MF 38	Tiller	International
MF 39	Cultivator	International
MF 137	Cultivator	International
MF 567	Cultivator	International
MF 21	Cultivator	Mexico
MF 259	Cultivator	N. America
MF 938	Tiller	S. Africa
MF 23	Cultivator	U.K.

ONE WAY DISC HARROWS

Model		Source
MF 63	Sundercut	Australia
MF 67	Sundercut	Australia
MF 360	Wide Level Disc Harrow	N. America
MF 30	One Way Disc Harrow	S. Africa

TOOL CARRIERS

Model		Source
MF 110	Tool Carrier	Australia
MF 351/352 Tool Carrier		Australia
MF 560	Tool Carrier	Australia
MF 50/70/80/100 Tool Carrier		Mexico

SUBSOILERS

MF 27	Subsoiler	Australia
MF 37	Subsoiler	Australia
MF 27-10 Subsoiler		India
MF 36	Subsoiler	Mexico
MF 12	Subsoiler	S. Africa
MF 35	Subsoiler	S. Africa
MF 112	Subsoiler	S. Africa
MF 24	Subsoiler	U.K.
MF 25	Subsoiler	U.K.

TRANSPORT AND TRAILERS

MF 12	Transporter	Australia
MF 802	Trailer	Brazil
MF 812	Transporter	Brazil
MF 2-10	Transporter	India
	4t. Trailer	India
MF 27-10 Trailer		India
MF 28-10 Trailer		India
MF 55	Trailer	International
MF 200	Low Loader	U.K.
MF 200	Trailer	U.K.
MF 200	Trailer	U.K.
MF 200	Trailer	U.K.

BLADES AND SOIL SCOOPS

MF 21	Blade	Australia
MF 818	Blade	Brazil
MF 17-10 Blade		India
MF 226/227 Blade		N. America
MF 63	Grader	S. Africa
MF 125	Scoop	S. Africa

ROTARY CUTTERS

Model		Source
MF 880	Rotary Cutter	Brazil
MF 77	Rotary Cutter	S. Africa

LOADERS AND CRANES

MF 14	Jib Crane	Australia
MF 800	Jib Crane	Brazil
MF 12-10	Jib Crane	India
MF 216/236	Loader	N. America
MF 80	Loader	U.K.

SPREADING AND FERTILISING

MF 110/130	Spreader	N. America
MF 160	Spreader	N. America
MF 205	Spreader	N. America
MF 19	Spreader	U.K.
MF 100	Slurry Tanker	U.K.

OTHERS

MF 1	Post Hole Digger	Australia
MF 338	Drag Scraper	Australia
MF 420	Tru Line Driver	Australia
MF 23-10	Culti-Wheel	India
MF 1007	Paddy Disc Harrow	India

Source: M-F Worldwide Catalogue, 1980

M-F POCKET CATALOGUE 1985

TRACTORS

MF 1010, 1020, 1030 Compact Tractors
MF 152 Special Tractor
MF 158 Fruit Tractor
MF 230 Tractor
MF 240 Tractor
MF 250 2WD Tractor
MF 250 4WD Tractor
MF 265 2WD Tractor
MF 265 4WD Tractor
MF 290 2WD Tractor
MF 290 4WD Tractor
MF 675 4WD Tractor
MF 675 2WD Tractor

MF 690 2WD Tractor
MF 690 4WD Tractor
MF 698T 2WD Tractor
MF 698T 4WD Tractor
MF 699 2WD Tractor
MF 699 4WD Tractor
MF 2645 2WD Tractor
MF 2645 4WD Tractor
MF 2685 2WD Tractor
MF 2685 4WD Tractor
MF 2725 2WD Tractor
MF 2725 4WD Tractor
MF 4840 Articulated Tractor
MF 4880 Articulated Tractor
MF 234 Crawler
MF 254 Crawler
MF 274 Crawler
MF 294 Crawler

HARVESTING

MF 8 Plot Combine
MF 16 Combine
MF 20 Combine
MF 24 Combine
MF 27 Combine
MF 29 Combine
MF 31 Combine
MF 860-6 Combine
MF 860-8 Combine
MF 865 Combine
MF 2 Baler
MF 3 Baler
MF 4 Baler
MF 1455E Round Baler
MF 1565 Round Baler
MF 70 Rotary Mower
MF 70 Mower Conditioner

FARM IMPLEMENTS

Implements for Compact Tractors
MF 160 Fixed Plough
MF 262 Reversible Plough
MF 137 Flexible Tine Cultivator
MF 305 Cultivator
MF 315 Cultivator
MF 280 Tandem Disc Harrow
MF 520 Tandem Disc Harrow
MF 30 Drill
MF 38 Tiller
MF 100 Slurry Tanker
MF 110 Slurry Tanker
MF 75 Loader
MF 80 Loader
MF 85 Loader

M-F POCKET CATALOGUE 1985

TRACTORS

MF 1010, 1020, 1030 Compact Tractors
MF 152 Special Tractor
MF 158 Fruit Tractor
MF 230 Tractor
MF 240 Tractor
MF 250 2WD Tractor
MF 250 4WD Tractor
MF 265 2WD Tractor
MF 265 4WD Tractor
MF 290 2WD Tractor
MF 290 4WD Tractor
MF 675 4WD Tractor
MF 675 2WD Tractor

MF 690 2WD Tractor
MF 690 4WD Tractor
MF 698T 2WD Tractor
MF 698T 4WD Tractor
MF 699 2WD Tractor
MF 699 4WD Tractor
MF 2645 2WD Tractor
MF 2645 4WD Tractor
MF 2685 2WD Tractor
MF 2685 4WD Tractor
MF 2725 2WD Tractor
MF 2725 4WD Tractor
MF 4840 Articulated Tractor
MF 4880 Articulated Tractor
MF 234 Crawler
MF 254 Crawler
MF 274 Crawler
MF 294 Crawler

HARVESTING

MF 8 Plot Combine
MF 16 Combine
MF 20 Combine
MF 24 Combine
MF 27 Combine
MF 29 Combine
MF 31 Combine
MF 860-6 Combine
MF 860-8 Combine
MF 865 Combine
MF 2 Baler
MF 3 Baler
MF 4 Baler
MF 1455E Round Baler

MMF 1565 Round Baler
MF 70 Rotary Mower
MF 70 Mower Conditioner

FARM IMPLEMENTS

Implements for Compact Tractors
MF 160 Fixed Plough
MF 262 Reversible Plough
MF 137 Flexible Tine Cultivator
MF 305 Cultivator
MF 315 Cultivator
MF 280 Tandem Disc Harrow
MF 520 Tandem Disc Harrow
MF 30 Drill
MF 38 Tiller
MF 100 Slurry Tanker
MF 110 Slurry Tanker
MF 75 Loader
MF 80 Loader
MF 85 Loader

Model, Serial Number and Engine Data for Tractors, Combines, Industrials etc.

The following data tables have been assembled from several sources. The main ones are Massey Ferguson in the UK, the USA and France; FERMEC; DV Schiller of Massey Ferguson in Canada; Delbert Gentner; the *Wild Harvest* Massey Collectors' magazine; also *Data Book No. 6 Massey-Harris,* by Alan C King and the Ontario Agricultural Museum. The data should not be regarded as absolutely definitive and readers will note that there are some inconsistencies. No attempt has been made to reconcile the inconsistencies, the objective has simply been to bring together as much published and archival data as possible. Readers should be aware that the range of years presented for each model is possibly not the complete range in some cases — I have simply reproduced what data I could gather together. Where hyphens, question marks or gaps appear no data is available.

No serial number data has come to hand for the Bull and M-H Parrett design tractors. However, M-H production of Parrett tractors is reportedly 125 in 1918-1919, 382 in 1920, 39 in 1921, 25 in 1922 and only 1 in 1923 when production was terminated.

Table 1
Wallis tractor serial numbers

Year first built	Model	Serial number
1912-1913	Bear 4-30 and Fuel Save 30-50	201-210
1913	Cub C 15-20 Fuel Save	
1913-1917	Cub (C and D)	1001-1660
1915	Cub J	10001-13505
1916	Cub K	14442-23156
1919	K-3 (3 wheel model K)	14001-14441
1919	Motor cultivator	Experimental only
1920	TC general purpose	Experimental only
1922	Cub OK	23200-25644
1926	Cub certified standard	25645-40000
1926	Cub OKO	40001-50000
1926	Certified Combine 20-30	50001-52000
1927	Certified Combine 20-30	52001-69000

The 20-30 became rebadged as the Massey-Harris 20-30 when Wallis was taken over in 1928.

The serial number 69000 marked the end of the Massey-Harris 20-30 line.

Table 2
Massey-Harris U frame and General Purpose tractor serial numbers

Year	Model	Serial number
1930	General Purpose 4WD (Hercules engine)	300000-303000
1936	General Purpose 4WD (M-H OHV engine)	303001-355000
1931-1935	25 Green	69001-69970
1936	25 Green	69970-71044
	69970 was the first with V fan belt and new brakes	
1937	25 Green	71045-73111
	71045 was the first with 4 ring piston	
1937-1938	25 Green	71045-73111
1937	25 Industrial Green	90001-90200
1938-1939	25 Red A gears	73112-85000
1938-1939	25 Red B gears	85001-90000
1929	12	100101-107000
1930	12 Orchard	200000-200250
1930	12 Industrial	250001-250026
1936	Pacemaker Green	107001-109837
	10768 was the first 4 ring piston on 8 December	
1936		
1936	Pacemaker Green Orchard	200251-200412
1938	Pacemaker Red twin power gas	109838-120000
1938	Pacemaker Red distillate	120001-130000
1938	Pacemaker Red twin power gas Orchard	200403-201000
1938	Pacemaker Red twin power gas Vineyard	201042-201500
1938	Pacemaker Red distillate Vineyard	201501-202000
1938	Pacemaker Red distillate	204001-206000
1936-1937	Challenger Green	130001-133366
	131594 was the first 4 ring piston	
1938	Challenger Red twin power gas	133367-14000
1938	Challenger Red distillate	140001-144000

Table 3
Massey-Harris tractor serial numbers after the U frame tractors

Year	Model	Serial number
1939-41? maybe only two years	The General Tractor There is no certainty as to which serial number range is correct	1FA 000-1FA 6886 also 000-0614 and 1000-6886
1938	101 Senior standard	355001-355602
1939		355603-356791
1940		356792-358187
1941		358188-358868
1942		358869-358974
1943		358975-359457
1944		359457-360926
1945		360927-362519
1946		362520-363647

Year	Model	Serial number
1941	102 Senior standard	365001-365201
1942		365202-366061
1943		366062-366182
1944		366183-367352
1945		367353-367423
1938	101 Senior rowcrop	255001-256084
1939		256085-257280
1940		257281-258768
1941		258769-259761
1942		259762-260429
1943		260430-260795
1944		260796-263019
1945		263020-264999
1945		270001-270144
1946		270145-272506
1942	102 Senior rowcrop	265001 265043
1943		265044-265077
1944		265078-265287
1939	101 Junior standard	377001-377927
1940		377928-379549
1941		379550-379814

Year	Model	Serial number
1942		379815-379854
1943		379855-380640
1944		380641-382568
1945		382569-384297
1946		384298-385641
1939	101 Junior rowcrop	375001-376157
1940		376158-377000
1940		395001-395569
1941		395570-397636
1942		397637-398595
1943		398596-399999
1943		500001-500002
1944		500003-502433
1945		502434-503778
1946		503779-505513
1939	102 Junior standard	385001-385203
1940		385204-385449
1941		385450-386098
1942		386099-386661
1943		386662-387000
1943		390001-390007
1944		390008-390993
1945		390994-391912
1946		391913-392749
1939	102 Junior rowcrop	387001-387030
1940		387031-387126
1941		387127-387418
1942		387419-387600
1943		387601-387843
1944		387844-388239
1945		388240-388994
1946		388995-389172
1940	203 (201G)	91201-91541
1941	(242 Chrysler engine)	91541-91690
1942		91691-91702
1940	203G (202G)	95000-95001
1941	(330 Continental engine)	95002-95181
1942		95182-95222
1944		95223-95294
1946		95295-95337
1947		95338-95342
1940	203D or 201 (203) KS	98001-98027
1941	(330 Continental engine)	98028-98363
1942		98364-98673
1943		98674-98806
1944		98807-99688
1946		99689-100119
1947		100120-100131
1941	81 Standard	425001-425677
1942		425678-425756
1944		425757-425779
1945		425780-426802
1946		426803-427574
1941	81 Rowcrop	400001-403167
1942		403168-403353
1944		403354-403363
1945		403364-404663
1948		404664-406601
1941	82 Standard	435001-435278
1942		435279-435451
1943		435452-435457
1945		435458-435737
1946		435738-436159

Year	Model	Serial number
1941	82 Rowcrop	420001-420054
1942		420055-420273
1945		420274-420306
1946		420307-420425
1946	20 gas rowcrop	1001-1579
1947		1580-3583
1948		3584-5195
1946	20 GS standard	1001
1947		1002-2229
1948		2230-2661
1947	20 K standard	1001-1818
1948		1819-2431
1947	20 K rowcrop	1001-1353
1948		1354-1644
1948	22 G standard	1001-1541
1949		1542-3207
1950		3208-4532
1951		4533-5716
1952		5717-6253
1948	22 gas rowcrop	1001-2095
1949		2096-4579
1950		4580-7623
1951		7624-10136
1952		10137-10783
1952	21 (Colt)	1001-1416
1953		1417-2669
1952	22	20001-29584
1953		20585-20623
1952	23 (Mustang)	1001-1665
1953		1666-4345
1954		4346-4552
1955		4553-4772
1956		4773-4832
1948	22 K standard	1001-1316
1949		1317-1487
1950		1488-1569
1951		1570-1747
1952		1748-1823
1948	22 K rowcrop	1001-1153
1949		1154-1335
1950		1336-1557
1951		1558-1775
1952		1776-1827
1952	30	30001-30595
1953		30596-30600
1946	30 gas standard	1001
1947		1002-2119
1948		2120-3193
1949		3194-5567
1950		5567-7490
1951		7491-8695
1952		8696-9337
1946	30 gas rowcrop	1001
1947		1002-3385
1948		3386-6824
1949		6825-9344
1950		9345-13815
1951		13816-17933
1952		17934-19382
1947	30 K standard	1001-1893
1948		1894-3250

Year	Model	Serial number
1949		3251–3530
1950		3531–3860
1951		3861–4170
1947	30 K rowcrop	1001–1224
1948		1225–2009
1949		2010–2392
1950		2393–2718
1951		2719–3179
1952	33	1001–2054
1953		2055–6616
1954		6617–9781
1955		9782–12607
1956	333	20001
1957		22649–22748
1946	44 gas standard	1001–1140
1947		1141–1870
1948		1871–4527
1949		4528–9580
1950		9581–13725
1951		13726–17058
1952		17059–19117
1946	30 gas rowcrop	1001
1947		1002–2047
1948		2048–5317
1949		5318–13821
1950		13822–21814
1951		21815–31189
1952		31190–33890
1953		40001
1953		43700–47060
1946	44 K standard	1001–1010
1947		1011–1440
1948		1441–3597
1949		3598–4826
1950		4827–6018
1951		6019–6758
1952		6786–6822
1952		40001
1953		43700–47060
1947	44 K rowcrop	1001–1078
1948		1079–1855
1949		1856–2598
1950		2599–3328
1951		3329–4203
1952		40001
1953		43700–47060
1948	44 diesel standard	1001–1022
1949		1023–2179
1950		2180–3988
1951		3989–5638
1952		5639–6396
1952		40001
1953		43700–47060
1948	44 diesel rowcrop	1001–1003
1949		1004–2482
1950		2483–4703
1951		4704–5656
1952		40001
1952		43700–47060
1953		
1952	44 butane standard	1001–1460
1952	44 butane rowcrop	1001–1460

Year	Model	Serial number
1947	44-6 gas standard	1001–2000
1948		2001–2600
1950		2601–2729
1946	44-6 gas rowcrop	1001
1947		1002–2982
1948		2983–4754
1949		4755–5254
1950		5255–5508
1951		5509–5928
1950	44 GS vineyard	1001–1030
1951		1031
1952		40001
1953		43700
1950	44 GS orchard	1001–1100
1951		1101–1120
1952		40001
1953		43700
1950	44 DS orchard	1001–1001
1951		1002–1034
1951	44 GRA (high altitude)	1001–1163
1952		1164–1269
1951	44 GSA (high altitude)	1001–1054
1952		1055–1065
1953	44 Special G and D	50001
1954		51364
1955		58067(?)–60719
1956	444	70001
1957		73989
1958		77000–77131
1946	55 standard	1001
1947		1116
1948		2132
1949		3581
1950		5468
1951		6399–7077
1952		10001
1953		13017
1954		15299
1955		17059–17888
1946	55 K standard	1001
1947		1013
1948		1554
1949		3033
1950		4078
1951		4808
1952		5503–5504
1952		10001
1953		13017
1954		15299
1955		17059–17888
1949	55 D standard	1001
1950		1022
1951		2058
1952		2822–2964
1952		10001
1953		13017
1954		15299
1955		17059–17888
1949	55 (GSH and GIWH) (Riceland and Hillside)	1001
1950		1035
1951		1216–1509

Year	Model	Serial number
1952		10001
1953		13017
1954		15299
1955		17059-17888
1949	55 K	1001
1950	(Riceland and Hillside)	1013
1951		1110-1230
1952		10001
1953		13017
1954		15299
1955		17059-17888
1950	55 D	1001
1951	(Riceland and Hillside)	1152
1952		1452-1516
1952		10001
1953		13017
1954		15299
1955		17059-17888
1951	55 GSA, GSWA, GSHA	1001
1952		1025-1026 (GSWA)
1952		10001
1953		13017
1954		15299
1951	55 GISH	1002
1952	(gas western) (GSW)	1083-1109
1952		10001
1953		13017
1954		15299
1951	55 DISH-DSW	1001
1952	(diesel western)	1190-1212
1952		10001
1953		13017
1954		15299
1955	555	20001
1956		20133
1957		21133
1958		22950-23012
1955	MH 50	500001
1956		500473
1957		510764-515707
1948	M-H 744 (U.K.)	201-400
1949		401-1400
1950		1401-4400

After 1950 the production year is indicated by a letter starting with F for 1951, G for 1952, H for 1953 and J for 1954. It is reported that only about two hundred 744s were made at the Manchester factory before production was transferred to Kilmarnock in Scotland

Year	Model	Serial number
1954	M-H 745 and 745 S	Reportedly about
1958	(U.K.)	11,000 made

745 serial numbers started with J for 1954 and ran to N for 1958 The 745S only made in 1958.

Year	Model	Serial number
1953	M-H I-162	1001-1026
1954	M-H I 330G	1001-1006 (Navy)
1955	M-H I-244 (no PTO)	1001-1019 (Navy)
1956		1020-1038 (Navy)
1956		3001-3180 (Air Force)
1957		3181-3427 (Air Force)
1955	M-H FSI-244	2001-2218
1956	(Air Force with PTO)	2219-2243
1956	M-H 303 industrial	1001-1075

Year	Model	Serial number
1957	(Work Bull)	1076-1193
1958		1194-1599
1956	M-H 404 industrial	1001-1050
1957	(Work Bull)	1051-1118
1947	M-H Pony (Canada)	PGS 1001-1320
		PGA 1001-1002
1948		PGS 1321-4162
		PGA 1003-3514
		PGA 1001A-1570A
1949		PGA 1571A-10816A
1950		PGA 10817A-13725A
		PGS 4163-4328
1951		PGA 13726-18224
1952		PGA 18225-22006
1953		PGA 22007-22668
1954		PGA 22669-23853
1954	M-H Pacer (U.S.A.)	PGA 50001-51612
1955		PGA 51613-52770
1956		PGA 52771-53730
1957	M-H Model Pony (U.S.A.) (special Pony made to use up stocks)	PGA 24049-24319

Serial nos. 23854-24048 were not used
PGS = standard axle. PGA = adjustable axle.

Table 4
Code to the suffix letters of 20, 20K, 22, 22K, 30, 30K, 44, 44K, 44B, 44D, 44(6), 55, 55K, 55B, 55D

A	–	high altitude engine
B	–	butane (LPG) fuel
D	–	diesel fuel
F	–	foot clutch
G	–	gasoline
H	–	hand clutch
K	–	low grade fuel
O	–	orchard
R	–	rowcrop
S	–	standard model
V	–	vineyard model
W	–	wide axle

Table 5
Ferguson and early Massey Ferguson tractor serial numbers

Year	Model	Serial number
1933	Ferguson Black tractor (U.K.)	Prototype – one only
1936	Ferguson model A	1-550 Coventry
1939	(U.K.)	Climax engine
		551-1354
		David Brown engine

There is evidence to suggest that Coventry Climax and David Brown engines were both fitted from about serial no. 250-500

Slightly more than 1,354 may have been produced

Year	Model	Serial number
1939	Ford Ferguson (U.S.A.)	1-14643
1940		14644-47842
1941		47843-92362
1942		92363-107754
1943		107755-131782
1944		131783-174637
1945		174638-204128
1946		204129-267288
1947		267289-306221

N.B. 9N model = petrol, 9NAN = TVO for U.K.,
2N = utility model: steel wheels, no starter or dynamo

Year	Model	Serial number
1946	TE-20 (U.K.)	1-315
1947		316-20894

TE Continental engine and TEA Standard engine tractors were built side by side up to 48000 then the Continental engine was dropped

Year	Model	Serial number
1948		20895-77772
1949		77773-116461
1950		116462-167836
1951		167837-241335

The 85mm engine replaced the 80mm engine at 172501

1948		20895-77772
1949		77773-116461
1950		116462-167836
1951		167837-241335

The 85mm engine replaced the 80mm engine at 172501

1952		241336-310779

12 volt electrics were introduced at 250001

1953		310780-367998
1954		367999-428092
1955		428093-488578
1956		488579-517651

1948	TO-20 (U.S.A.)	1-1807
1949		1808-14659
1950		14660-39162
1951		39163-60000

1951 August	TO-30 (U.S.A.)	60001-72679
1952		72680-108644
1953		108645-125958
1954		125959-140000

1954	TO-35 (U.S.A.)	140001-140005
1955		140006-167156
1956		167157-171740
1957		171741-178215

1958	TO-35 gas del	178216-188850
1959		188851-203679

Year	Model	Serial number
1960		203680-207426
1958	TO-35 gas sp	183348-185503
1959		185504-203197
1960		203198-209483
1958	TO-35 diesel	180742-187718
1959		187719-203359
1960		203360-203679
1960	MF 35	203202-211071
1961	MF 35 diesel 3-cylinder (U.S.A.)	211072-223895
1962		223896-237274
1963		237275-247604
1964		247605-254512
1963	MF 35 Turf (U.S.A.)	656000150-656000614
1964		656000615-656000892
1963	MF 35 Utility (U.S.A.)	655000279-655001253
1964		655001254-655001754
1956	Ferguson 40 (U.S.A.)	400001-405670
1957		405671-409097
1956	FE-35 (U.K.)	1001-9225
1957		9226-79552
1958		79553-105067
1959		125068-171470

Last Grey and gold tractor 74655
Last 23C engine 166595, first A3-152 engine 166596

1960		171471-220613
1961		220614-267527
1962		267528-307230
1963		307231-352254
1964		352255-388382

MF 35X with Multipower introduced December 1962

1958	MF 65 (765) (U.K.)	500001-510450
1959		510451-520568
1960		520569-533179
1961		533180-551732
1962		551733-572324
1963		572325-593027
1964		593028-614024

First A4.203 engine fitted at 531453
Multipower introduced in August 1962

1959	MF 702 (U.K.)	700001-700140
		700141-701678
1966	MF 3303/5 (U.K.)	914000-
1967	MF 2203/5 (U.K.)	835000-
1958	MF 50 (U.S.A.)	515708-522692
1959	MF 50 gas and LPG	522693-528612
1960		528163-528465
1961		528466-530415
1962		530416-533849
1963		533850-536640
		536641-537996
1962	MF 50 diesel (U.S.A.)	530417-533850

The MF 50 replaced the M-H 50 and Ferguson 40 at the end of the two line policy

1956	M-H-F 202 (U.S.A.)	300001-300028
1957		300029-301171
1960		305108-306....
1960	MF 204 (U.S.A.)	341381-3419..
1957	MF 65 (U.S.A.)	650000-650023
1958		650024-661163
1959	gas and LPG	661164-671652
1960		671653-680210

Year	Model	Serial number
1961		680210-686310
1962		686313-694782
1963		694782-704387
1964		704388-710787
1965		710788-710886
1959	MF 65 diesel (U.S.A.)	667229-671378
1960		671379-680208
1961		686311-694775
1958	MF 85 gas (U.S.A.)	800001-800047
1959	gas and LPG	800048-804354
1960		804355-807750
1961		807751-808563
1960	MF 85 diesel (U.S.A.)	804545-807750
1961		808107-808563
1959	MF 88 gas and LPG (U.S.A.)	880001-881452
1960	MF 88 diesel	881453-882229
1961		882230-882495
1956	M-H-F 202 (U.S.A.)	300001-300028
1957		300029-301171
1960	MF 202 (U.S.A.)	305108-306168
1961		306168-306778
1962		306789-307918
1960	MF 204 (U.S.A.)	341381-341986
1961		341985-342647
1962		342648-343182
1961	MF 90 (U.S.A.)	810000-810376
1962	MF 90 gas	810674-
1962	MF 90 diesel	810377-813385
1963		813385-816866
1964		816867-819762
1965		819763
1961	MF Super 90 WR (U.S.A.)	885000-885009
1962		885010-886155
1963		886156-887383
1964		887384-888581
1965		888582-888771
1958-62	MF 95 (U.S.A.)	3025 sold
1962-65	MF 97 (U.S.A.)	4100 sold

The 95 and 97 tractors were from Minneapolis Moline

1959-60	MF 98 (U.S.A.)	500 made

The 98 tractor was made by Oliver

Year	Model	Serial number
1961	MF 203 (U.S.A.)	659000001-659000680
1962	MF 203 diesel	659000688-659001379
1961	MF 205 (U.S.A.)	659100001-659100375
1962	MF 205 diesel	659100378-659100712
1961	MF 356 (U.S.A.)	670000001-670000149
1962	MF 356 gas	670000176-670000601
	MF 356 diesel	670000147-670000610
1962	MF 304 gas (U.S.A.)	119750001-119750018
	MF 304 diesel	119750002-119750019
1962	MF 302 diesel (U.S.A.)	119700001-119700017
	MF 302 gas	119000002-119700016
1962	MF 35 diesel utility (U.S.A.)	655000003-655000240
	MF 35 gas utility	655000001-655000236
	MF 35 gas turf special	656000001-656000105

Table 6
Some North American tractor serial number data 1958-1976

Model	Year	Start serial number	Finish serial number
MF 135	1964	641000003	641004221
	1965	641004422	641016740
	1966	641016741	641024445
	1967	new serial number system	
MF 150	1964	642000003	642000858
	1965	642000859	642003945
	1966	642003946	642005473
	1967	new serial number system	
MF 165	1964	643000003	643000480
	1965	643000481	643007762
	1966	643007763	643014672
	1967	new serial number system	
MF 175	1965	644000008	644001493
	1966	644001494	644003040
	1967	new serial number system	
MF 180	1965	645000007	645002422
	1966	645002423	645004712
	1967	new serial number system	
MF 1100	1965	650000174	650001966
	1966	650001997	650005481
	1967	new serial number system	
MF 1130	1965	651500022	651500081
	1966	651500082	651501612
	1967	new serial number system	
MF 202	1958	301172	303157
	1959	303158	305107
	1960	305108	306168
	1961	306169	306778
	1962	306779	307922
	1963	307923	309221
	1964	309222	310066
	1965	310067	311083
	1966	311084	311823
	1967	new serial number system	
MF 203	1961	659000001	659000680
	1962	659000681	659001378
	1963	659001379	659001766
	1964	659001767	659002053
	1965	659002054	659002666
	1966	659002667	659003097
	1967	new serial number system	
MF 204	1959	340001	341380
	1960	341381	341985
	1961	341986	342647
	1962	342648	343181
	1963	343182	343835
	1964	343836	344308
	1965	344309	345102

Model	Year	Start serial number	Finish serial number
	1966	345103	345804
	1967	new serial number system	
MF 205	1961	65910000	659100375
	1962	659100376	659100711
	1963	659100712	659100969
	1964	659100970	659101164
	1965	659101165	659101446
	1966	659101447	659101637
	1967	new serial number system	
MF 302	1962	119700000	119700016
	1963	119700017	119700178
	1964	119700179	119700524
	1965	119700525	119700858
	1966	119700859	119701248
	1967	new serial number system	
MF 304	1962	119750000	119750018
	1963	119750019	119750162
	1964	119750163	119750505
	1965	119750506	119750770
	1966	119750771	119751199
	1967	new serial number system	
MF 356	1961	670000000	670000146
	1962	670000147	670000612
	1963	670000613	670001038
	1964	670001039	670001332
	1965	670001333	670001608
	1966	670001609	670002063
	1967	new serial number system	
MF 402	1959	000001	000435
	1960	not built	
	1961	000436 upward	
MF 1001	1958	100001	100151
	1959	100152	100499
	1960	not built	
	1961	100500	
MF 2135 Utility	1964	646000001	646000189
	1965	646000190	646001464
	1966	646001465	646002460
	1967	new serial number system	
MF 2135 Turf	1964	648000001	648000080
	1965	648000081	648000645
	1966	648000646	648001021
	1967	new serial number system	
MF 2500	1966	138400004	138400345
	1967	new numbering system	
MF 3165 Utility	1964	647000001	647000013
	1965	647000014	647001000
	1966	647001001	647002279
	1967	new serial number system	
MF 3165 Turf	1966	649000004	649000171
	1967	new serial number system	

Source: MF North America 1977 and 1981

Table 7
UK made FE35/MF35 tractor serial number prefixes

Chassis
   Normal width   S
   Vineyard   V
   Industrial   J
   High clearance   C

Engine
   Petrol 6:1   G
   Petrol 6.6:1★   H
   Diesel 23C engine   D
   TVO   K
   Lamp oil   L
   Diesel A3.152 engine   N
   Gas (butane)   B

Clutch
   Single   F
   Dual   M

★high altitude

Table 8
North American tractor serial numbers November 1st, 1967-1980

( ) indicates last year of production

"A" line tractors

Agricultural: MF135(75), 150(75), 165(75), 175(75), 180(74), 230, 245, 255, 275, 285.

Industrial: MF20, 30, 31, 40, 50, 302(68), 304(68), 356(69), 2135(68), 2200(72), 2500(74), 3165(69).

Year	Start serial number	Finish serial number
1967	9A10001	9A39835
1968	9A39836	9A63157
1969	9A63158	9A87324
1970	9A87325	9A107518
1971	9A107519	9A128140
1972	9A128141	9A152024
1973	9A152025	9A179543
1974	9A179544	9A205691
1975	9A205962	9A229222
1976	9A229223	9A254044
1977	9A254045	9A276934
1978	9A276935	9A296945
1979	9A296946	9A323744
1980	9A323745	9A339343

"B" line tractors

Agricultural: MF1080(72), 1085, 1100(72), 1105, 1130(72), 1135, 1150(72), 1115.

Year	Start serial number	Finish serial number
1967	9B10001	9B14962
1968	9B14963	9B18672
1969	9B18673	9B23485
1970	9B23486	9B28226
1971	9B28227	9B31957
1972	9B31958	9B36840
1973	9B36841	9B42685
1974	9B42686	9B49352
1975	9B49353	9B57729
1976	9B57730	9B66275
1977	9B66276	9B74240
1978	9B74241	9B76058

"C" line tractors

Agricultural: MF1500(74), 1505, 1800(74), 1805.

Year	Start serial number	Finish serial number
1970	9C001001	9C001005
1971	9C001006	9C001911
1972	9C001912	9C002463
1973	9C002464	9C003024
1974	9C003025	9C004056
1975	9C004057	9C005809
1976	9C005810	9C007058
1977	9C007059	9C007858

"R" line tractors

Agricultural: MF2700, 2800, 2675, 2705, 2745, 2775, 2805.

Year	Start serial number	Finish serial number
1976	9R000001	9R000047
1977	9R000048	9R000601
1978	9R000602	9R002781
1979	9R002782	9R006752
1980	9R006753	9R010307

"D" line tractors

MF 4840, 4880.

Year	Start serial number	Finish serial number
1978	9D001001	9D001007
1979	9D001008	9D001840
1980	9D001841	9D002752

Source: MF North America, 1977 and 1981

Table 9
MF lawn and garden tractors, tillers, snow throwers and snowmobile serial numbers

Model	Year	Start serial no.	Finish serial no.
MF 7 Lawn (recoil)	1968	00001	01147
	1969	01148	03066
	1970	03067	06901
	1971	06902	09314
	1972	09315	10978
	1973	10979	12978
MF 7 Lawn (electric start)	1968	200001	204256
	1969	204257	211416
	1970	211417	223306
	1971	223307	231497
	1972	231498	237555
	1973	237556	243527
MF 7 Lawn (hydrostatic)	1968	400001	400053
	1969	400054	401485
	1970	401486	404171
	1971	404172 upward	
MF 8 Lawn (hydrostatic)	1972	500001	501716
	1973	501717	503931
	1974	503932	507933
	1975	507934	508960
MF 8 Lawn (recoil)	1974	100001	101825
	1975	101826	102475
MF 8 (electric start)	1974	300001	306915
	1975	306916	310762
MF 10 L and G	1966	00001	06015
	1967	06016	14044
	1968	14045	16181
	1969	16182	19155
	1970	19156	23898
	1971	23899	26126
	1972,1973, 1974	not built	
	1975	26127	28226
	1976	28227	29526
MF 10 L and G (variable speed)	1972	800001	803351
	1973	803352	806982
	1974	806983	810480
	1975	810481	812842
	1976	812843	814942
MF 12 L and G (hydrostatic)	1967	500001	502903
	1968	502904	506951
	1969	506952	510577
	1970	510578	515383
	1971	515384	517708
	1972	517709	518279
MF 14 L and G	1972	0001	2360
	1973	2361	3645
	1974	3646	6145
	1975	6146	7498
	1976	7499	8799

Model	Year	Start serial no.	Finish serial no.
MF 16 L and G	1975	200001	202650
	1976	202651	203901
MF 5 Riding mower	1971	0001	3811
	1972	3812	5049
	1973	not built	
	1974	5050	6149
MF 6 Riding mower (became 626)	1971	500001	503708
	1972	503709	506058
	1973	506059	506958
	1974	not built	
	1975	506959	511111
MF 8 Riding mower (became 832)	1975	701653	708238
MF 24S Mower	1967	10000	16001
MF 24S DLX Mower	1967	32501	33000
MF 210 Walk behind rotary mower	1971	0001	2088
	1972	2089	4928
MF 310 Walk behind rotary mower	1971	0001	0871
	1972	0872	2363
MF 22 Tiller	1967	8001	8500
MF 26 Tiller	1967	8501	9000
MF 253 Tiller	1975	002000	002500
	1976	002501	003626
MF 254 Tiller	1971	100001	100221
	1972	100222	100978
	1973	100979	101633
	1974	101634	102256
	1975	102257	103170

Model	Year	Start serial no.	Finish serial no.
MF 255 Tiller	1971	200001	200875
	1972	200876	201528
	1973	201529	202179
	1974	202180	204854
	1975	204855	205905
	1976	205906	206931
MF 256 Tiller	1975	300001	301050
	1976	301051	302276
MF 550 Tiller	1973	0001	0530
	1974	0531	1100
	1975	1101	2148
	1976	2149	2849
MF 650 Tiller	1967	0001	1350
	1968	1351	2200
	1969	2201	4926
	1970	not built	
	1971	4927	5373
	1972	5374	5812
	1973	5813	6300
	1974	6301	6982
	1975	6983	9196
MF 227 Snowblower	1971	0001	1486
	1972	1487	1936
MF 228 Snowblower	1971	00001	00350
	1972	00351	01936
	1973	01937	27500
	1974	27501	28093
MF 305 Snowblower	1976	000001	001000
MF 308 Snowblower	1976	000001	001000
MF 520 Snow thrower	1972	200001	200557
	1973	200558	200968

Model	Year	Start serial no.	Finish serial no.
	1974	200969	201542
	1975	201543	202043
	1976	202044	202617
MF 620 Snow thrower	1966	0001	0996
	1967	0997	1503
	1968	1504	3843
	1969	3844	5043
	1970	5044	5598
	1971	5599	6469
	1972	6470	8611
	1973	8612	9224
	1974	9225	10571
	1975	10572	11072
	1976	11073	11276
MF 720 Snow thrower	1968	100001	100717
	1969	100718	102917
	1970,1971	not built	
	1972	102918	104167
	1973	104168	104586
	1974	104587	105186
	1975	105187	105669
Ski-whiz 297 Snowmobile	1968	0001	0864
	1969	0865	1864
Ski-whiz 300 Snowmobile	1972	0001	1870
Ski-whiz 300S Snowmobile	1969	100001	105162
	1970	105163	109152
	1971	109153	109163
Ski-whiz 304S Snowmobile	1973	10001	10700
	1974	10701	11165
Ski-whiz 304T Snowmobile	1973	301001	301050
Ski-whiz 340T Snowmobile	1972	51001	51715
Ski-whiz 344T Snowmobile	1973	60001	61001
	1974	61002	61965
Ski-whiz 350SS Snowmobile	1969	300001	302027
	1970	302028	306327
Ski-whiz 380 Snowmobile	1968	200001	200970
	1969	200971	202341
Ski-whiz 400SST Snowmobile	1970	400001	402928
	1971	402929	403853
Ski-whiz 400T Snowmobile	1972	100001	101919
	1973	101920	102355
Ski-whiz 400WT Snowmobile	1972	150001	151881
	1973	151882	151940
Ski-whiz 404ST Snowmobile	1973	110001	110680
	1974	110681	111710
Ski-whiz 404WT Snowmobile	1973	160001	161101
	1974	160908	161101
Ski-whiz 440T Snowmobile	1972	200001	202690

Model	Year	Start serial no.	Finish serial no.
Ski-whiz 440WT Snowmobile	1972	250001	252185
	1973	252186	252430
Ski-whiz 444ST Snowmobile	1973	210001	211000
	1974	211001	212040
Ski-whiz 444WT Snowmobile	1973	260001	260570
	1974	260751	261070
Ski-whiz 500ST Snowmobile	1969	500001	503021
	1970	503022	505724
	1971	505725	506097
Ski-whiz formula I Snowmobile	1970	200001	201293
	1971	201294	201501
Ski-whiz formula II Snowmobile	1971	340001	340126
Ski-whiz formula III Snowmobile	1971	700001	700500
Ski-whiz formula IV Snowmobile	1971	800001	801500
Ski-whiz special Snowmobile	1971	600001	600124
Massey Chinook Snowmobile	1975	687562	689365
	1976	094652	095853
Massey Whirlwind 340 Snowmobile	1975	686262	694225
	1976	094655	094954
Massey Whirlwind 440 Snowmobile	1975	684760	694233
	1976	094249	
095454Massey Cyclone 340 Snowmobile	1975	684404	684752
Massey Cyclone 440 Snowmobile	1975	684153	684402
Massey Storm 440 Snowmobile	1976	094654	097051

Source: MF North America, 1977

Table 10
Serial numbers for loaders, backhoes and forklifts

Model	Year	Start serial no.	Finish serial no.
MF 32 Loader	1969	00001	01526
	1970	01527	03322
	1971	03323	04890
	1972	04891	08200
	1973	08201	08949
	1974	08950	09130
	1975/76	nos. not in sequential order	
MF 32-A Loader	1976	000001	000006
MF 34 Loader	1969	100001	100511
	1970	100512	101996
	1971	101997	102609
	1972	102610	106855
	1973	106856	107152
	1974/75/76	nos. not in sequential order	
MF 34-A Loader	1976	000001	000010
MF 38 Loader	1966	3913	4735
	1967	4736	5426
	1968	5427	5858
	1969	5859	6258
	1970	6259	6433
	1971	6434	6983
MF 90 Loader	1966	0001	0304
	1967	0305	0500
	1968	0501	0839
	1969	0840	1100
	1970	1101	1631
	1971	1632	1985
MF 95 Loader	1966	0201	0485
	1967	0486	0585
	1968	0586	0885
	1969	0886	1100
	1970	1101	1230
	1971	1231	1430
MF 99 Loader	1966	41891	42111
	1967	42112	42272
MF 100 Loader	1966	102742	103378
	1967	103379	104461
	1968	104462	105653
	1969	105654	106343
MF 200 Loader	1966	209274	211619
	1967	211620	213450
	1968	213451	215909
	1969	215910	217381
MF 225 Loader	1972	0001	1070
	1973	1071	1239
	1974	1240	1319
	1975	1320	1515
MF 235	1972	0001	0494
	1973	0495	2000
	1974	2001	3140
	1975	3141	4400
MF 236 Loader	1975	1001	1311
	1976	1312	2788
MF 245	1972	0001	1027
	1973	1028	1290
	1974	1291	1565
	1975	1566	1934
	1976	1935	2000
MF 246	1976	1001	1447
MF 300 Loader	1966	1524	2317
	1967	2318	2751
	1968	2752	2777
	1969	2778	2873
	1970	2874	3482
	1971	3483	4199
	1972	4200	5100
	1973	5101	5906
	1974/75/76	nos. not in sequential order	

Model	Year	Start serial no.	Finish serial no.
MF 300A Loader	1976	000001	000004
MF 52 Backhoe	1967	100001	100186
(was 212)	1968	100187	100540
	1969	100541	101027
	1970	101028	101337
	1971	101338	101811
	1972	101812	102297
	1973	102298	102908
	1974/5/76	nos. not in sequential order	
MF 52A Backhoe	1976	000001	000002
MF 54 Backhoe	1966	0001	1105
(was 232)	1967	1106	1581
	1968	1582	2129
	1969	2130	3140
	1970	3141	4039
	1971	4040	4704
	1972	4705	6504
	1973	6505	7596
	1974		
	1975		
	1976		10355
MF 54A Backhoe	1976	000001	000071
MF 54S	1966	500001	500384
	1967	500385	500531
	1968	not built	
	1969	500352	500594
	1970	500595	500826
	1971	500827	500996
	1972	500997	501164
	1973	501165	501248
	1974/75/76	nos. not in sequential order	
MF 185 Backhoe	1966	0426	0682
	1967	0683	0789
MF 320 Backhoe	1966	0966	1258
	1967	1259	1260
MF 325 Backhoe	1966	0092	0412
	1967	0413	0498
	1968/69	not built	
	1970	0499	0539
MF 7 Forklift	1966	0520	0532
	1967	0533	0554
	1968	0545	0554
	1969	0555	0618
MF 204 Forklift	1966	2079	2445
	1967	2446	2519
MF 4500 Forklift	1975	400001	400307
	1976	400308	400399
	1977	400400	400646
	1978	400647	400841
MF 6500 Forklift	1975	600001	600390
	1976	600391	600580
	1977	600581	601025
	1978	601026	601360

Source: MF North America, 1977

Table 11
Serial numbers for construction and forest machinery, 1966-1980

Model	Year	Start serial no.	Finish serial no.
CRAWLERS			
MF 200B LDR and	1966	70200001	70201007
Dozer (was MF 200),	1967	70201008	70202973
and MF 2244 Loader	1968	70202974	70204520
and Dozer	1969	70204521	70204800
	1970	70204801	70208730
	1971	70208731	70209388
	1972	70209389	70210289
	1973	70210290	70211459
	1974	70211460	70212999
	1975	70213000	70213420
	1976	70213421	70214143
	1977	70214144	70214143
	1978	70214977	70215196
MF D200C Loader	1978	2767000001	2767000050
MF D200C Dozer	1978	2768000001	2768000050
MF 300 LDR	1969	1020100001	1020100228
	1970	1020100229	1020100756
	1971	1020100757	1020100928
	1972	1020100929	1020101234
	1973	1020101235	1020101534
	1974	1020101535	1020101884
	1975	1020101885	1020102041
	1976	1020102042	1020102216
	1977	1020102217	1020102495
	1978	1020102496	1020102585
MF 300 Dozer	1969	1020200001	1020200032
	1970	1020200033	1020200275
	1971	1020200276	1020200395
	1972	1020200396	1020200425
	1973	1020200426	1020200461
	1974	1020200462	1020200570
	1975	1020200571	1020200602
	1976	1020200603	1020200667
	1977	1020200668	1020200786
	1978	1020200787	1020200822
MF 336 LDR	1967	7090504	7091117
	1968	7091118	7091501
	1969	7091502	7092069
	1970	7092070	7092078
MF 3366 Dozer	1967	6090090	6090101
	1968	6090102	6090760
	1969	6090761	6091108
	1970	6091109	6091383
MF 400 LDR	1971	1060100178	1060100470
	1972	1060100471	1060100730
	1973	1060100731	1060101067
	1974	1060101068	1060101358
	1975	1060101359	1060101469
MF 400C Loader	1977	2100100001	2100100178
	1978	2100100179	2100100489
	1976	1060101470	1060101742
MF 400 Dozer	1971	1060200001	1060200115
	1972	1060200116	1060200320
	1973	1060200321	1060200457

Model	Year	Start serial no.	Finish serial no.	Model	Year	Start serial no.	Finish serial no.
	1974	1060200458	1060200597	MF 33 All wheel	1968	100001	100025
	1975	1060200598	1060200741	steering	1969	100026	100064
	1976	1060200742	1060200778		1970	100065	100100
MF 400C Loader	1977	5000200173	5000200324		1971	100101	100128
	1978	5000200235	5000200445		1972	100129	100204
MF 500 LDR	1968	1010100020	1010100060		1973	100205	100260
	1969	1010100061	1010100248		1974	100261	100319
	1970	1010100249	1010100496		1975	100320	100377
	1971	1010100497	1010100538		1976	100378	100440
	1972	1010100539	1010100608	MF 33 Front wheel	1968	20001	20011
	1973	1010100609	1010100688	steering	1969	20012	20014
	1974	1010100689	1010100796	MF 33 Rear wheel	1968	300001	300075
	1975	1010100797	1010100851	steering	1969	300076	300084
	1976	1010100852	1010100891		1970	300085	300118
MF 500 Dozer	1968	1010200030	1010200041		1971	300119	300172
	1969	1010200042	1010200164		1972	300173	300305
	1970	1010200165	1010200496		1973	300306	300376
	1971	1010200497	1010200637		1974	300377	300404
	1972	1010200638	1010200677		1975	300405	300462
	1973	1010200678	1010200871	MF 44 All wheel	1968	10001	10042
	1974	1010200872	1010201177	steering	1969	10043	10090
	1975	1010201178	1010201405		1970	10091	10114
	1976	1010201406	1010201466		1971	10115	10129
MF 600C Loader	1975	31003014	31006092	MF 44 Front wheel	1968	20001	20004
	1976	31006093	31008191	steering	1969	20005	20200
MF D600C Dozer	1975	30904133	30906081	MF 44 Rear wheel	1968	30001	30044
	1976	30906082	30908157	steering and diesel	1969	30045	30052
MF D700C Dozer	1975	31105394	31105572	all wheel steering	1970	30053	30073
	1976	31105573	31108231	after 1968	1971	30074	30085
EXCAVATORS					1972	30086	30111
MF350 Excavator	1968	5010100020	5010100142	MF 44B	1973	3020300001	3020300095
MF 450S Excavator	1968	5020100005	5020100087		1974	3020300096	3020300435
	1969	5020100088	5020100338		1975	3020300436	3020300687
	1970	5020100339	5020100794		1976	3020300688	3020300726
	1971	5020100795	5020101055	MF 44C	1975	77600001	77604474
	1972	5020101056	5020101256		1976	77604475	77608287
	1973	5020101257	5020101708	MF 55	1968	100001	100050
	1974	5020101709	5020102226		1969	100051	100141
	1975	5020102227	5020102428		1970	100142	100233
					1971	100234	100257
FORESTRY					1972	100258	100334
MF 220 Skidder	1970	10001	10187		1973	100335	100385
	1971	10188	10232		1974	100386	100459
	1972	10233	10259		1975	100460	100498
MF 320 Skidder	1976	000001	000179		1976	100499	100514
MF 2200 Treever	1965	0001	0058	MF 55C	1975	77704360	77706187
	1966	0059	3132		1976	77706188	77708363
	1967	3133	3304	MF 60	1978	9E100001	9E100174
	1968	3305	3419	Backhoe/Loader	1979	9E100175	9E100698
	1969	3420	3487		1980	9E100699	9E100961
	1970	3488	3587	MF 66	1970	600001	600043
WHEEL LOADERS					1971	600044	600103
MF 470	1964	4001	4050		1972	600104	600109
	1965	4051	4155		1973	600110	600146
	1966	4156	4256		1974	600147	600197
	1967	4266	4556		1975	600198	600232
	1968	4557	4663		1976	600233	600244
	1969	4664	4812	MF 66C	1975	77404365	77406065
	1970	4813	4912		1976	77406066	77408421
MF 11	1970	F156	F287	MF 77	1970	700001	700011
	1971	F288	F695		1971	700012	700045
	1972	F696	H1109		1972	700046	700061
	1973	H1110	J1469		1973	700062	700066
	1974	J1470	K1775		1974	700067	700104
	1975	K1776	L2065				

Model	Year	Start serial no.	Finish serial no.
	1975	700105	700138
	1976	700139	700143
MF 77C	1975	77503523	77503762
	1976	77503763	77503934
MF 88	1970	800001	800022
	1971	800023	800057
	1972	800058	800080
	1973	800081	800081
	1974	800082	800093
	1975	800094	800134
	1976	800135	800154
MF 70 BH/LDR	1969	100001	100190
	1970	100191	100433
	1971	100434	100537
	1972	100538	100814
	1973	100815	100946
	1974	100947	101086
	1975	101087	101192
	1976	101193	101270
	1973	300001	300060
	1974	300061	300187
	1975	300188	300272
	1976	300273	300441
MF 711B Skid steer loader (was 711)	1974	001	738
	1975	739	1143
	1976	1144	1241
MF 811 Skid steer loader	1974	001	007
	1975	008	163
	1975	164	407

Source: MF North America, 1977 and 1981.

Table 12
MF Compact tractor serial numbers based on fiscal years

Model	Year	Start serial no.	Finish serial no.
MF 205	1978	2744000101	2744000314
	1979	2744000315	2744000682
	1980	2744000683	2744001512
MF 205-4	1979	2753000101	2753000676
	1980	2753000677	2753000916
MF 210	1978	2746000101	2746000960
	1979	2746000961	2746001710
	1980	2746001711	2746002699
MF 210-4	1979	2754000101	2754000710
	1980	2754000711	2754000763
MF 220	1978	2748000101	2748000299
	1979	2748000300	2748000551
	1980	2748000552	2748000749
MF 220-4	1979	2756000101	2756000519
	1980	2756000520	2756000867

Table 13
Some engines fitted to post U frame M-H tractors according to serial numbers

Model	Engine	Serial no. data
101 Junior	124 Continental	375001-376985 rowcrop
		377001-378713 standard
	140 Continental	3376986-376999, 395001-399682 rowcrop
		378714-380642 standard
		387001-387884 distillate rowcrop
		385001-386985 distillate standard
	162 Continental	399683-505513 rowcrop
		380463-385641 standard
		387844-389172 distillate rowcrop
		386985-392750 distillate standard
101 Super and Senior	201.3 Chrysler	255001-258285 rowcrop
		355001-357870 standard
	217 Chrysler	258286-260017 rowcrop
		357871-358918 standard
	226 Continental	260018-2/2506 rowcrop
		258919-365000 standard
102 Senior	244 Continental	265001-265286 distillate rowcrop
		365001-367423 distillate standard

Table 14
Some engines fitted to post U frame M-H tractors

Model	Fuel	Engine
81	Gas	Continental F 124
82	Kerosene	Continental F 124
101	Gas	Chrysler T 57
		Chrysler T 81
		Chrysler T 105
101 Super	Gas	Chrysler T 96
		Chrysler T 116
101 Senior	Gas	Continental F 226

Chrysler 201.3 and 217 engines were also fitted to the 101 senior and super tractors

Model	Fuel	Engine
101 Junior	Gas	Continental F 124
		Continental F 140
		Continental F 162
102 Senior	Kerosene	Continental A 244
102 Junior	Kerosene	Continental F 140
		Continental F 162
102 Junior	Gas	Continental F 124
		Continental F 140
		Continental F 162
102 Senior	Gas	Continental F 226
201	Gas	Chrysler T 100
		Chrysler T 120
		Chrysler 242
202	Gas	Continental M 290
		Continental 330
203	Kerosene	Continental M 330 D
203	Gas	Continental M 330
General		Hercules IXA
20	Gas	Continental F 124
20	Kerosene	Continental F 140
22	Gas	Continental F 140
22	Kerosene	Continental F 140
30	Gas	Continental F 162
30	Kerosene	Continental F 162
33	Non diesel	M-H E 201
33	Diesel	M-H ED 201
333	Gas	M-H E 208
333	L P Gas	M-H E 208
333	Diesel	M-H ED 208
44	Gas	M-H H 260 G
44	Kerosene	M-H H 260 K
44	L P Gas	M-H H 260 B
44	Diesel	M-H HD 260
44 (6)	Gas	Continental F 226
44 special	Non diesel	M-H H 260
44 special	Diesel	M-H HD 260
444	Gas	M-H H 277
444	L P Gas	M-H H 277
444	Diesel	M-H HD 277
744 (U.K.)	Diesel	Perkins P6
745 and 745S (U.K.)	Diesel	Perkins P4
55 G	Gas	M-H J 382 G
55	Kerosene	M-H J 382 K
55	L P Gas	M-H J 382 B
55	Diesel	M-H JD 382
555	Diesel	M-H JD 382
Pony	Gas	Continental N 62
Pony 811, 812		

Model (French)	Fuel	Engine
Pony 820 (French)	Diesel	Simca Hanomag
Pacer 16		Continental Y 91
Colt 21		Continental F 124
Mustang 23		Continental F 140

Table 15
Some engines fitted to some early M-H reaper threshers and combines

Model	Engine	HP
No. 6	Buda	26
No. 7	Buda	25
No. 9	Continental	30
No. 9 A	Buda	25
No. 9 B	Continental	30
No. 11	Hercules	26
No. 14	Hercules	48
No. 15	Hercules	31
No. 17	Hercules	31
No. 20	Chrysler	65
No. 50		21
No. 21	Chrysler T 125	
No. 21 A	Chrysler 6 T 112	
Clipper self propelled	Continental F 162	30
No. 26	Chrysler IND 30	
No. 27	Chrysler IND 8A	
No. 222	Continental F 162-4B1	

Table 16
M-H tractor and engine identification data from a workshop manual

Model	Fuel	Ser. no. range	Cylinders	Compression	Engine cu. in.	Engine model
RC 20	Gas	20GR–1001 & up	4	6.7:1	124	Cont. F124
RC 20K	Dist.	20KR–1001 & up	4	5:1	1140	Cont. 140
Std. 20	Gas	20GS–1001 & up	4	6.7:1	124	Cont. 124
Std. 20k	Dist.	20KS–1001 & up	4	5:1	140	Cont. 140
RC 30	Gas	30GR–1001 & up	4	6:1	162	Cont. F162
RC 30K	Dist.	30KR–1001 & up	4	5:1	162	Cont. F162
Std. 30	Gas	30GS–1001 & up	4	5.6:1	162	Cont. F162
Std. 30K	Dist.	30KS–1001 & up	4	5:1	162	Cont. F162
RC 44	Gas	44GR–1001 & up	4	5.6:1	260	M-H H260G
RC 44K	Dist.	44KR–1001 & up	4	4.6:1	260	M-H H260G
Std. 44	Gas	44GS–1001 & up	4	5.6:1	260	M-H H260G
Std. 44K	Dist.	44KS–1001 & up	4	4.6:1	260	M-H H260G
RC 44(6)	Gas	44-6GR–1001 & up	6	6:1	226	Cont. F226
Std. 55	Gas	55GS–1001 & up	4	5.6:1	382	M-H J382G
Std. 55K	Dist.	55KS–1001 & up	4	4.6:1	382	M-H J382K
RC 81	Gas	400001–406601	4	6.7:1	124	Cont. F124
Std. 81	Gas	425001–427574	4	6.7:1	124	Cont. F124
RC 82	Dist.	420001–420425	4	5:1	140	Cont. 140
Std. 82	Dist.	435001–436159	4	5:1	140	Cont. F140
RC 101	Gas	255001–258285	6	6.7:1	201	Chrys. T57,T81,T105
Std. 101	Gas	355001–357870	6	6.7:1	201	Chrys. T57,T81,T105
RC 101 Super	Gas	258286–260717	6	6.8:1	217	Chrys. T96,T116
Std. 101 Super	Gas	357871–359424	6	6.8:1	217	Chrys. T96,T116
RC 101 Jr–102G Jr.	Gas	375001–376713	4	6.5:1	124	Cont. F124
		376986–399682	4	6.7:1	140	Cont. F140
		399683–505513	4	6:1	162	Cont. F162
Std. 101 Jr–102G Jr.	Gas	377001–378713	4	6.7:1	124	Cont. F124
		378714–380462	4	6.5:1	140	Cont. F140
		380463–385641	4	6:1	162	Cont. F162
RC 101 Sr–102G Sr.	Gas	260718–272506	6	6:1	226	Cont. F226
Std. 101 Sr–102G Sr.	Gas	358919–363647	6	6:1	226	Cont. F226
RC 102 Jr.	Dist.	387000–387225	4	5:1	140	Cont. F140
		387226–389172	4	5:1	162	Cont. F162
Std. 102 Jr.	Dist.	385001–385467	4	5:1	140	Cont. F140
		385468–392750	4	5:1	162	Cont. F162
RC 102 Sr.	Dist.	265002–265287	6	4.8:1	244	Cont. A244
Std. 102 Sr.	Dist.	365001–367423	6	4.8:1	244	Cont. A244
Std. 201	Gas	91201–91703	6	6.8:1	242	Chrys. T120
Std. 202	Gas	95001–95223	6	6.2:1	290	Cont. M290
Std. 203	Dist.	98001–100131	6	4.8:1	330	Cont. M330D
Std. 203G	Gas	95224–95342	6	5.8:1	330	Cont. M330

Table 17
Comparative specifications of some post-war M-H tractors

Model	Type	Fuel	No. of Cyl- inders	Bore	Stroke	Piston Displa. cu.in.	Horsepower				Speeds, M.P.H.					
							BELT		DRAWBAR		1st	2nd	3rd	4th	5th	Reverse
							rated	max.	rated	max.						
Pony		Gasoline	4	2³/₈″	3¹/₂″	62	10.34	12.16	8.31	11.08	2.74	3.59	7.00			3.22
22	Standard	Gasoline	4	3³/₁₆″	4³/₈″	140	26.85	31.59	17.93	23.91	2.79	3.98	5.24	14.80		2.79
22	Row Crop	Gasoline	4	3³/₁₆″	4³/₈″	140	26.85	31.59	17.93	23.91	2.79	3.98	5.24	14.80		2.79
22K	Standard	Kerosene	4	3³/₁₆″	4³/₈″	140	★20.40	24.00	★13.50	18.00	2.79	3.98	5.24	14.80		2.79
22K	Row Crop	Kerosene	4	3³/₁₆″	4³/₈″	140	★20.40	24.00	★13.50	18.00	2.79	3.98	5.24	14.80		2.79
30	Standard	Gasoline	4	3⁷/₁₆″	4³/₈″	162	29.99	35.28	20.42	27.23	2.19	3.06	3.82	5.35	10.71	2.48
30	Row Crop	Gasoline	4	3⁷/₁₆″	4³/₈″	162	29.99	35.28	20.42	27.23	2.58	3.61	4.51	6.31	12.63	2.93
30K	Standard	Kerosene	4	3⁷/₁₆″	4³/₈″	162	★23.35	27.50	★16.50	22.00	2.19	3.06	3.82	5.35	10.71	2.48
30K	Row Crop	Kerosene	4	3⁷/₁₆″	4³/₈″	162	23.35	27.50	16.50	22.00	2.58	3.61	4.51	6.31	12.63	2.93
44	Standard	Gasoline	4	3⁷/₈″	5¹/₂″	260	39.98	47.04	31.02	41.36	2.21	3.33	4.43	5.75	12.28	2.89
44	Row Crop	Gasoline	4	3⁷/₈″	5¹/₂″	260	39.98	47.04	31.02	41.36	2.58	3.61	4.51	6.31	12.63	2.93
44K	Standard	Kerosene	4	3⁷/₈″	5¹/₂″	260	33.53	39.45	27.64	36.85	2.21	3.33	4.43	5.75	12.28	2.89
44K	Row Crop	Kerosene	4	3⁷/₈″	5¹/₂″	260	33.53	39.45	27.64	36.85	2.58	3.61	4.51	6.31	12.63	2.93
44D	Standard	Diesel	4	3⁷/₈″	5¹/₂″	260	36.58	43.04	29.61	39.48	2.21	3.33	4.43	5.75	12.28	2.89
44D	Row Crop	Diesel	4	3⁷/₈″	5¹/₂″	260	36.58	43.04	29.61	39.48	2.58	3.61	4.51	6.31	12.63	2.93
744D	Standard	Diesel	6	3¹/₂″	5″	288.6		41.00		35.00	2.21	3.33	4.43	5.75	12.28	2.89
744D	Row Crop	Diesel	6	3¹/₂″	5″	288.6		41.00		35.00	2.58	3.61	4.51	6.31	12.63	2.93
55	Standard	Gasoline	4	4¹/₂″	6″	382	52.18	61.39	40.65	54.20	2.96	4.22	5.22	12.07		2.54
55K	Standard	Kerosene	4	4¹/₂″	6″	382	46.32	54.49	37.12	49.49	2.96	4.22	5.22	12.07		2.54
55D	Standard	Diesel	4	4¹/₂″	6″	382	★46.00	54.00	36.3	46.00	2.96	4.22	5.22	12.07		2.54

★H.P. Figures, Engineer Estimates   Speeds shown above are for Tractors on Rubber and are approximate only

Table 18
Ferguson TE and TO tractor designations

Model	Production period	Fuel	Type
MADE IN U.K.			
TE20	1946–1948	Petrol	Continental engine
TEA20 to 172598	1947–1951	Petrol	Standard 80mm engine
TEA20 from 172599	1951–1956	Petrol	Standard 85mm engine
TEB20	1946–1948	Petrol	Narrow width Continental engine
TEC20		Petrol	Narrow width (?) Standard engine
TED20	1949–1956	TVO	Normal width
TEE20	1949–1956	TVO	Normal width
TEF20	1951–1956	Diesel	Normal width
TEH20	1950–1956	Lamp oil	Normal width
TEJ20	1950–1956	Lamp oil	Narrow width
TEK20	1952–1956	Petrol	Vineyard
TEL20	1952–1956	TVO	Vineyard
TEM20	1952–1956	Lamp oil	Vineyard
TEP20	1952–1956	Petrol	Full industrial
TER20	1952–1956	TVO	Full industrial
TES20	1952–1956	Lamp oil	Full industrial
TET20	1952–1956	Diesel	Full industrial
TEP20	1952–1956	Petrol	Semi industrial

Model	Production period	Fuel	Type
MADE IN U.K.			
TE20	1946–1948	Petrol	Continental engine
TEA20 to 172598	1947–1951	Petrol	Standard 80mm engine
TEA20 from 172599	1951–1956	Petrol	Standard 85mm engine
TEB20	1946–1948	Petrol	Narrow width Continental engine
TEC20		Petrol	Narrow width (?) Standard engine
TED20	1949–1956	TVO	Normal width
TEE20	1949–1956	TVO	Normal width
TEF20	1951–1956	Diesel	Normal width
TEH20	1950–1956	Lamp oil	Normal width
TEJ20	1950–1956	Lamp oil	Narrow width
TEK20	1952–1956	Petrol	Vineyard
TEL20	1952–1956	TVO	Vineyard
TEM20	1952–1956	Lamp oil	Vineyard
TEP20	1952–1956	Petrol	Full industrial
TER20	1952–1956	TVO	Full industrial
TES20	1952–1956	Lamp oil	Full industrial
TET20	1952–1956	Diesel	Full industrial
TEP20	1952–1956	Petrol	Semi industrial

Table 19
Ferguson TE 20
early engine numbers

Engine	Engine numbers
80mm petrol	S.1E–S.100204E
85mm petrol	S.100501E–S.117000E
	S.100501EY–S.100777EY
	(Atlas Engineering)
	SC.1E–SC.102,519E
	S.201EX–S245EX (Experimental)
85 mm V.O.	S.120501E–S.250501E
90 mm V.O.	SD.1E–SD.10E
85mm L.O.	SB.1E–SB.13000E
Diesel	SA.1E–SA.47006E
Spares engines	Add S to number e.g. S.112389ES
Duplicate numbers	Add D to number e.g. S.116392ED
Duplicate numbers	This occurred at the end of the 85 mm petrol (S…E) range, so that engine numbers ran:
	S.116998E
	S.116999E
	S.117000E
	S.117000ED
	S.116999ED
	S.116998ED

Table 20
Massey-Harris and
Massey Ferguson Combine
serial numbers

Model	Type	Series	Year	First	Last
15 and 17	PT	950/951	1937–46	No records	
			1947	K4100	K5112
			1948	W4700	W5649
			1948	W6650	W6699
			1949	10000	11974
			1950	11975	12900
			1951	12901	13680
			1952	13681	14633
			1953	14634	15333
20	SP		1938–41	No records	
21	SP	952 canvas table	1941–46	No records	
			1947	K1	K3499
			1948	W0	W4699
21	SP	952 auger table	1941–46	No records	
			1947	K5200	K6400
			1948	W5650	W6649
			1948	W8700	W13371
			1949	1	10279
222	Reaper thresher		1947	K3500	K4099
26	SP	956	1948	W6700	W8699
			1948	W13400	W14506
			1949	1	4493
			1949	25000	25817
			1950	25818	30435
			1951	30436	35646
			1952	35647	41443
27	SP	964	1949	75001	75025
			1950	75026	83191
			1951	83192	93663
			1952	93664	104613
35	SP	915	1958	91500001	91500404
			1959	91500405	91503305
			1960	91503306	91506505
			1961	not built	
			1962	91506506	91506980
			1963	124406981	124407530
			1964	124407531	124408131
Super 35	SP	1244	1963	6981	7530
35	PT	922	1959	92200001	92200300
			1960	92200301	92201501
			1961	92201502	92201877
			1962	92201878	92202327
			1963	not built	
			1964	92202328	92202427
Clipper	PT		1938	5001	5075
			1939	5101	7400
			1940	7501	10500
			1941	12001	14300
			1942	20001	23115
			1943	25001	26542
			1944	27001	29740
			1945	30001	32219
			1946	35001	39000
			1947	40001	43340
			1948	44001	51585
			1949	52001	62500

Model	Type	Series	Year	First	Last
			1950	63001	74350
			1951	75001	89900
			1952	96001	99240
50 Clipper	SP	922	1651	95001	95100
			1952	95101	95170
				200001	200801
			1953	200802	201500
				202001	204971
			1954	205001	208913
			1955	209001	212000
			1956	215001	217221
			1957	215001	221550
			1958	221551	222775
			1959	222776	223802
60	SP	965	1953	250000	250099
			1954	250300	251904
			1955	251095	252460
			1956	252461	253576
			1957	253577	254590
			1958	254591	255284
60	PT	968	1953	250100	250299
			1954	300000	300985
			1955	300986	302309
			1956	302310	303511
			1957	303512	304391
			1958	304392	305536
70	SP		1953	42000	43499
72	SP	940	1959	1	1377
			1960	1378	2571
			1961	2572	2853
			1962	2854	3153
			1963	3154	3653
			1964	3654	3988
			1965	3989	4113
72	PT	941	1959	1	1002
			1960	1003	1202
			1961	1203	1502
			1962	not built	
			1963	1503	1802
			1964	1803	1962
80	SP	966	1952	200000	200286
			1953	200287	204878
			1954	204879	207644
			1955	207645	209939
			1956	209940	212512
82	SP	917	1957	213778	215956
			1958	215957	219338
			1959	219340	222232
			1960	222233	223969
			1961	223970	225636
			1962	225697	226636
			1963	226638	227217
90	SP	967	1953	125000	133148
			1954	133149	140071
			1955	140072	144304
			1956	144305	148067
92	SP	918	1957	149178	152615
			1958	152618	157118
			1959	157119	163156
Super 92	SP	930	1960	1	3607
			1961	3608	8221
			1962	8222	12041
			1963	12042	15313
			1964	15314	15907
			1965	15908	16087

Model	Type	Series	Year	First	Last
Super 92 Hillside	SP	933	1961	1	110
205	SP	1398	1966	1	201
			1967	202	1011
			1968	1012	1161
			1969	1169	1526
			1970	1527	1751
300	SP	1167	1962	1	50
			1963	51	2252
			1964	2253	5716
			1965	5717	8539
			1966	8540	11451
			1967	11452	13988
			1968	13989	15885
			1969	15886	17226
			1970	17227	18375
			1971	18376	19175
			1972	19176	20280
			1973	20281	21055
			1974	21056	21855
			1975	21856	22775
			1976	22776	23567
			1977	23568	24015
405	PT	1330	1966	1	485
			1967	486	1090
			1968	not built	
			1969	1091	1390
			1970	1391	1590
			1971	not built	
			1972	1591	1750
410	SP	1200	1964	1	3659
			1965	3660	7882
			1966	7883	11753
			1967	11754	15062
			1968	15063	17462
			1969	17463	20091
			1970	20092	21013
			1971	21014	22993
			1972	22994	25273
510	SP	1201	1964	1	901
			1965	902	3052
			1966	3053	6017
			1967	6018	9076
			1968	9077	11428
			1969	11429	14430
			1970	14431	15946
			1971	15947	18736
			1972	18737	21267
			1973	21268	23701
			1974	23702	26828
			1975	26829	29098
			1976	29099	31663
			1977	31664	33977
540	SP	2428	1978	1	818
			1979	819	1855
			1980	1856	2370
			1981	2371	2885
550	SP	2393	1978	1	650
			1979	651	2781
			1980	2782	4894
			1981	4895	5306
			1982	5307	5946
			1984	5947	6661
			1988	6662	6726
750	SP	1696	1973	1	2105
			1974	2106	4548

Model	Type	Series	Year	First	Last
			1975	4549	7489
			1976	7490	10197
			1977	10198	13712
			1978	13713	16536
			1979	16539	19595
			1980	19596	22479
751	PT	2019	1979	1	1000
			1980	1001	2260
760	SP	1746	1971	1	10
			1972	11	510
			1973	511	1466
			1974	1467	2479
			1975	2474	4063
			1976	4064	5828
			1977	5829	7662
			1978	7663	9412
			1979	9413	11175
			1980	11176	13173
850/855	SP	1696	1981	22480	24661
			1982	24662	25657
			1983	25658	26795
			1984	26796	27543
			1985	27544	27908
			1986		
			1987	27909	28108
851	PT	2019	1981	2261	2610
			1982	2611	3160
852	PT	2019	1983	1	225
			1984	226	475
860/865	SP	1746	1981	13174	15223
			1982	15224	16558
			1983	16559	18227
			1984	18228	19114
			1985	19115	20331
			1986	20332	20361
			1987	20362	20561
8560	SP	5245	1986	1	172
			1987	173	445
8590	SP	5235	1987	1	100
5650	SP	2730	1989	3241	4025
			1990	4026	
8450	SP		1989	57289303572	
			1990	57289304520	
			1991	57289304543	
8460	SP		1989	57299401874	
			1990	57299402383	
			1991	57299402903	
Sweet corn harvester		1848	1970	10001	10025
				10026	10050

Sources: MF North America 1996 and 1977, and "Wild Harvest. Massey Collectors News." Vol. 9 No. 2, 1992

Table 21
Periods of production of tractors made in France 1951-1994

Model	Period of production	Model	Period of production
811 Pony	1951-1953	MF 2680	1979-1984
812 Pony	1953-1958	MF 2640	1979-1984
820 Pony	1957-1962	MF 2620	1980-1984
MF 821	1958-1962	MF 145 Mk 3	1980-1982
MF 865	1960-1964	MF 168	1982-1986
MF 835	1959-1963	MF 168 S	1982-1986
MF 825	1960-1963	MF 158 F	1982-1986
MF 42/8	1961-1965	MF 158 V	1982-1986
MF 37/8	1962-1965	MF 152	1982-1986
MF 20/25	1962-1965	MF 152 V	1982-1986
MF 30/8	1963-1965	MF 152 S	1982-1986
MF 65 Mk2	1963-1965	MF 145 V/S	1982-1986
MF 165 HX 211	1965-1969	MF 135.8-V	1982-1986
MF 145 HX 210	1965-1972	MF 2720	1982-1984
MF 140 HX 208 209	1965-1972	MF 690	1982-1987
MF 135	1965-1972	MF 298	1982-1984
MF 122	1965-1969	MF 675	1982-1987
MF 133 HX 218	1967-1972	MF 2725	1984-1987
MF 165 Mk 3	1968-1973	MF 2685	1984-1987
MF 178/8	1969-1972	MF 2645	1984-1986
MF 155	1970-1972	MF 2625	1984-1986
MF 1080/8	1970-1976	MF 699	1984-1987
MF 185	1972-1976	MF 698 T	1984-1987
MF 188	1972-1976	MF 3090	1986-1990
MF 165 DL	1972-1976	MF 3080	1986-1992
MF 168	1972-1976	MF 3070	1986-1993
MF 155 DL	1972-1976	MF 3060	1986-1994 onwards
MF 158 DL	1972-1976	MF 3050	1986-1994 onwards
MF 158 Mk 3	1972-1981	MF 3680	1987-1991
MF 152	1972-1979	MF 3650	1987-1990
MF 148	1972-1976	MF 3630	1987-1990
MF 133 DL	1972-1977	MF 3610	1987-1990
MF 135 DL	1972-1977	MF 3065	1987-1994 onwards
MF 595	1975-1982	MF 3655	1990-1994 onwards
MF 590	1976-1982	MF 3645	1990-1994 onwards
MF 285	1976-1980	MF 3125	1990-1994 onwards
MF 575	1976-1982	MF 3115	1990-1993
MF 275	1976-1983	MF 3095	1990-1994 onwards
MF 260	1976-1983	MF 3690	1991-1994 onwards
MF 245	1976-1982	MF 3670	1991-1994 onwards
MF 148 Mk 3	1976-1982	MF 3635	1992-1994 onwards
MF 235	1976-1983	MF 3085	1992-1994 onwards
MF 133 Mk 3	1976-1983	MF 3120	1993-1994 onwards
MF 135	1976-1981	MF 3075	1993-1994 onwards
MF 168	1977-1983	MF 3065 S Visioporteur	1993-1994 onwards
MF 255	1977-1983	MF 3065 Visioporteur	1993-1994 onwards
MF 292	1978-1983	MF 3060 Visioporteur	1993-1994 onwards
MF 250	1978-1981	MF 3050 Visioporteur	1993-1994 onwards

Source: Recherches conception et production: Marketing FDC Massey Ferguson. 1994. Wall chart

Table 22
Production periods of some Italian made MF tractors 1971-1994

Model	Period of production
MF 140 DL	1971-1976
MF 1134	1977-1985
MF 1114	1977-1985
MF 274	1978-1984
MF 254	1978-1986
MF 194 F	1984-1988
MF 184 S	1984-1988
MF 184 F	1984-1988
MF 174 S	1984-1988
MF 174 F	1984-1988
MF 284	1984-1987
MF 264	1984-1987
MF 194 S	1986-1988
MF 164 S	1986-1988
MF 164 S	1986-1988
MF 174 V	1987-1988
MF 164 V	1987-1988
MF 154 V	1987-1988
MF 394 SF	1989-1994 onwards
MF 384 SF	1989-1994 onwards
MF 374 VSF	1989-1994 onwards
MF 364 VSF	1989-1994 onwards
MF 354 VSF	1989-1994 onwards
MF 396 C/CF	1990-1994 onwards
MF 376 C/CF	1990-1994 onwards
MF 394 SF "E/S"	1992-1994 onwards
MF 384 SF "E/S"	1992-1994 onwards
MF 374 SF "E/S"	1992-1994 onwards
MF 374 V "E/S"	1993-1994 onwards
MF 364 VSF "E/S"	1993-1994 onwards
MF 354 VSF "E/S"	1993-1994 onwards

Source: Recherches conception et production:
Marketing FDC Massey Ferguson. 1994. Wall chart

Table 23
Production periods of German produced MF tractors

Model	Period of production
MF 142	1974-1977
MF 132	1974-1977
MF 1132	1976-1979
MF 1102	1976-1979

Table 24
Serial number and production data for U.K. produced Massey Ferguson tractors

Model	Year	Start	Finish
MF 135	1965	101	30282
	1966	30283	67596
	1967	67597	93304
	1968	93305	117428
	1969	117429	141425
	1970	141426	162199
	1971	400001	403517
	1972	403518	419582
	1973	419583	432708
	1974	432709	445601
	1975	445602	457866
	1976	457867	469334
	1977	469335	479192
	1978	479193	487349
	1979	487350	490714
MF 148	1972	600001	612152
	1973	602153	604448
	1974	604449	605577
	1975	605578	607702
	1976	607703	609158
	1977	609159	609968
	1978	609969	610892
	1979	610893	610982
MF 148 Turkey	1976	540001	543653
	1977	543654	544604
MF 165	1965	500001	512206
	1966	512207	530824
	1967	530825	547383
	1968	547384	563700
	1969	563701	581456
	1970	581457	599744
	1971	599745	608557
	1971	100001	103621
	1972	103622	116361
	1973	116362	126447
	1974	126448	135053
	1975	135036	145436
	1976	145437	155686
	1977	155687	164417
	1978	164418	171501
	1979	171502	173696
MF 168	1975	255967	258064
	1976	258065	259958
	1977	259959	260616
	1978	259959	260616
	1979	260997	261173
MF 175	1965	700001	705672
	1966	705673	714168
	1967	714169	722679
MF 175S	1968	650000	652063
	1969	652064	653721
	1970	653722	656010
	1971	656011	657362
MF 175 Turkey	1976	285001	286150
MF 178	1967	722680	722700
	1968	722701	732183

Model	Year	Start	Finish
	1969	732184	740325
	1970	740326	747282
	1971	747283	753108
MF 185	1971	300000	302832
	1972	302833	310397
	1973	310398	315221
	1974	315222	319922
	1975	319923	326110
	1976	326111	332106
	1977	332107	335210
	1978	335211	339754
	1979	339755	340103
MF 188	1971	350000	350005
	1972	350006	353296
	1973	353297	357062
	1974	357063	360783
	1975	360784	365088
	1976	365089	368349
	1977	368350	370155
	1978	370156	371305
	1979	371306	371333
MF 20	1970	803826	804545
	1971	804546	805201
	1972	805202	805918
	1973	805919	806578
	1974	806579	807207
	1975	807208	808001
	1976	808002	808944
	1977	808945	809551
MF 203/205 Mk. 1	1961	701679	702600
	1962	702061	703576
	1963	703577	706885
	1964	706886	708776
	1965	708777	709202
Mk. 2	1965	830001	831474
MF 20B	1979	855001	855215
	1980	855216	855435
	1981	855436	855559
	1982	855560	855743
	1983	855744	855893
	1984	855894	855913
	1985	855914	855996
	1986	53 produced	
MF 20D	1978	850001	850033
	1979		
	1980	850238	850390
	1981	850391	850451
	1982	850452	850481
	1983	810001	810367
	1984	810368	810781
	1985		
	1986	94 produced	
	1987	50 produced	
	1988	144 produced	
MF 20E	1982	850484	850612
	1983	850613	850718
	1984	850719	850845
	1985	850846	850974
	1986	82 produced	
MF 2135	1965	800001	800707
	1966	800708	801396
	1967	801397	802273
	1968	802274	802986
	1969	802987	803825
MF 2203/5	1965	831000	831474

Model	Year	Start	Finish
	1966	831475	832974
	1967	832975	835549
	1968	835550	836911
	1969	836912	838137
	1970	838138	838161
MF 230	1983	535001	535731
	1984	535732	535957
	1986	324 produced	
	1987	287 produced	
	1988	371 produced	
	1989	388 produced	
	1990	2327 produced	
	1991	232 produced	
	1992	208 produced	
	1993	154 produced	
	1994	139 produced	
MF 240	1979	500001	505098
	1980	505099	513211
	1981	513212	518906
	1982	518907	524436
	1983	525135	530000
	1983	550001	551832
	1984	551833	557557
	1985	557558	562419
	1986	562420	563863
	1987	4126 produced	
	1988	3049 produced	
	1989	2832 produced	
	1990	2327 produced	
	1991	1861 produced	
	1992	2433 produced	
	1993	2420 produced	
	1994	2335 produced	
MF 245	1978	530001	530012
MF 250	1983	622001	623944
	1984	623945	627275
	1985	627276	629952
	1986	629953	631553
MF 250C	1986	454 produced	
MF 253	1988	558 produced	
	1989	763 produced	
	1990	750 produced	
	1991		
	1992	367 produced	
	1993	637 produced	
	1994	593 produced	
MF 265	1978	175001	175002
	1979	178333	185204
	1981		
	1982		
	1983	194428	197922
	1984	197923	201408
	1985	201409	204137
	1986	204138	206356
MF 265C	1986	599 produced	
MF 270	1982	286152	286178
	1983	286179	287173
	1984	287174	287958
	1985	287959	288432
	1986	288433	288861
MF 275	1979	210001	210958
	1980	210959	212631
	1981		
	1982	220950	221502
	1983	221503	222272

Model	Year	Start	Finish	Model	Year	Start	Finish
	1984	222273	223378	MF 30E	1983	900501	900628
	1985	223379	224495		1984	900629	901186
	1986	224496	225351		1985	900187	901222
	1987			MF 3303/5	1966	814000	814184
	1988				1967	814185	816529
	1989	656 produced			1968	816530	819436
	1990	1056 produced			1969	819437	822778
	1991	1055 produced			1970	822779	822903
	1992	549 produced		MF 340	1989	44 produced	
	1993	596 produced			1990	252 produced	
	1994	662 produced			1991	155 produced	
MF 275C	1986	119 produced			1992	82 produced	
MF 275 Iraq	1980	214001	215242		1993	42 produced	
	1981	215243	220349	MF 340 C	1991	10 produced	
MF 283	1986	288 produced			1992	40 produced	
	1987				1993	22 produced	
	1988			MF 342 C	1993	105 produced	
	1989				1994	93 produced	
	1990	49 produced		MF 350	1986	44 produced	
	1991	2 produced			1987	158 produced	
	1992	11 produced			1988	111 produced	
	1993	301 produced			1989	82 produced	
	1994	433 produced			1990	57 produced	
MF 285	1979	340104	341000		1991	51 produced	
MF 290	1979	341001	342989		1992	21 produced	
	1980	371334	371427		1993	5 produced	
	1983	386913	389877	MF 350 C	1987	32 produced	
	1984	389878	393088		1988	298 produced	
	1985	393089	394999		1989	195 produced	
	1986	1875 produced			1989	87 produced	
	1989	94 produced			1990	145 produced	
	1990	291 produced			1991	117 produced	
	1991	1820 produced			1992	73 produced	
	1992	1593 produced			1993	26 produced	
	1993	914 produced		MF 352 C	1993	81 produced	
	1994	1757 produced			1994	151 produced	
MF 290C	1986	506 produced		MF 355	1986	45 produced	
MF 290 Iraq	1980	347001	348073		1987		
	1981	348074	350000		1988	244 produced	
	1982				1989	184 produced	
	1983	395000	398000		1990	122 produced	
MF 290-2	1985	393089	394999		1991	15 produced	
	1985	398676	399999		1992	13 produced	
	1985	400001	400063		1993	1 produced	
	1985	721917	723931	MF 355 C	1986	134 produced	
MF 298	1983	702586	703061		1987	209 produced	
	1984	703062	703698		1987	184 produced	
	1985	703699	704134		1988	197 produced	
	1986	799 produced			1989	213 produced	
MF 30	1969	900001	900042		1990	99 produced	
	1970	900043	900177		1991	25 produced	
	1971	900178	900283		1992	43 produced	
	1972				1993	10 produced	
	1973			MF 360	1986	529 produced	
	1974	900407	900475		1987	876 produced	
	1975	900476	900566		1988	794 produced	
	1976	900567	900659		1989	315 produced	
	1977	900660	900679		1990	138 produced	
	1978	900679	900680		1991	13 produced	
MF 30D	1982	900099	900152	MF 360	1986	529 produced	
	1983	900153	900237		1987	876 produced	
	1984	900238	900284		1988	794 produced	
	1985	900285	900362		1989	315 produced	
MF 30D C	1986	51			1990	138 produced	
MF 30E	1983	900501	900628		1991	13 produced	

Model	Year	Start	Finish	Model	Year	Start	Finish
	1992	5 produced			1993	870 produced	
	1993	2 produced			1994	687 produced	
MF 360 C	1987	432 produced		MF 383 C	1991	173 produced	
	1988	628 produced			1992	162 produced	
	1989	303 produced			1993	267 produced	
	1990	90 produced			1994	256 produced	
	1991	27 produced		MF 390	1986	538 produced	
	1992	6 produced			1987	2181 produced	
MF 362	1990	527 produced			1988	1607 produced	
	1991	591 produced			1989	1624 produced	
	1992	427 produced			1990	2195 produced	
	1993	590 produced			1991	1600 produced	
	1994	655 produced			1992	1354 produced	
MF 362 C	1989	20 produced			1992	16 produced	
	1990	1083 produced			1993	1505 produced	
	1991	410 produced			1994	1818 produced	
	1992	727 produced		MF 390 C	1986	340 produced	
	1993	1168 produced			1987	841 produced	
	1994	1194 produced			1988	2166 produced	
MF 365	1986	279 produced			1989	2258 produced	
	1987	1181 produced			1990	1939 produced	
	1988	1011 produced			1991	1406 produced	
	1989	894 produced			1992	1378 produced	
	1990	559 produced			1992	55 produced	
	1991	329 produced			1993	1813 produced	
	1992	407 produced			1994	1831 produced	
	1993	338 produced		MF 390T	1989	133 produced	
	1994	345 produced			1990	122 produced	
MF 365 C	1986	121 produced			1991	74 produced	
	1987	615 produced			1992	34 produced	
	1988	944 produced			1993	63 produced	
	1989	744 produced			1994	271 produced	
	1990	461 produced		MF 390T C	1989	85 produced	
	1991	594 produced			1990	377 produced	
	1992	404 produced			1991	421 produced	
	1993	284 produced			1992	527 produced	
	1994	184 produced			1993	983 produced	
MF 372 C	1991	46 produced			1994	1260 produced	
	1992			MF 392	1991	14 produced	
	1993	67 produced			1992	36 produced	
	1994	116 produced			1993		
MF 375	1986	49 produced			1994	72 produced	
	1987	1384 produced		MF 393	1992	21 produced	
	1988	1462 produced			1993	112 produced	
	1989	1321 produced			1994	141 produced	
	1990	869 produced		MF 393 C	1992	69 produced	
	1991	583 produced			1993	131 produced	
	1992	431 produced			1994	151 produced	
	1993	464 produced		MF 396	1992	35 produced	
	1994	559 produced			1993	51 produced	
MF 375 C	1986	119 produced			1993	97 produced	
	1987	596 produced			1994	97 produced	
	1988	874 produced		MF 396 C	1992	29 produced	
	1989	1069 produced			1993		
	1990	718 produced			1994	91 produced	
	1991	658 produced		MF 398	1986	88 produced	
	1992	436 produced			1987	330 produced	
	1993	534 produced			1988	279 produced	
	1994	470 produced			1989	160 produced	
MF 382	1994	17 produced			1990	282 produced	
MF 382 C	1992	34 produced			1991	345 produced	
	1993	210 produced			1992	177 produced	
	1994	361 produced			1993	119 produced	
MF 383	1986	240 produced			1994	276 produced	
	1987	629 produced		MF 398 C	1986	145 produced	
	1988	432 produced					
	1989	999 produced					
	1990	1086 produced					
	1991	1363 produced					
	1992	490 produced					

Model	Year	Start	Finish	Model	Year	Start	Finish
	1987	234 produced					
	1988	587 produced		MF 50 F/S	1979	875001	875006
	1989	445 produced		MF 550	1976	615001	615192
	1990	256 produced			1977	615193	616870
	1991	173 produced			1978	616871	618927
	1992	151 produced			1979	618928	619911
	1993	206 produced			1980	619912	620530
	1994	253 produced			1981	620531	620721
MF 399	1986	84 produced		MF 565	1976	650001	651187
	1987	408 produced			1977	651188	653458
	1988	816 produced			1978	653459	656253
	1989	697 produced			1979	656254	657826
	1990	822 produced			1980	657827	658851
	1991	503 produced		MF 575	1976	265001	265891
	1992	366 produced			1977	265892	267644
	1993	683 produced			1978	267645	269141
	1994	1268 produced			1979		
MF 399 C	1986	84 produced			1980	270028	271270
	1987	219 produced		MF 590	1976	375001	375904
	1988	5454 produced			1977	375904	377117
	1989	611 produced			1978	377118	378837
	1990	791 produced			1979	278837	379927
	1991	699 produced			1980	379928	381381
	1992	663 produced		MF 590 Denmark	1977	398001	398408
	1993	942 produced		MF 675	1981	720001	720020
	1994	1038 produced			1982	720021	720918
MF 40	1970	868162	839412		1983	720919	721914
	1971	839413	840279	MF 690	1981	700001	700008
	1972	840280	841072		1982	700009	700164
	1973	841073	841783		1983	701165	702486
	1974	841784	842271	MF 702	1959	700001	700140
	1975	842272	842806		1960	700141	701678
	1976	842807	843305	T70	1994	30 produced	
	1977	843306	843923	T70 C	1993	14 produced	
	1978				1994	46 produced	
	1979			T80	1994	50 produced	
	1980			T80C	1993	25 produced	
	1981	865546	865696		1994	80 produced	
	1982			T98	1994	21 produced	
	1983	865697	865973	T98C	1994	55 produced	
MF 50	1970	829904	825865				
	1971	825866	828857				
	1972	828858	831273				
	1973	831274	832841				
	1974	832842	833902				
	1975	833903	835245				
	1976	835246	836528				
	1977	836529	837888				
	1978	837889	838927				
	1979						

(Data supplied by MF)

Table 25
Serial number prefixes for
U.K. built tractors

A	Torque converter
B	High clearance (transmission)
C	Single clutch
D	Petrol engine (non current)
E	Hi. clearance (non current)
F	Multi power pump
G	Auxiliary hydraulic pump
H	Heavy duty (front axle)
J	Side PTO
K	Sealed brakes
L	Less differential lock (non current)
M	8 speed transmission
N	Bord-na-Mona
P	IPTO
R	Side IPTO
S	Hi-flow pump 2 speed, 2 shafts
T	Hi-flow pump 1 speed, 1 shaft
U	Mk. 2 gearbox multi power
Z	Mk. 2 gearbox 8 speed

Source: MF circulars

Table 26
MF 1200 and 1250 tractor
serial numbers

MF 1200

H101 FG - J218 FG	These tractors were issued with random numbers, therefore the cut in of certain changes cannot be identified
XJ 103 74 FG - XK 103 130 FG	These tractors are numbered in sequence
K 900 001 FG	Onwards in sequence
Note well	Two different types of serial number may be quoted on a document or serial number plate. The complete number of the later of the two numbers is more relevant
D (or M) suffix	High capacity auxiliary hydraulic pump
F	Multi Power transmission
G	Standard capacity auxiliary hydraulic pump
M	Eight speed transmission
1972	H 101-149
1973	J 120 - J 200 and J 10374 - J 103119
1974	K 103120 - K 103130 and K 900001
1975	L 900229 -
1976	L 900748 -
1977	L 901021 -
1978	L 901508 -
1979	L 901845 - 902059

MF 1250

1979	903001 -
1980	903046
1981	903193 -
1982	903257 - 903257

Source: MF data sheets

Table 27
Some Landini tractor model numbers and engine data

(all Perkins engines unless indicated)

Landini series	MF series	Year introduced	HP	Engine
Footstep series small				
"30"	"204"			
R 5830	MF 254-2	1984	53	AD 3-152 S
R 6030	MF 264-2	1985	58	AT 3-152
R 6830	MF 274-2	1984	67	A 4-236
R 7830	MF 284-2	1984	75	A 4-236
R 8830	MF 294-2	1984	83	A 4-248
DT 5830	MF 254-4	1984	53	AD 3-152 S
DT 6030	MF 264-4	1985	58	AT 3-152
DT 6830	MF 274-4	1984	67	A 4-236
DT 7830	MF 264-4	1984	75	A 4-236
DT 8830	MF 294-4	1984	83	A 4-248
"60"	"303"			
R 5860	MF 353-2	1988	53	AD 3-152 S
R 6060	MF 363-2	1988	60	AT 3-152
R 6860	MF 373-2	1988	67	A 4-236
R 7860	MF 383-2	1988	74	A 4-236
R 8860	MF 393-2	1988	83	A 4-248
R 7860 HC	MF 383-2 HC	1988	74	A 4-236
R 8860 HC	MF 393-2 HC	1988	83	A 4-248
DT 5860	MF 353-4	1988	53	AD 3-152 S
DT 6060	MF 363-4	1988	60	AT 3-152
DT6860	MF 373-4	1988	67	A 4-236
DT 7860	MF 383-4	1988	74	A 4-236
DT 8860	MF 393-4	1988	83	A 4-248
DT 7869 HC	MF 383-4 HC	1988	74	A 4-236
DT 8860 HC	MF 393-4 HC	1988	83	A 4-248
Semiplatform and Cab small series				
"40"	"204 - SAP"			
R 5840	MF 254-2 SP	1985	53	AD 3-152 S
R 6040	MF 264-2 SP	1985	58	AT 3-152
R 6840	MF 274-2 SP	1985	67	A 4-236
DT 5840	MF 254-4 SP	1985	53	AD 3-152 S
DT 6040	MF 264-4 SP	1985	58	AT 3-152
DT 6840	MF 274-4 SP	1985	67	A 4-236
"70"	"303 - S"			
R 5870	MF 353-2 S	1988	53	AD 3-152 S
R 6070	MF 363-2 S	1988	60	AT 3-152
R 6870	MF 373-2 S	1988	67	A 4-236
R 7870	MF 383-2 S	1988	74	A 4-236
R 8870	MF 393-2 S	1988	83	A 4-248
DT 5870	MF 353-4 S	1988	53	AD 3-152 S
DT 6070	MF 363-4 S	1988	60	AT 3-152
DT 6870	MF 373-4 S	1988	67	A 4-236
DT 7870	MF 383-4 S	1988	74	A 4-236
DT 8870	MF 393-4 S	1988	83	A 4-248
"Blizzard"	"303 LX"			
R 50	MF 353-2 LX	1992	53	AD 3-152 S
R 60	MF 363-2 LX	1992	60	AT 3-152
R 65	MF 373-2 LX	1992	67	A 4-236
R 75	MD 383-2 LX	1992	74	A 4-236
R 85	MF 393-2 LX	1992	83	A 4-248

R 95	MD 393T-2 LX	1993	90	AT 4-236
DT 50	MF 353-4 LX	1992	53	AD 3-152 S
DT 60	MD 363-4 LX	1992	60	AT 3-152
DT 65	MF 373-4 LX	1992	67	A 4-236
DT 75	MF 383-4 LX	1992	74	A 4-236
DT 85	MF 393-4 LX	1992	83	A 4-248
DT 95	MF 393T-4 LX	1993	90	AT 4-236
Small, cab series				
"50"	"204 - S"			
R 6550	MF 274-2 S	1980	67	A 4-236
R 7550	MF 284-2 S	1980	75	A 4-236
R 8550	MF 294-2 S	1980	83	A 4-248
DT 6550	MF 274-4 S	1980	67	A 4-236
DT 7550	MF 284-4 S	1980	75	A 4-236
DT 8550	MF 294-4 S	1980	83	A 4-248
"80"	"307"			
R 6880	MF 377-2	1988	67	A 4-236
R 7880	MF 387-2	1988	74	A 4-236
R 8880	MF 397-2	1988	83	A 4-248
R 9080	MF 987T-2	1989	90	AT 4-236
R 9880	MF 1007-2	1989	94	AT 4-236
R 6880 View Master	MF 377-2 Steep Nose	1989	67	A 4-236
R 7880 View Master	MF 387-2 Steep Nose	1989	74	A 4-236
R 8880 View Master	MF 397-2 Steep Nose	1989	83	A 4-248
DT 6880	MF 377-4	1988	67	A 4-236
DT 7880	MF 387-4	1988	74	A 4-236
DT 8880	MF 397-4	1988	83	A 4-248
DT 9080	MF 397T-4	1989	90	AT 4-236
DT 9880	MF 1007-4	1989	94	AT 4-236
DT 8880 HC	MF 397-4 HC	1989	83	A 4-248
DT 9880 HC	MF 1007-4 HC	1989	94	AT 4-236
DT 6880 View Master	MF 377-4 Steep Nose	1989	67	A 4-236
DT 7880 View Master	MF 387-4 Steep Nose	1989	74	A 4-236
DT 8880 View Master	MF 397-4 Steep Nose	1989	83	A 4-248
"Special" range				
"Frutteto"	"Frutteto 104"			
R 5530 V	MF 154-2 V	1987	53	AD 3-152 S
R 6030 V	MF 164-2 V	1987	58	AT 3-152
R 6530 V	MF 174-2 V	1987	67	A 4-236
DT 5530 V	MF 154-4 V	1987	53	AD 3-152 S
DT 6030 V	MF 164-4 V	1987	58	AT 3-152
DT 6530 V	MF 174-4 V	1987	67	A 4-236
R 5530 F	MF 154-2 S	1983	53	AD 3-152 S
R 6030 F	MF 164-2 S	1986	58	AT 3-152
R 6530 F	MF 174-2 S	1983	67	A 4-236
R 7530 F	MF 184-2 S	1983	75	A 4-236
R 8530 F	MF 194-2 S	1985	83	A 4-248
DT 5530 F	MF 154-4 S	1983	53	AD 3-152 S
DT 6030 F	MF 164-4 S	1986	58	AT 3-152
DT 6530 F	MF 174-4 S	1983	67	A 4-236
DT 7530 F	MF 184-4 S	1983	75	A 4-236
DT 8530 F	MF 194-4 S	1985	83	A 4-248
DT 5530 L	MF 154-4 F	1986	53	AD 3-152 S
DT 6030 L	MF 164-4 F	1987	58	AT 3-152
DT 6530 L	MF 174-4 F	1985	67	A 4-236
DT 7530 L	MF 184-4 F	1983	75	A 4-236
DT 8530 L	MF 194-4 F	1985	83	A 4-248
R 5560 V	MF 354-2 V	1988	47	AD 3-152
R 6060 V	MF 364-2 V	1989	60	AT 3-152
R 6560 V	MF 374-2 V	1989	67	A 4-236
DT 5560 V	MF 354-4 V	1988	47	AD 3-152
DT 6060 V	MF 364-4 V	1989	60	AT 3-152
DT 6560 V	MF 374-4 V	1989	67	A 4-236

R 5560 F	MF 354-2 S	1989	53	AD 3-152 S
R 6060 F	MF 364-2 S	1989	60	AT 3-152
R 6560 F	MF 374-2 S	1989	67	A 4-236
R 7560 F	MF 384-2 S	1989	74	A 4-236
R 8560 F	MF 394-2 S	1989	83	A 4-248
DT 5560 F	MF 354-4 S	1989	53	AD 3-152 S
DT 6060 F	MF 364-4 S	1989	60	AT 3-152
DT 6560 F	MF 374-4 S	1989	67	A 4-236
DT 7560 F	MF 384-4 S	1989	74	A 4-236
DT 8560 F	MF 394-4 S	1989	83	A 4-248
DT 5560 L	MF 354-4 F	1989	53	AD 3-152 S
DT 6060 L	MF 364-4 F	1989	60	AT 3-152
DT 6560 L	MF 374-4 F	1989	67	A 4-236
DT 7560 L	MF 384-4 F	1989	74	A 4-236
DT 8560 L	MF 394-4 F	1989	83	A 4-248
R 5560 F-GE	MF 354-2 S GE	1990	53	AD 3-152 S
R 6060 F-GE	MF 364-2 S GE	1990	60	AT 3-152
R 6560 F-GE	MF 374-2 S GE	1990	67	A 4-236
R 7560 F-GE	MF 384-2 S GE	1990	74	A 4-236
R 8560 F-GE	MF 394-2 S GE	1990	83	A 4-248
DT 5560 F-GE	MF 354-4 S GE	1990	53	AD 3-152 S
DT 6060 F-GE	MF 364-4 S GE	1990	60	AT 3-152
DT 6560 F-GE	MF 374-4 S GE	1990	67	A 4-236
DT 7560 F-GE	MF 384-4 S GE	1990	74	A 4-236
DT 8560 F-GE	MF 394-4 S GE	1990	83	A 4-248
"Frutteto Advantage"	"Frutteto Executive"			
R 55 VP-VQ	MF 354-2 VQ	1994	53	AD 3-152 S
R 60 VP-VQ	MF 364-2 VQ	1994	60	AT 3-152
R 65 VP-VQ	MF 374-2 VQ	1994	67	A 4-236
R 75 VP-VQ	MF 384-2 VQ	1994	74	A 4-236
DT 55 VP-VQ	MF 354-4 VQ	1994	53	AD 3-152-S
DT 60 VP-VQ	MF 364-4 VQ	1994	60	AT 3-152
DT 65 VP-VQ	MF 374-4 VQ	1994	67	A 4-236
DT 75 VP-VQ	MF 384-4 VQ	1994	74	A 4-236
R 55 F	MF 354-2 SQ	1992	53	AD 3-152 S
R 60 F	MF 364-2 SQ	1992	60	AT 3-152
R 65 F	MF 374-2 SQ	1992	67	A 4-236
R 75 F	MF 384-2 SQ	1992	74	A 4-236
R 85 F	MF 394-2 SQ	1992	83	A 4-248
DT 55 F	MF 354-4 SQ	1992	53	AD 3-152 S
DT 60 F	MF 364-4 SQ	1992	60	AT 3-152
DT 65 F	MF 374-4 SQ	1992	67	A 4-236
DT 75 F	MF 384-4 SQ	1992	74	A 4-236
DT 85 F	MF 394-4 SQ	1992	83	A 4-248
R 55 L	MF 354-2 FQ	1992	53	AD 3-152 S
R 60 L	MF 364-2 FQ	1992	60	AT 3-152
R 65 L	MF 374-2 FQ	1992	67	A 4-236
R 75 L	MF 384-2 FQ	1992	74	A 4-236
R 85 L	MF 394-2 FQ	1992	83	A 4-248
DT 55 L	MF 354-4 FQ	1992	53	AD 3-152 S
DT 60 L	MF 364-4 FQ	1992	60	AT 3-152
DT 65 L	MF 374-4 FQ	1992	67	A 4-236
DT 75 L	MF 384-4 FQ	1992	74	A 4-236
DT 85 L	MF 394-4 FQ	1992	83	A 4-248
	MF 354-2 AQ	1992	53	AD 3-152 S
	MF 364-2 AQ	1992	60	AT 3-152
	MF 374-2 AQ	1992	67	A 4-236
	MF 384-2 AQ	1992	74	A 4-236
	MF 394-2 AQ	1992	83	A 4-248
DT 55 GT	MF 354-4 AQ	1992	53	AD 3-152 S
DT 60 GT	MF 364-4 AQ	1992	60	AT 3-152
DT 65 GT	MF 374-4 AQ	1992	67	A 4-236
DT 75 GT	MF 384-4 AQ	1992	74	A 4-236
DT 85 GT	MF 394-4 AQ	1992	83	A 4-248
R 55 FP	MF 354-2 SP	1993	53	AD 3-152 S
R 60 FP	MF 364-2 SP	1993	60	AT 3-152

R 65 FP	MF 374-2 SP	1993	67	A 4-236
R 75 FP	MF 384-2 SP	1993	74	A 4-236
R 85 FP	MF 394-2 SP	1993	83	A 4-248
DT 55 FP	MF 354-4 SP	1993	53	AD 3-152 S
DT 60 FP	MF 364-4 SP	1993	60	AT 3-152
DT 65 FP	MF 374-4 SP	1993	67	A 4-236
DT 75 FP	MF 384-4 SP	1993	74	A 4-236
DT 85 FP	MF 394-4 SP	1993	83	A 4-248
R 55 LP	MF 354-2 FP	1993	53	AD 3-152 S
R 60 LP	MF 364-2 FP	1993	60	AT 3-152
R 65 LP	MF 374-2 FP	1993	67	A 4-236
R 75 LP	MF 384-2 FP	1993	74	A 4-236
R 85 LP	MF 394-2 FP	1993	83	A 4-248
DT 55 LP	MF 354-4 FP	1993	53	AD 3-152 S
DT 60 LP	MF 364-4 FP	1993	60	AT 3-152
DT 65 LP	MF 374-4 FP	1993	67	A 4-236
DT 75 LP	MF 384-4 FP	1993	74	A 4-236
DT 85 LP	MF 394-4 FP	1993	83	A 4-248
	MF 354-2 AP	1993	53	AD 3-152 S
	MF 364-2 AP	1993	60	AT 3-152
	MF 374-2 AP	1993	67	A 4-236
	MF 384-2 AP	1993	74	A 4-236
	MF 394-2 AP	1993	83	A 4-248
DT 55 GTP	MF 354-4 AP	1993	53	AD 3-152 S
DT 60 GTP	MF 364-4 AP	1993	60	AT 3-152
DT 65 GTP	MF 374-4 AP	1993	67	A 4-236
DT 75 GTP	MF 384-4 AP	1993	74	A 4-236
DT 85 GTP	MF 394-4 AP	1993	83	A 4-248
R 55 GE	MF 354-2 GE	1993	53	AD 3-152 S
R 60 GE	MF 364-2 GE	1993	60	AT 3-152
R 65 GE	MF 374-2 GE	1993	67	A 4-236
R 75 GE	MF 384-2 GE	1993	74	A 4-236
R 85 GE	MF 394-2 GE	1993	83	A 4-248
DT 55 GE	MF 354-4 GE	1993	53	AD 3-152 S
DT 60 GE	MF 364-4 GE	1993	60	AT 3-152
DT 65 GE	MF 374-4 GE	1993	67	A 4-236
DT 75 GE	MF 384-4 GE	1993	74	A 4-236
DT 85 GE	MF 394-4 GE	1993	83	A 4-248
"Large" series				
R 10000	MF 1014-2	1980	105	A 6-3544
R 12500	MF 1114-2		125	A 6-3544
R 13000		1984	120	A 6-3544
R 14500	MF 1134-2		145	AT 6-3544
DT 10000	MF 1014-4	1980	105	A 6-3544
DT 12500	MF 1114-4		125	A 6-3544
DT 13000		1984	120	A 6-3544
DT 14500	MF 1134-4		145	AT 6-3544
"Large Legend" series				
DT 115		1994	110	1006-6HR2
DT 130		1994	112	1006-6TLR2
DT 145		1994	138	1006-6THR2
DT 105		1994	103	
"Large" series imported				
Vanguard 110		1992	110	1006-6HR
Vanguard 130		1992	130	1006-6T7
DT 16550	MF 3655-4	1990	160	1006-6TW
DT 17500	MF 3670-4	1993	175	620-DS★
DT 19000	MF 3680-4	1990	190	612-SA★
DT 19500	MF 3690-4	1993	200	612-DS★

★Valmet
Source: Landini

Table 28
Engines fitted to some Ferguson and MF agricultural tractors sold on the North American market

(P = Perkins, C = Continental, GM = General Motors, CAT = Caterpillar, VAL = Valmet, MM = Minneapolis Moline, CUM = Cummins, M = Mercedes)

Tractor model	Diesel	Gas	LP
Ferguson 20		Z 120 (C)	
Ferguson 30		Z 129 (C)	
MF 25	A4.107 (P)		
MF 130	A4.107 (P)		
TO 35	Standard 23C/137.8	Z-134 4 Cyl (C)	
Ferguson 40		Z-134 4 Cyl (C)	
MF 35	Standard 23C/137.8	Z-134 4 Cyl (C)	
FE 35	A3.152 (P)		
MF 35	A3.152 (P)	Z-134 4 Cyl (C)	
MF 50	A3.152 (P)	Z-134 4 Cyl (C)	Z-134 4 Cyl (C)
MH 50		Z-134 4 Cyl (C)	Z-134 4 Cyl (C)
MF 135	AD3.152.7 DLX (P)	Z-145 4 Cyl (C)	
MF 135		Z-134 4 Cyl (C) AG3.152 (P)	
MF 150	AD3.152.7 (P)	Z-145 4 Cyl (C) AG3.152 (P)	Z-145 4 Cyl (C)
MF 135 English	AD3.152 (P)		
MF 254-4	AD3.152 (P)		
Landini RDT5500	AD3.152 (P)		
MF 230	AD3.152 (P)	Z-145 4 Cyl (C)	
MF 235	AD3.152 (P)	Z-145 4 Cyl (C)	
MF 245	AD3.152 (P)	Z-145 4 Cyl (C)	
MF 250	AD3.152 (P)		
MF 240	AD3.152 (P)		
MF 231	AD3.152 (P)		
MF 253	AD3.152 (P)		
MF 364S	AD3.152 (P)		
MF 360	ATD3.152 (P)		
MF 65	A4.203 (P)	G176 Cl (C)	LPG 176 Cl (C)
MF 65 U	A4.203 (P)	G176 Cl (C)	LPG 176 Cl (C)
MF 65	AD4.203 (P)	G176 Cl (C)	LPG 176 Cl (P)
MF 65 U	AD4.203 (P)	AG4.212 Cl (P)	
MF 165	AD4.203 (P)	AG4.212 Cl (P)	LPG 176 Cl (C)
MF 165 U	AD4.203 (P)	AG4.212 Cl (P)	
MF 255	AD4.203 (P)	AG4.212 Cl (P)	
MF 255	AD4.236 (P)	AG4.212 (P)	
MF 175	A4.236 (P)	G4.206 (C)	
MF 175		AG4.236 (P)	
MF 180	A4.236 (P)	G4.206 (C)	
MF 180		AG4.236 (P)	
MF 265	AD4.236 (P)	AG4.236 (P)	
MF 270	AD4.236 (P)		
MF 290	248 (P)		
MF 670	AD4.236 (P)		
MF 375	A4.236 (P)		
MF 390T	AT4.236 (P)		
MF 398	AT4.236 (P)		
MF 3070	AT4.236 (P)		
MF 374S	A4.236 (P)		
MF 384S	A4.236 (P)		
MF 362	A4.236 (P)		

MF 261	A4.236 (P)		
MF 393	AT4.236 (P)		
MF 274-4	A4.236 (P)		
Landini RDT 6500	A4.236 (P)		
Landini RDT 6530	A4.236 (P)		
MF 184-4	A4.236 (P)		
Landini RDT 7500	A4.236 (P)		
MF 374S	A4.236 (P)		
MF 3050			
MF 3075	1004.4 (P)		
MF 690	A4.248 (P)		
MF 282	A4.248 (P)		
MF 275	A4.248 (P)		
MF 294-4	A4.248 (P)		
Landini RDT 8500	A4.248 (P)		
Landini RDT 8550	A4.248 (P)		
MF 290	A4.248 (P)		
MF 690	A4.248 (P)		
MF 283	A4.248 (P)		
MF 383	A4.248 (P)		
MF 390	A4.248 (P)		
MF 394S	A4.248 (P)		
MF 3060	A4.248 (P)		
MF 290	A4.248 (P)		
MF 85	HD 277 (C)	G223-G242 (C)	LPG 223 (C)
MF 88	HD 227 (C)	G242 (C)	LPG 242 (C)
MF Super 90	A4.300 (P)	G242 (C)	LPG 242 (C)
MF 1080	A4.318 (P)		
MF 1085	A4.318 (P)		
MF 285	A4.318 (P)		
MF 298	A4.318 (P)		
MF 295	A4.318 (P)		
MF 698	A4.318 (P)		
MF 399	A6.354 (P)		
MF 1100	A6.354 (P)		
Landini RDT 10000	A6.354 (P)		
Landini RDT 12500	A6.354 (P)		
Landini RDT 14500	AT6.354 (P)		
MF 2675	A6.354 (P)		
MF 2640	A6.354 (P)		
MF 1130	AT6.354 (P)		
MF 1135	AT6.354 (P)		
MF 2705	A6.354 (P)		
MF 1105	A6.354 (P)		
MF 95	MM425.5 (MM)		
MF Super 97	MM504 (MM)		
MF 98	GM 371 (MM)		
MF 3090	A6.354 (P)		
MF 3630	AT6.354.4 (P)		
MF 3650	ATC6.354 (P)		
MF 3505	A6.354 (P)		
MF 3525	AT6.354 (P)		
MF 3545	AT6.354 (P)		
MF 3120	AT1006 (P)		
MF 3140	AT1006 (P)		
MF 3660	AT1006 (P)		
MF 3660	AWT1006 (P)		
MF 399	A1006 (P)		
MF 396	A1006 (P)		
MF 3670	620 DS (VAL)		
MF 3670	612 DS (VAL)		

MF 3680	612 DS (VAL)
MF 3690	612 DS (VAL)
MF 1150	AV8.510 (P)
MF 1155	AV8.540 (P)
MF 2745	AV8.540 (P)
MF 2775	AV8.640 (P)
MF 2800	ATV8.640 (P)
MF 2805	ATV8.640 (P)
MF 4800	V903 (CUM)
MF 4840	V903 (CUM)
MF 4880	VT903 (CUM)
MF 4900	VT903 (CUM)
MF 1500	C-573(V8) (CAT)
MF 1505	C3208(V8-636 ci) (CAT)
MF 1800	C-636(V8) (CAT)
MF 1805	C3208(V8-636 ci) (CAT)
MF 5200	12.7L (Detroit Dsl) (GM)
MF 5200	855 (CUM)
MF 3065	T4.236 (P)
MF 3065	AT4.236 (P)

Source: Delbert Gentner, MF North America

Table 29
Engines fitted to some harvesting equipment sold on the North American market

(P = Perkins, C = Continental, CH = Chrysler,
M = Mercedes, GM = General Motors Chevrolet)

Model	Diesel	Gas	LP
MF 300	AD4.203 (P)	6-225 Cl (CH)	
MF 205		6-170 Cl (CH)	
MF 35		4-F 140 (C)	
MF S-92	A6.305 (P)	6 Cyl 265 Cl (CH)	
MF 72		6 Cyl 230.2 Cl (CH)	
MF 82		6 Cyl 230.2 Cl (CH)	
MF 92		6 Cyl 251 Cl (CH)	
MF 410	A4.300 (P)	GM 292-6 (GM)	
MF 510`	A6.354 (P)	GM 327(V8) (GM)	
MF 540	A4.318 (P)		
MF 550	A6.354 (P)		
MF 750	A6.372 (P)	GM 350(V8) (GM)	
MF 750	AT6.354 (P)		
MF 760	AT6.354 (P)		
MF 760	AV8.540 (P)		
MF 850	A6.372 (P)		
MF 850	AT6.354 (P)		
MF 855	AT6.354 (P)		
MF 860	AT6.354 (P)		
MF 860	AV8.540 (P)		
MF 865	AV8.540 (P)		
MF 5650	A6.354 (P)		
MF 8560			
MF 8570	Cummins 6 CTA		
MF 8450	OM 352A (M)		
MF 8460	OM 421A (M)		
MF 885 Swather	A4.236 (P)		
MF 34 Swather	Cont 4-F-140 Cl (C)		
MF 44 Swather	Cont 4-F-162 Cl (C)		

Source: Delbert Gentner, MF North America

Table 30
A collation of some Massey Ferguson tractor model numbers and engine models by series

Model	Engine (Perkins unless indicated)
"100" series	
122	A4.99
130	A4.107
132	Eicher tractor
133	A3.144
135	AD3.152
139	Eicher tractor
140S	AD3.152
142	Eicher tractor
145	AD3.152
145V	AD3.152
147 (Spain)	AD3.152S
148	AD3.152S
150	AD3.152
152	AD3.152S
155	AD4.203
157 (Spain)	AD4.203
158 (also V & F)	AD4.203
165	AD4.203/212
168	A4.236
175	A4.236
175S	A4.236
177	A4.236
178	A4.248
180	AD4.236
185	A4.248
188	A4.248
"200" series	
230	AD3.152
231	AD3.152
235	AD3.152
240	AD3.152
245	AD3.152
250	AD3.152S
252	AT3.152.4
253	AT3.152.4
254	AD3.152S
255	AD3.152S
260	AD54.203
261	AD4.236
265	A4.236
270	AD4.236
274	A4.236
275	A4.236
283	A4.248
285	A4.248
290	A4.248
292 (Brazil)	ATA.236
294 (USA)	A4.248
296 (Brazil)	A6.354.4
297 (Brazil)	A6.354.4
298	A4.3182
299 (Brazil)	ALT6.354.4
233 (Landini)	AD3.152

Model	Engine (Perkins unless indicated)
253 (Landini)	AD3.152
263 (Landini)	T3.152.4
273 (Landini)	A4.236
283 (Landini)	A4.236
293 (Landini)	A4.248
"300" series	
342	AD3.152S
350	AD3.152S
352	AT3.1524
355	AT3.1524
360	AT3.1524
362	A4.236
363 Landini	AT3.1524
365	A4.236
372	A4.236
375	A4.236
382	A4.248
383 USA	A4.248
383 HC Landini	A4.236
390	A4.248
390T	AT4.236
393	A4.248
393 USA	AT4.236
396 USA	1006
398	AT4.236
399	A6.3544
333 Landini	AD3.152
353 Landini	AD3.152S
373 Landini	A4.236
377 Landini	A4.236
387 Landini	A4.236
397 Landini	A4.248
"2000/3005" series	
2620	A6.354.4
2640	A6.354.4
2680	AT6.3544
2720	AT6.3544
2625 (Europe)	A6.354.4
2645	A6.3544
2685	AT6.3544
2725	AT6.3544
2770 USA	AV8.640
2800 USA	ATV8.640
2675 USA	6.354.4
2705 USA	6.354.4
2745 USA	AV8.540
2775 USA	V8.640
2805 USA	V8.640
3505 USA	6.354.4
3525 USA	T6.354.4
3545 USA	T6.354.4
Crawlers	
124C	AD3.152
144C	AD3.152
164C	AD4.203
134C	AD3.152
154C	AD3.152
174C	A4.236
184C	A4.248
234C	3 cyl
254C (also CF)	AD3.152S
264C (also CF)	T3.1524

Model	Engine (Perkins unless indicated)
274C (also CF)	A4.236
294C	A4.236
376	4.236
396	A4.248
396C	AT4.236
394C	A4.248
244CF	AD3.152S
1114C	6.354.4
1124C	AT6.354.4

Industrial crawlers	
3366L (Landini) crawler loader	AD4.300
244 (Landini) crawler shovel	A3.152

Source: Kindly compiled by Rory Day of the Tractor and Machinery magazine

Table 31
Engines fitted to some MF industrials sold on the North American market

(P = Perkins, C = Continental)

Model	Diesel	Gas	LP
MF 811	A4.108 (P)		
MF 203	A3.152.7 (P)		
MF 205	A3.152.7 (P)		
MF 202		4-Z134 (C)	
MF 204		4-Z134 (C)	
MF 203	AD3.152 (P)		
MF 205	AD3.152 (P)		
MF 2135	A3.152.7 (P)	4-Z134 (C)	
MF 2200	A3.152.7 (P)	4-Z134 (C)	AG3.152 (P)
MF 2244	A3.152.7 (P)		
MF 200	A3.152.7 (P)		
MF 2500	A3.152.7 (P)		AG3.152 (P)
MF 40	A3.152.7 (P)		AG3.152 (P)
MF 4500	A3.152.7 (P)		AG3.152 (P)
MF 30B	A3.152.7 (P)		
MF 30E	A3.152.7 (P)		
MF 20D	A3.152.7 (P)		AG3.152 (P)
MF 20C	A3.152.7 (P)		AG3.152 (P)
MF 356	A4.203.5 (P)		
MF 356	AD4.203.5 (P)	GF193 (C)	
MF 302	AD4.203.5 (P)	GF193 (C)	
MF 50	AD4.203.5 (P)		
MF 50A	AD4.203.5 (P)		
MF 304	AD4.203.5 (P)		
MF 470	AD4.236 (P)		
MF 3165	AD4.203 (P)		
MF 30	AD4.203 (P)		
MF 40B	AD4.203 (P)		
MF 50D	A4.236 (P)		
MF 60TDL	A4-4.236 (P)		
MF 40C	A4.236 (P)		
MF50E	A4.236 (P)		
MF 50C	A4.236 (P)		

Model	Diesel	Gas	LP
MF 50F	A4.236 (P)		
MF 6500	A4.236 (P)	AG4.236 (P)	
MF 350 Excavator	A4.248 (P)		
MF 35 Loader	A4.248 (P)		
MF 300 Crawler	A4.248 (P)		
MF 220 Skidder	A4.248 (P)		
MF 11 S.L	A4.248 (P)		
MF 3366 Crawler	A4.300 (P)		
MF 70 BLT	A4.318 (P)		
MF 3366 Crawler	A4.318 (P)		
MF 320 Skidder	A4.318 (P)		
MF 44 Loader	A6.354 (P)		
MF 450 Excavator	A6.354 (P)		
MF 400 Crawler	A6.354 (P)		
MF 80 TBL	A6.354 (P)		
MF 44-B Loader	A6.354 (P)		
MF 500 Crawler	AV8.510 (P)		
MF 55 Loader	AV8.510 (P)		

Source: Delbert Gentner, MF North America

Table 32a
Machine nomenclature for recent MF industrials

Machine	Product	Machine type series
EX20	Mini Excavator	Excavator
PL10	Power Line (600 series)	Farm handlers
SS10	516	Skid sters
SS11	516XP	Skid steers
SS12	518	Skid steers
SS13	518XP	Skid steers
SS14	514	Skid steers
SS15	513	Skid steers
4027	Power skids	Drive trains (tugs)
5102	30E	Lo-line
5103	50E 2WD	Lo-line
5157	50E 4WD	Lo-line
5218	40E	Lo-line
5347	Series T	Backhoes
5348	Series 90 SShift	Backhoes
5349	Series 90 CMount	Backhoes
5443	Series S	Backhoes
5683	506	Skid steers
5684	505	Skid steers
5890	503	Skid steers
5970	508	Skid steers
9086	504	Skid steers
2882	50D	

Hence a machine number might read EX20 T 1234 in which case EX 20 = machine identity no., T = year of manufacture and 1234 = machine serial number.

Source: FERMEC International 1997

Table 32b
Year indicator for MF industrial serial numbers

A	1965
B	1966
C	1967
D	1968
E	1969
F	1970
G	1971
H	1972
J	1973
K	1974
L	1975
M	1976
N	1977
P	1978
R	1979
S	1980
T	1981
V	1982
W	1983
X	1984
Y	1985
A	1986
B	1987
C	1988
D	1989
E	1990
F	1991
G	1992
H	1993
R	1994
S	1995
T	1996

Source: FERMEC International. 1997

Table 33
UK MF industrials year (fiscal) of manufacture, models and year serial

Year	Model	First serial number	Last serial number
1970	MF20	803823	804545
	MF40	838309	839412
	MF50	822757	825865
1971	MF20	804546	805185
	MF30	900177	900283
	MF40	839413	840279
	MF50	825866	828857
1972	MF20	805186	805917
	MF30	900284	900360
	MF40	840280	841074
	MF50	828858	831272
1973	MF20	805918	806576
	MF30	900361	900406
	MF40	841075	841783
	MF50	831273	832841
	MF50B	J000503	J002323
1974	MF20	806577	807207
	MF30	900407	900475
	MF40	841784	842271
	MF50	832842	833901
	MF50B	K002324	K003916
1975	MF20	807208	808000
	MF30	900476	900566
	MF40	842272	842803
	MF50	833902	835245
	MF50B	L3917	L5528
1976	MF20	808001	808944
	MF30	900567	900659
	MF40	842804	843302
	MF50	835246	836520
	MF50B	M5529	M7498
1977	MF20	808945	809548
	MF30	900660	900677 Final
	MF40	843303	843920
	MF50	836521	837879
	MF50B	N7499	N10041
1978	MF20	809549	810033
	MF40	843921	844264
	MF50	837880	938915
	MF50B	P10042	P12519
	MF20D	850000	850033
1979	MF20	810034	810205 Final
	MF20B	855000	855211
	MF20D	850034	850235
	MF40	844265	844396 Final
	MF40 Phase III	865000	865271
	MF50	838916	840010 Final
	MF50 Phase III	875001	875005
	MF50B	R12520	R15056
1980	MF20B	855212	855435
	MF20D	850236	850391
	MF40	865272	865543
	MF50	875006	875801
	MF50B	S15057	S16190 (last machine from Knowsley)
	MF50B	S20001 (first Manchester machine)	S20963
	MF30C	900001	900030

1981	MF20B	855436		855557
	MF20D	850392		850450
	MF40	865544		865696
	MF50	875802		876404
	MF30C	900031		900074
	MF50B 2WD	T20964		T21821 Final
	MF50B 4WD	T001		T114 Final
	MF50B II 2WD	2871T001		2871T560
	MF50B II 4WD	2872T001		2872T157
1982	MF20B	855558		8555720
	MF20D	850451		850481
	MF20E	850482		850563
	MF30C	900075		900096
	MF30D	900097		900119
	MF40	865697		865909
	MF50	876405		876893
1983	MF20B	855721		855888
	MF20E	850564		850715
	MF30D	900119		900217
	MF40	865910		865973
	MF50	876894		877172
	MF20D New	810206		810235
	MF30E	900504		

Source: FERMEC International. 1997

Table 34
Italian-made industrial machines: models and last serial number of the year

Model	1973	1974	1975	1976	1977
300 loader	1596	1924	2041	2247	2516
300 dozer	465	586	606	685	790
D300B			034	060	
400 loader	1100	1367	1472	1774	1812
400 dozer	484	612	745	777	
D400B			048	089	190
D400C			022	198	342
D400C LPG				009	065
D400C DD				092	358
500 loader	701	800	852	892	926
500 dozer	884	1183	1427	1472	1521
350S	513				
450S	1729	2169	2345	2626	2639
33RWS	812	896	956	976	
44RWS	791				
44B	114	455	708	725	
55	618	747	845	859	
450D					306

Source: FERMEC International. 1997

Table 35
Serial number data for some French built combines and balers 1960-1966

			(first machine built in year)				
Machine	1960	1961	1962	1963	1964	1965	1966
892 combine	10114	11548	13190	13905	14481	15325	
99/8 baler						15506	16312
15/8 baler					1001	1253	3067
20/8 baler					50001	50587	53598
803 baler				50000	50927		
10.8 baler				★	18692		
510/8 combine							5501

★ 2001 to 2117 then new numbers from 15118

Source: Massey Ferguson S.A. 1966

Table 36
Some serial number data for 410 and 510 combines

	(serial number of last machine built in year of production)		
Model	1968	1969	1970
410	D 1155	E 1905	F 2758
510	D 1744	E 2879	F 4500

(N.B. 3544 of the 410 model and 6254 of the 510 model were built)

Source: Massey Ferguson

Table 37
Serial number data for some German built combines 1964-1969

Year	Machine	First no.	Last no.
1954	MF 630	A 1	A 31
1955		B 32	B 360
1956		C 631	C 4029
1957		D 4030	D 9275
1958	MF 630 S	E 9276	E 14112
1959		F 14113	F 16801
		G 16802	G 19819
		I 22560	I 25223
1963	MF 30	KD 3001	KD 4000
1964		LD 4001	LD 4781
1965		MD 4782	MD 5761
1966		ND 5762	ND 6841
1967		OD 6842	OD 7969
1968		PD 7970	PD 8642
1969		QD 8643	
1961	MF 31	HB 001	HB 011
1962		IB 012	IB 262
1963		KB 263	KB 1612
1964		LB 1613	LB 3043
1965		MB 3044	MB 4634
1966		NB 4635	NB 6264
1967		OB 6265	OB 7564
1968		PB 7565	PB 8109
1969		QB 8110	
1957	MF 685	685001	685009
1958		EA 10	EA 362
1959	MF 685 S	FA 363	FA 1737
1960		GA 1738	GA 2652
1961		HA 2768	HA 4693

Year	Machine	First no.	Last no.	Year	Machine	First no.	Last no.
1962		IA 4694	IA 7178	1963		KE 128	KE 1032
1963		KA 7179	KA 7528	1964		LE 1033	LE 1547
1961	MF 86	HC 001	HC oo6	1965		ME 1548	ME 1847
1962		IC 007	IC 154	1966		NE 1848	NE 2177
1963		KC 155	KC 849	1967		OE 2178	
1964		LC 850	LC 1455	1966	MF 71	NDA 1	NDA 550
1965		MC 1456	MC 2365	1967		ODA 551	ODA 1180
1966		NC 2366	NC 3455	1968		PDA 1181	PDA 1225
1967		OC 3456	OC 4730	1970		QDA 1226	
1968		PC 4731		1964	MF 15	1001	1252
1963	MF 87	KF 001	KF 025	1965		1253	3060
1964		LF 026	LF 1359	1966		3061	4981
1965		MF 1360	MF 3029	1967		5146	
1966		NF 3030	NF 4989	1968			
1967		OF 4990	OF 6294	1969		7096	
1968		PF 6295		1964	MF 20	50001	50586
1960	MF 892	10114	11547	1965		50587	53597
1961		11548	13189	1966		53598	60081
1962		13190	13904	1967		60227	
1963		13905	14480	1968			
1964		14481	15325	1969		65548	
1965	MF 99	15506	16311	1966	MF 8	NEA 1001	NEA 1165
1966		16312		1967		OEA 1166	OEA 2210
1964	MF 500	V 3131	3413	1968		PEA 2311	PEA 3055
1965		V 4658	4737	1969		QEA 3056	
1966	MF 510	5501	5927	1968	MF 158	QEA 500	QEA 525
1967		6173	7000	1969		QEA 526	
1968		7001	7746	1969	MF 186	QHA 1003	
1969		7747		1968	MF 187	PGA 1000	PGA 1310
1962	MF 70	IE 001	IE 127	1969		QGA 1311	

Source: Massey Ferguson

Table 38
Serial numbers of some French
produced tractors 1963-1969

Model	Code	1963	(last number of fiscal year 31st October) 1964	1965	1966	1967	1968	1969
MF 25	SNMY	1018748						
	SNFY	2003774						
	ENMY	11416						
	VNMY	102099						

The MF 25 was manufactured from 1961-1963

Model	Code	1963	1964	1965	1966	1967	1968	1969
MF 30	SNMY	1104656	1111477	1112003				
	SNFY	2125599	2126485	2126550				
	ENMY	15326	15654	15692				
	VNMY	250547	250620	250620				
	A.VNMY		201449	201529				
	CNMY	30324	30379	30382				
MF 35	SNMY	67966	68134	68134				
	ENMY	110401	110473	110473				
	SNMY-S		73804	74395				
	ENMY-S		111925	112039				
	VNMY-S		121035	121182				
	SNMWY		160714	160714				
	ENMY		170523	170523				
	VNMWY		175526	175536				
	SNFY		123700	123700				

The MF 35 was manufactured from 1962-1965

Model	Code					
MF 65	SNMY	126083	126083	126083		
(Mk II)	CNMY	150375	150375	150375		
	SNDMY	127595	129527	129974		
	CNDMY	151573	151874	151923		
	SNMWY	135614	136603	136834		
	CNMWY	155543	155836	155856		
MF 130	SNMY			376606	381989	385261	386831	387858
	SNFY			421577	422121	422500	422616	422651
	ENMY			430735	431131	431278	431420	431449
	VNMY			437410	438366	438881	439459	440063
	CNMY			446549	446682	446711	446725	446725
	JNMY			452635	452654	452664	452664	
	JNFY			458540	458546	458554	458554	

The MF 130 was first manufactured in November 1964

Model	Code					
MF 133	SNMY				187500/600557	604197
	ENMY				188629/610501	610713
	VNMY				172406/613511	613889
MF 135	SNDMY	255602	262159	268438	273718/620570	625362
	SNDM					
	SNDF			286596	286596	
	SNDFY	277154	277497	278992	279302	645710
	ENDMY	290785	291152	291484	291841/647501	647908
	ENDFY		296541	296641	296641	
	SNDMWY	298750	299144	299553	300321/650502	651035
	SNDMY.L					654743
	SNDMWL					660330
	ENDMWY	304515	304532	304549	304555	
	VNDMY	142098	142815	143458	143953/659501	
	VNDMWY	147524	147542	147560	147531	660330
MF 165	SNDMY	323032	325804	328330	328901	
(AD.203	SNDMY-M	342025	342952	343635	343741	
engine)	CNDMY	347728	347936	348090	348100	
	SNDMWY	354557	355928	356666	356952	
	SNDMWY-M	364756	365024	365239	365247	
	CNDMWY	368660	368784	368846	368851	
MF 165	SNDMY				462459/669528	671998
(AD.212	SNDMY-M				480317/681505	684149
engine)	CNDMY				484729/697501	697723
	SNDMWY				486850	487456
	SNDMWY-M				493124	493270
	CNDMWY				494512	494636
MF 175S	SNDMY					330725
	SNDMW-Y					334539
MF 178	SNDMY					402723
	SNDMW-Y					414072

NB. 1. Numbers separated by an oblique indicate 6 speed/8 speed versions

2. The above tractor nomenclatures apply only to sales outside France.
   Within France the MF 35 was known as the MF 37 and the MF 135 as the MF 140

Source: Massey Ferguson

Serial numbering system for FE35, 765 and 702/203/205 tractors and engines

(A reproduction of an MF circular)

ADVICE

The method of identifying the type of FE35 Tractor and Engine will be basically similar to that used previously for TE20 types. Each FE35 Tractor and Engine will be allocated a Serial Number with prefix and suffix letters which will indicate the particulars relevant to that type.

TRACTOR SERIAL NUMBERS

The Serial Numbers for the Tractors will start at 1001 and each number will have usually three prefix letters. However, as and when alternative refinements become available the number of prefix letters will be extended as necessary to a fourth and perhaps a fifth letter.

The existing prefixes are as follows:

Chassis

First Letter	*Prefix Letter*
Normal Width (Agricultural)	S
Vineyard	V
Industrial	J
High clearance	C

Engine

Second Letter	*Prefix Letter*
Petrol (6:1 compression ratio)	G
High Altitude Petrol (6.6:1 compression ratio)	H
Diesel (23C)	D
V.O.	K
L.O.	L
3A.52	N

Clutch

Third Letter	*Prefix Letter*
Single Clutch (Standard Model)	F
Dual Clutch (De-Luxe Model)	M

Example

The Serial Number SDM1076 would indicate that Tractor Serial No. 1076 was a Standard Model with Diesel Engine and Dual Clutch, whereas JGF1088 was an Industrial Tractor with Petrol engine (6:1CR) and single clutch.

Each type of engine will start at Serial No. 1 and will have:

(a) Two prefix letters to indicate the engine type.

(b) The suffix letter "E" to denote it is an engine number.

(c) An additional suffix letter to indicate the type of clutch.

In the case of Petrol Engines only, the first letter following the suffix "E" will indicate a normal or high compression ratio, therefore, these engines will have three suffix letters whereas all other engines will have two.

The complete range of Prefixes and Suffixes to cover the engine units is as follows:

87 m/m Petrol

6:1 Compression Ratio with Single Clutch	SF – ELS
6:1 Compression Ratio with Dual Clutch	SF – ELD
6:6.1 Compression Ratio with Single Clutch	SF – EHS
6:6.1 Compression Ratio with Dual Clutch	SF – EHD

87 m/m V.O.

With Single Clutch	SG – ES
With Dual Clutch	SG – ED

87 m/m L.O.

With Single Clutch	SH – ES
With Dual Clutch	SH – ED

Diesel (3⁵/₁₆ bore)

With Single Clutch	SJ – ES
With Dual Clutch	SJ – ED

Example

The Engine No. SF123EHD would indicate that Engine No. 123 would be an 87 m/m Petrol with a 6.6:1 Compression Ratio and Dual Clutch.

SPARE ENGINES

No Engine Numbers will be duplicated except in the case of engines for Spares, when, as in the past, the suffix "S" will be added for identification purposes.

Example: SF123EHD/S

Enter on Card Index under FE35. Tractor 'S' - Serial Numbering 'N' - Numbering.

MF765 SEMI-INDUSTRIAL TRACTOR CODES

The following code letter prefixes have been established and advised to you as follows:

Prefix 'J'	—	All Units
Prefix 'JM'	—	Fitted with Standard Transmission
Prefix 'JA'	—	Fitted with Instant Reverse Transmission
Prefix 'JMY'	—	Fitted with Standard Transmission and Diff Lock
Prefix 'JAY'	—	Fitted with Instant Reverse Transmission and Diff Lock

702/203/205 INDUSTRIAL TRACTORS

Prefix 'D'	—	"Standard" Engine 702 only
Prefix 'N'	—	Perkins Engine - 203/205
Prefix 'M'	—	Regular Transmission - 203
Prefix 'A'	—	"Funk" Transmission - 205
Prefix 'Y'	—	Differential Lock fitted

FE35

SGF - Petrol - Single Clutch - SF – ELS
SGM - Petrol - Double Clutch - SF – ELD
SHF - Petrol High Alt. Single Clutch - SF –EHS
SHM - Petrol High Alt. Double Clutch - SF – EHD
VGF - Petrol Vine Single Clutch - SF – ELS
JGF - Petrol Ind. Single Clutch - SF –ELS
JGM - Petrol Ind. Double Clutch - SF – ELD

SKF - V.O. - Single Clutch - SG - ES
SKM - V.O. - Double Clutch -SG - ED
VKF - V.O. - Vine Single Clutch - SG - ES
JKF - V.O. - Ind. Single Clutch - SG -ES
JKM - V.O. - Ind. Double Clutch - SG - ED
SDF - Diesel - Single Clutch - SJ - ES
SDM - Diesel - Double Clutch - SJ - ED
VFD - Diesel Vine Single Clutch - SJ - ES
JDF - Diesel Ind. Single Clutch - SJ - ES
JDM - Diesel Ind. Double Clutch - SJ - ED
SLF - L.O. - Single Clutch - SH - ES
SLM - L.O. - Double Clutch - SH - ED
VLF - L.O. Vine - Double Clutch - SH - ES
JLF - L.O. Ind. - Single Clutch - SH - ES
JLM - L.O. Ind. - Double Clutch - SH - ED
SBF - Butane - Single Clutch -
SBM - Butane - Double Clutch -
1956 - 1001 to 9225
1957 - 9226 to 79552
1958 - 79553 to 125067
1959 - 125068 to 171470
1960 - 171471 to
1961 -

All French produced tractors — serial number system

(Reproduction of an MF Service Bulletin 15th April 1974)

French produced tractors are numbered systematically as follows:

The first group of letters show the type of tractor and year of manufacture.

A letter indicating the tractor sub-type:
  S — Normal Width
  E — Narrow
  V — Vineyard
  C — High Clearance
  R — 4 Wheel Drive, Normal Clearance

A letter indicating the type of transmission:
  W — Multi-Power without facility for Hydraulic Operation of Trailer Brakes
  F — 4 Wheel Drive, 8 Speed Gearbox with facility for Hydraulic Operation of Trailer Brakes
  T — 4 Wheel Drive, Multi-Power Tractor with facility for Hydraulic Operation of Trailer Brakes

A letter indicating that special tyres have been fitted:
  L or M — For Rear Tyres
  B — For Front Tyres

A letter showing the manufacturing year: This commences on 1st September. (For example, code letters M for 1974 will first be used on 1st September 1973).

B	— 1971	W	— 1976
R	— 1972	G	— 1977
C	— 1973	H	— 1978
M	— 1974	Z	— 1979
E	— 1975	A	— 1980

The three figures immediately following the letter notation indicate the day of manufacture in the year beginning with the first working day in September. The first number will be '101'.

All French produced tractors — serial number system

(Reproduction of an MF Service Bulletin 30th October 1980)

French produced tractors are numbered as follows:

The first group of numbers show the tractor model followed by a figure '8' — denoting French manufacture and then one or two letters denoting type, as follows:
  S — Normal Width
  E — Narrow
  V — Vineyard
  R — 4 Wheel Drive,
and
a letter indicating the type of transmission:
  W — Multi-Power without facility for hydraulic operation of trailer brakes
  F — 4 Wheel Drive, 8 speed gearbox with facility for hydraulic operation of trailer brakes
  T — 4 Wheel Drive, Multi-Power, with facility for hydraulic operation of trailer brakes

NOTE: No letter is used where basic transmission is fitted, e.g. 8 speed.

The second line shows the year of manufacture and day of build.
  A letter indicating the year of manufacture:
  NOTE: The French Company's fiscal year commences on the 1st September of the preceding year until the following August 31st.

J	— 1981	L	— 1986
S	— 1982	U	— 1987
B	— 1983	V	— 1988
K	— 1984	N	— 1989
T	— 1985		

(Example — Code Letter 'S' for 1982 will first be used for tractors built on the 1st September, 1981)

The three figures immediately following the letter notation, indicate the day of manufacture in the year, beginning with the first *working* day in September. The first number will be 101.

The next set of three figures show (independent of tractor model) the order in which that tractor was manufactured on the working day indicated.

The third line shows the engine serial number.

Example — An MF595 2 wheel drive, normal width tractor, with a Multi-Power transmission, leaving the assembly line first on the 5th September, 1980, will be stamped on the serial number plate as follows:

Top Line	595 8SW
Centre Line	J 105001
Bottom Line	F 00000 G

MF tractor serial number effective points starting 1982

Model	Year							
	1982	1983	1984	1985	1986	1987	1988	1989
UK								
240		524172	552016	557882	562369	V01001	N01001	P01001
250		621838	624021	627250	629926			
253							N01001	P01001
270		286152	287179	288016	288425			
283				393474	723784			
290		386453	389947	393422	723909			
298		702586	703062	703760	704095			
360					U01001	V01001	N01001	P01001
375					U01001	V01001	N01001	P01001
383					U01001			
390					U01001	V01001	N01001	P01001
390T								P01001
398					U01001	V01001	N01001	P01001
399					U01001	V01001	N01001	P01001
MEXICO								
282S	KC24457S	KD26466S						
282H	KC25226H	KD25218H						
BRAZIL								
283						00001	00102	01202
POLAND								
231								P17001
ITALY								
254-4	2229282	2229927	22210485	222M01750	22202733	22203556		
274-4	22111297	22112162	22112828	221N02384	22103628	22104826		
294-4	2235938	2236290	2236511	223D00915	22301652	22302505		
154S-2					13300288	133A00489	133C00645	133C00791
154S-4					23300755	233A01012	233C01304	233C01511
174S-2					13200653	132A00912	132C01178	132C01413
174S-4					23201344	232A01754	232C02271	232C02679
194S-2								141D00136
194S-4								241D00393
194F-2					14000014	140D00024	140D00037	140D00062
194F-4					24000129	240D00382	240D00925	240D01456
364S								P01001
374S								P01001
384S								P01001
394S								P01001
FRANCE								
670		B207021 K183027	T101001	L101001	U031001			
690		B197022 K181026	T101001	L101001	U031001			
698		B201031 K186009	T101001	L101001	U031001			
699			T101001	L101001	U031001			
2640	S276213	B160217 K181026						
3505		K241203	T101201	L101201	U031201			
3525		K241213	T101201	L101201	U031201			
3545		K242206	T101201	L101201	U031201			
3050					U031001	V001001	N001001	P001001
3060					U031001	V001001	N001001	P001001

Model	Year							
	1982	1983	1984	1985	1986	1987	1988	1989
3070					U031001	V001001	N001001	P001001
3090					U031001	V001001	N001001	P001001
3505						V001201		
3525						V001201		
3545						V001201		
3630						V001001	N001001	P001001
3650						V001001	N001001	P001001
3680							N293001	P001001

JAPAN

Model	1982	1983	1984	1985	1986	1987	1988	1989
1010-2	00101	00613	10901	11727	12471	13902	14433	14549
1010-4	40101	40607	40809	41491	42317	43683	44498	44696
1010H-2						13953	14455	14549
1010H-4						43640	44370	44696
1020-2		00101	00411	00809	01548	02394	02707	02768
1020-4		40101	40395	40549	41002	41787	42273	42532
1020H-2						02319	02707	02768
1020H-4						41709	42343	42641
1030-2			00101	00820	01501			
1030-4			40101	40600	41245			
1030L-2					02067	02542	03139	03285
1030L-4					41713	42167	42594	42953
1035-2					00100	00315		00540
1035-4					40100	40377	40691	40936
1040-2			00101	00155	00552			
1040-4			40101	40351	40562			
1045-2					00100	00234		00334
1045-4					40100	40275	40566	40757

Source: D. Gentner

All French-produced tractors serial number letter change indicating year of manufacturer

(Reproduction of an MF circular 2nd May 1983)

The French fiscal year ran from 1st September of the previous year until 31st August of the current year.

Example:
1st September 1981 to 31st August 1982 was the 1982 fiscal year.

However, from 1983 the MF fiscal year changed to 1 February to the following 31st January.

TRACTORS
In the case of *tractors* where will be two fiscal year periods for 1983.

The first period, from 1st September 1982 until 31 January 1983, is denoted by the prefix letter 'B' in the serial number. The second period, from 1st February 1983 until 31st January 1984, will have the prefix letter 'K', starting with serial number K101001.

From thereon the prefix letter denoting the year of manufacture will be:

T — 1984		V — 1987	
L — 1985		N — 1988	
U — 1986			

Tractor serial numbers (French production) letter changes indicating year of manufacture

(From an MF circular 19th September 1984)

The chart below gives the manufacturing period and year identification letter for French produced tractors since 1971:

Fiscal Year	Year Letter	Manufacturing Period
1971	B	Sept 1970 – Aug 1971
1972	R	Sept 1971 – Aug 1972
1973	C	Sept 1972 – Aug 1973
1974	M	Sept 1973 – Aug 1974
1975	E	Sept 1974 – Aug 1975
1976	W	Sept 1975 – Aug 1976
1977	G	Sept 1976 – Aug 1977
1978	H	Sept 1977 – Aug 1978
1979	Z	Sept 1978 – Aug 1979
1980	A	Sept 1979 – Aug 1980
1981	J	Sept 1980 – Aug 1981
1982	S	Sept 1981 – Aug 1982
1983	B	Sept 1982 – Jan 1983
1983	K	Feb 1983 – Jan 1984
1984	T	Feb 1984 – Jan 1985
1985	L	Feb 1985 – Jan 1986
1986	U	Feb 1986 – Jan 1987
1987	V	Feb 1987 – Jan 1988
1988	N	Feb 1988 – Jan 1989

The letter prefix to the serial number indicates the MF fiscal year of manufacture which runs from the 1st September of the previous year until 31st July of the current year until 1983.

From 1983 the fiscal year changed to 1st February to the following 31st January, see year letters B and K in the chart.

The three figures immediately following the letter notation indicate the day of manufacture in the year beginning with the first working day in September or February. The first number will be 101, excluding the first 4 weeks holiday in August, Christmas, weekends and public holidays (8 days).

The next set of three figures show tractor type and the order in which the tractor was manufactured on the day indicated. For example:

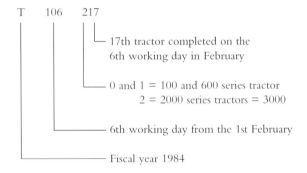

T   106   217

— 17th tractor completed on the 6th working day in February

— 0 and 1 = 100 and 600 series tractor
2 = 2000 series tractors = 3000

— 6th working day from the 1st February

— Fiscal year 1984

MF tractor serial numbers — UK production

(From an MF circular Novermber 1986)

Below is a summary of the serial number ranges of FM tractors for each M-F fiscal year from 1982 to 1985.

It is emphasised that, in this connection, the fiscal year used to run from the 1st November of the previous year to the 31st October of the current year.

However, from 1983, the MF fiscal year changed to start on the 1st February 1983 to the 31st January 1984. Therefore, there was a short period — 1st November 1982 to the 31st January 1983 — which is known as '1983 OLD fiscal year', and a full 12 month period — 1st February 1983 to the 31st January 1984 — which is known as '1983 NEW fiscal year'.

From the 1st February 1983, each fiscal year runs from 1st February each year to the following 31st January.

NB: For details of serial numbers of machines produced in France, please see Service Bulletin ADMIN 28-84.

SERIAL NUMBER OF FIRST TRACTOR OF MANUFACTURE

	1 November – 31 October	1 Nov – 31 Jan	1 February – 31 January			
TRACTOR MODEL	1982	1983 'OLD'	1983 'NEW'	1984	1985	1986
M-F 230	535001	535203	535241	535732	535955	536372
M-F 240	518907	524430	525615	552418	557882	562958
M-F 250	621006	621838	622117	624124	627250	630214
M-F 265	190605	194215	194988	198504	201631	204294
M-F 270	—	—	286256	287197	288017	288425
M-F 275	220683	221468	221539	222522	223408	224547
M-F 283	—	—	—	—	393474	724294★★
M-F 290	383320	386423	387058	390237	393422	724393★★
M-F 298	—	—	—	703129	703760	704169
M-F 550★	620722	—	—	—	—	—
M-F 565★	659159	—	—	—	—	—
M-F 575★	271595	—	—	—	—	—
M-F 590★	382238	—	—	—	—	—
M-F 675★	720001	720919	721408	—	—	—
M-F 690★	700001	701365	701958	—	—	—
M-F 1250★	903257	—	—	—	—	—

Certain of the above models are limited to certain special markets and are shown for record purposes only.

★ On the following models, UK production finished at the following serial numbers:
M-F 550 – 620767   M-F 575 – 271630   M-F 675 – 721914   M-F 1250 – 903322   M-F 565 – 659189   M-F 590 – 382396   M-F 690 – 702585
M-F 283/290 Tractors used serial numbers up to 400064, and then continued from serial number 721915 onwards

Tractor serial numbers (French production) M-F 3000 & MF 3600 series tractors, M-F 3500 & M-F 600 series tractors, M-F 2640 tractors

(From an MF circular 30th September 1988)

Dealer Service Bulletin 84-35, dated November 12, 1984, described the serial number system format.

Several changes to the numbering system and dealer questions indicate the need for further explanation.

All French built tractors use an alphabetical letter prefix (denoted by "A") and a six digit number (denoted by "#") format to define the full tractor serial number:

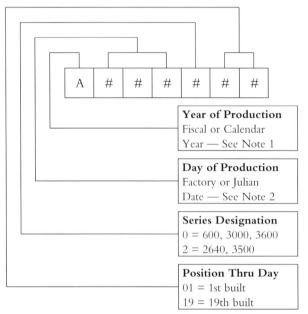

Year of Production
Fiscal or Calendar
Year — See Note 1

Day of Production
Factory or Julian
Date — See Note 2

Series Designation
0 = 600, 3000, 3600
2 = 2640, 3500

Position Thru Day
01 = 1st built
19 = 19th built

Year of Production Chart

Fiscal or Production Year	Year Alpha Letter	Manufacturing Period
1982	S	Sept 1981 – Aug 1982
1983	B	Sept 1982 – Jan 1983
1983	K	Feb 1983 – Jan 1984
1984	T	Feb 1984 – Jan 1985
1985	L	Feb 1985 – Jan 1986
1986	U	Feb 1986 – Dec 1986
1987	V	Jan 1987 – Dec 1987
1988	N	Jan 1988 – Dec 1988
1989	P	Jan 1989 – Dec 1989
1990	Q	Jan 1990 – Dec 1990

Note 1:
M-F Fiscal Year used from 1982 thru 1985. M-F Fiscal Year was September thru August, but changed to February thru January in 1983. See year letters B and K.

Starting February 1986, calendar year used.

Day of Production

Note 2:

Factory Day — The manufacture day in the year beginning with the first working day in September or February. The first number used is 101, excluding weekends or French holidays.

— Used from 1982 thru January 1986.

Julian Day — Actual calendar day. (January 1 is 001, February 1 is 032).

— Used from February 1986 onwards

Series Designation

0 = M-F 600   Series (670, 690, 698, 699)
0 = M-F 3000 Series (3050, 3060, 3070, 3090)
0 = M-F 3600 Series (3630, 3650, 3680)
2 = M-F 3500 Series (3505, 3525, 3545)
2 = M-F 2640

Position Thru Day

01 = First unit built during a day
02 = Second unit produced during the day
|
16 = Sixteenth unit produced during the day

Examples

1. M-F 3650 with serial number **N031002** translates to:
   - year of production was 1988
   - day of production was January 31 (thirty-first day)
   - 3600 series model
   - second tractor off the assembly line that day

2. M-F 3090 with serial number **V062016** translates to:
   - year of production was 1987
   - day of production was March 3 (sixty-second day)
   - 3000 series model
   - sixteenth tractor off the assembly line that day

3. M-F 3545 with serial number **L200201** translates to:
   - year of production was 1985
   - approximate day of production was mid June because:
       200 is the 100th factory work day from February 1
       100 divided by 5 work days per week equals 20 weeks
       20 weeks from February 1 is mid June
   - 3500 series model
   - first tractor off the assembly line that day

M-F 300/253/240 series tractors serial numbers identification

(From an MF circular September 30th 1988)

All M-F 300/253/240 series tractors are stamped with an alphabetical letter prefix, and followed with a five digit number sequence (example N 01001).

Also located on the s/n plate *before* the stamped serial number, will be the tractor model, (MF---), followed by the particular tractors base code (four numbers).

As an example:

MF360	= Model
5221	= Machine base code
N01001	= Complete serial number

The N indicated the fiscal year of build (1988).

The 01 would equal the week number of build within the fiscal year (1st week of February).

The 001 would indicate the number, in sequence of tractors built within the particular fiscal build week (1st tractor built in this build week).

Another example:
S/N V23264
V = 1987 fiscal 1987
23 = 23rd week of production
264 = 264th tractor build during that (23) week

Year of Production Chart

Fiscal Production Year	Year Alpha Letter	Manufacturing Period
1986	U	Feb 1986 – Jan 1987
1987	V	Feb 1987 – Jan 1988
1988	N	Feb 1988 – Jan 1989
1989	P	Feb 1989 – Jan 1990
1990	Q	Feb 1990 – Jan 1991

M-F 200/300/3000/3100/3600 series tractors — tractor serial numbers March 1991

M-F 200/300 Series Tractors	– UK Produced
M-F 231 Tractors	– Poland Produced
M-F 300 Series Tractors	– Italy Produced

The above tractors use an **ALPHA LETTER** plus a **5 DIGIT NUMBER** to form the **complete 6 character serial number.**

Serial numbers of this format breakdown as follows:
- the **ALPHA LETTER** defines the year of production.
- the **first 2 numeric characters** define the week of production.
- the **last 3 numeric characters** define the sequence of the tractor built during the week.

Example

The serial number "S04056" is defined as:
- "**S**" defines the year of production. In this case, "**S**" stands for production year **1991**. Refer to the Year of Production chart for **ALPHA LETTER** cross reference.
- "**04**" defines the 4th week of the calendar year or the **4th week of January 1991.**
- "**056**" defines the unit as the **56th** unit built that week.

M-F 3000/3100/3600 Series

Tractors	– France Produced

The above tractors use an **ALPHA LETTER** plus a **6 DIGIT NUMBER** to form the **complete 7 character serial number.**

Serial numbers of this format breakdown as follows:
- the **ALPHA LETTER** defines the year of production.
- the **first 3 numeric characters** define the calendar day of production.
- the **4th numeric character** defines the series designation. All M-F 3000/3100/3600 use "0" as the series designation.
- the **last 2 numeric characters** define the sequence of the tractor built during the day.

Example

The serial number "S031027" is defined as:
- "**S**" defines the year of production. In this case, "**S**" stands for production year **1991**. Refer to the Year of Production chart for **ALPHA LETTER** cross reference.
- "**031**" defines the 31st day of the calendar year or in this case **January 31, 1991.**
- "**0**" defines the series designation — M-F 3000/3100 /3600
- "**027**" defines the unit as the **27th** unit built that day (January 31, 1991).

M-F 200/300 Series Tractors	– UK Produced
M-F 231 Tractors	– Poland Produced
M-F 300 Series Tractors	– Italy Produced
M-F 3000/3100/3600 Series Tractors	– France Produced

Year of Production Chart

Production Year	Alpha Letter
1986	U
1987	V
1988	N
1989	P
1990	R
1991	S
1992	C
1993	D
1994	F
1995	M
1996	G
1997	H

Note 1:

On some early produced models, years of productions were based on M-F's fiscal year instead of the calendar year. Refer to DSB's TR 88-69, TR 88-70 and TR 84-35 for a fuller explanation.

Note 2:

DSB's TR 88-69 and TR 88-70 indicate **"Q" was to be used for production year 1990.** "Q" was not used, except for 6 weeks of production of the M-F 231 tractor. All other tractor models series and the remaining production of the M-F 231 used **"R".**

Examples

Example 1

MF 240 Tractor with serial number S10235

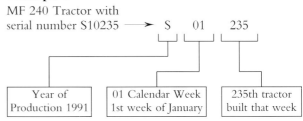

| Year of Production 1991 | 01 Calendar Week 1st week of January | 235th tractor built that week |

Example 2

MF 3140 Tractor with serial number S245018

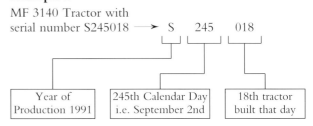

| Year of Production 1991 | 245th Calendar Day i.e. September 2nd | 18th tractor built that day |

Tractor serial numbers — year of builds
MF 231 tractors
MF 200/300 series UK tractors
MF 300 series Italian tractors
MF 3000/3100/3600 series tractors

Production Year	Alpha Letter
1986	U
1987	**V**
1988	N
1989	**P**
1990	R
1991	**S**
1992	A
1993	**B**
1994	C
1995	**D**
1996	E
1997	**F**

The above MF Series Tractors use an **ALPHABETIC LETTER** and a **5 or 6 DIGIT NUMBER** to form the **SERIAL NUMBER.**

- The **ALPHABETIC LETTER** of the serial number, for all above tractors, defines the **year of production.**
- The **first 2 DIGITS** of the **MF 200/300** Series Tractor serial number, defines the **calendar week** of production.
- The **first 3 DIGITS** of the **MF 3000/3100/3600** Series Tractors, defines the **calendar day** of production.
- The last **3 DIGITS** of the serial number, for all above tractors, defines the **sequence of the tractor built** during the build period (calendar week or calendar day).

Year of Production Chart

Production Year	Alpha Letter
1986	U
1987	V
1988	N
1989	P
1990	R
1991	**S**
1992	A
1993	B
1994	C
1995	D
1996	E
1997	F

Note 1: On some early produced models, years of productions were based on MF's fiscal year instead of the calendar year. Refer to DSB's TR 88-69, TR 88-70 and TR 84-35 for a fuller explanation.

Note 2: DSB's TR 88-69 and TR 88-70 indicate **"Q" was to used for production year 1990. "Q"** was not used, except for 6 weeks of production of the MF 231 tractor. All other tractor models series and the remaining production of the MF 231 used **"R".**

North American MF tractor plant month end serial no. production

Month	Year	"A" Line	"B" Line	"C" Line
Nov.	66	9A10001 to 9A13089	9B10001 to 9B10458	
Dec.	66	9A15325	9B10745	
Jan.	67	9A18128	9B11167	
Feb.	67	9A19489	9B11402	
March	67	9A21345	9B11713	
April	67	9A24621	9B12290	
May	67	9A28060	9B12924	
June	67	9A31394	9B13460	
July	67	9A34171	9B13832	
August	67	9A34885	9B13938	
Sept.	67	9A36897	9B14239	
Oct.	67	9A39835	9B14692	
Nov.	67	9A42288	9B15106	
Dec.	67	9A44628	9B15559	
Jan.	68	9A47148	9B16063	
Feb.	68	9A49256	9B16468	
March	68	9A50244	9B16656	
April	68	9A51609	9B16915	
May	68	9A54571	9B17455	
June	68	9A54571	9B17455	
July	68	9A56755	9B17880	
August	68	9A58217	9B18166	
Sept.	68	9A60705	9B18477	
Oct.	68	9A63157	9B18672	
Nov.	68	9A64636	9B18921	
Dec.	68	9A66316	9B19189	
Jan.	69	9A68112	9B19422	
Feb.	69	9A69227	9B19548	
March	69	9A71361	9B19741	
April	69	9A73680	9B20098	
May	69	9A76050	9B20631	
June	69	9A78407	9B21193	
July	69	9A81040	9B21873	
August	69	9A82427	9B22222	
Sept.	69	9A84472	9B22739	
Oct.	69	9A87324	9B23485	
Nov.	69	9A88323	9B23742	
Dec.	69	9A90221	9B24269	
Jan.	70	9A92301	9B24796	
Feb.	70	9A93869	9B25397	
March	70	9A96089	9B25883	
April	70	9A97915	9B26431	
May	70	9A99666	9B26632	
June	70	9A101826	9B27170	
July	70	9A104137	9B27591	
August	70	9A104828	9B27709	
Sept.	70	9A106559	9B28040	9C001001 & 9001002
Oct.	70	9A107518	9B28226	9C001006
Nov.	70	9A109576	9B28623	9C001006
Dec.	70	9A111625	9B29018	9C001059
Jan.	71	9A113805	9B29467	9C001142
Feb.	71	9A115717	9B29857	9C001280
March	71	9A116428	9B29996	9C001367
April	71	9A116428	9B29996	9C001367
May	71	9A116428	9B29996	9C001367

Month	Year	"A" Line	"B" Line	"C" Line
June	71	9A117426	9B30204	9C001431
July	71	9A120724	9B30853	9C001677
August	71	9A122995	9B31223	9C001735
Sept.	71	9A125538	9B31564	9C001804
Oct.	71	9A128140	9B31957	9C001911
Nov.	71	9A130706	9B32106	9C001951
Dec.	71	9A131907	9B32420	9C002033
Jan.	72	9A134096	9B32939	9C002108
Feb.	72	9A136375	9B33460	9C002128
March	72	9A138237	9B34009	9C002201
April	72	9A139539	9B34512	9C002262
May	72	9A141571	9B35198	9C002299
June	72	9A143701	9B35809	9C002355
July	72	9A146114	9B36445	9C002355
August	72	9A146591	9B36562	9C002355
Sept.	72	9A149008	9B36569	9C002373
Oct.	72	9A152024	9B36840	9C002463
Nov.	72	9A152444	9B36840	9C002463
Dec.	72	9A154503	9B37149	9C002463
Jan.	73	9A157400	9B37761	9C002463
Feb.	73	9A160148	9B38411	9C002466
March	73	9A162515	9B39107	9C002560
April	73	9A165255	9B39712	9C002611
May	73	9A168264	9B40318	9C002714
June	73	9A171075	9B40829	9C002805
July	73	9A171312	9B40872	9C002810
August	73	9A174376	9B41487	9C002880
Sept.	73	9A176652	9B41957	9C002931
Oct.	73	9A179543	9B42685	9C003024
Nov.	73	9A181521	9B43115	9C003101
Dec.	73	9A182760	9B43431	9C003183
Jan.	74	9A184962	9B44003	9C003285
Feb.	74	9A187035	9B44460	9C003329
March	74	9A189117	9B44973	9C003425
April	74	9A191824	9B45611	9C003510
May	74	9A194496	9B46277	9C003594
June	74	9A197048	9B46899	9C003623
July	74	9A199651	9B47556	9C003719
August	74	9A200483	9B47780	9C003779
Sept.	74	9A202578	9B48412	9C003887
Oct.	74	9A205691	9B49352	9C004056
Nov.	74	9A206620	9B50004	9C004174
Dec.	74	9A207680	9B50493	9C004226
Jan.	75	9A210066	9B51303	9C004355
Feb.	75	9A212637	9B52058	9C004465
March	75	9A214469	9B52876	Production Complete
April	75	9A217136	9B53729	Production Complete
May	75	9A219850	9B54523	Production Complete
June	75	9A221956	9B55361	Production Complete
July	75	9A224219	9B56239	Production Complete
Sept.	75	9A226334	9B56893	Production Complete
Oct.	75	9A229222	9B57729	Production Complete
Nov.	75	9A230263	9B58065	Production Complete
Dec.	75	9A232538	9B58734	Production Complete
Jan.	76	9A234902	9B59508	Production Complete
Feb.	76	9A237569	9B60345	Production Complete
March	76	9A240658	9B61263	Production Complete
April	76	9A243379	9B62122	Production Complete
May	76	9A245285	9B62992	Production Complete
June	76	9A248008	9B63926	Production Complete

Month	Year	"A" Line	"B" Line	"C" Line
				"R" Line
July	76	9A250639	9B64845	9R000013
August	76	9A250639	9B64845	9R000023
Sept.	76	9A252280	9B65436	9R000023
Oct.	76	9A254044	9B66275	9R000047
Nov.	76	9A256170	9B67103	9R000076
Dec.	76	9A257836	9B67771	9R000091
Jan.	77	9A259851	9B68547	9R000147
Feb.	77	9A261780	9B69282	9R000195
March	77	9A262204	9B70140	9R000217
April	77	9A265632	9B70863	9R000281
May	77	9A267053	9B71612	9R000359
June	77	9A269822	9B72512	9R000415
July	77	9A272299	9B73269	9R000462
August	77	9A272299	9B73269	9R000462
Sept.	77	9A274044	9B73580	9R000503
Oct.	77	9A276934	9B74240	9R000601
Nov.	77	9A279103	9B74943	9R000680
Dec.	77	9A280300	9B75181	9R000733
Jan.	78	9A281781	9B75291	9R000790
Feb.	78	9A283927	9B75508	9R000878
March	78	9A286350	9B75697	9R001050
April	78	9A287471	9B75697	9R001050
May	78	9A289717	9B75845	9R001280
June	78	9A292088	9B75960	9R001601
July	78	9A293660	9B76032	9R001826
August	78	9A294104	9B76058	9R001932
			(B-Line program complete)	
Sept.	78	9A295951		9R002420

Month	Year	"A" Line	"R" Line	4-W.D.	MF 60	"B" Line MF 285 Cab
Oct.	79	9A323744	9R006752	9D001840	9E100698	
Nov.	79	9A324352	9R006889	9D001968	9E100700	
Dec.	79	9A326168	9R007281	9D002101	9E100700	
Jan.	80	9A328824	9R007830	9D002259	9E100758	
Feb.	80	9A330136	9R008118	9D002323	9E100783	
March	80	9A332668	9R008621	9D002496	9E100855	
April	80	9A335188	9R009113	9D002637	9E100915	
May	80	9A335429	9R009157	9D002637	9E100915	
June	80	9A337038	9R009715	9D002692	9E100915	
July	80	9A339343	9R010307	9D002752	9E100961	
August	80	9A339343	9R010307	9D002752	9E100961	
Sept.	80	9A339343	9R010307	9D002752	9E100961	
Oct.	80	9A339343	9R010307	9D002752	9E100961	
Nov.	80	9A339343	9R010307	9D002752	9E100961	
Dec.	80	9A339343	9R010307	9D002752	9E100961	
Jan.	81	9A339343	9R010307	9D002752	9E100961	
Feb.	81	9A339343	9R010307	9D002828	9E100961	
March	81	9A341063	9R010705	9D002928	9E100961	
April	81	9A342762	9R011133	9D003022	9E100961	
May	81	9A344026	9R011537	9D003136	9E100961	
June	81	9A345414	9R011982	9D003280	9E100961	
July	81	9A346792	9R012388	9D003400	9E100961	
August	81	9A346792	9R012388	9D003452	9E100961	
Sept.	81	9A347948	9R012629	9D003452	9E100998	9B076241
Oct.	81	9A349122	9R012862	9D003452	9E101039	9B076336
Nov.	81	9A349469	9R012960	9D003459	9E101047	9B076342
Dec.	81	9A350583	9R013229	9D003514	9E101072	9B076360
Jan.	82	9A351537	9R013461	9D003583	9E101098	9B076445
Feb.	82	9A352762	9R013525	9D003668	9E101116	9B076462
March	82	9A353805	9R013525	9D003776	9E101117	9B076462
April	82	9A354679	9R013525	9D003869	9E101117	9B076462
May	82	9A354679	9R013525	9D003897	9E101117	9B076462
June	82					
July	82					
August	82					
Sept.	82					
Oct.	82					
Nov.	82					
Dec.	82					
Jan.	83					
Feb.	83					
March	83					
April	83					

4-WHEEL DRIVE

Month	Year			Month	Year	
Feb.	75	9C 4901				
March	75	9C 4993		July	76	9C 6793
April	75	9C 5107		Sept.	76	9C 6968
May	75	9C 5217		Oct.	76	9C 7058
June	75	9C 5352		Nov.	76	9C 7103
July	75	9C 5478		Dec.	76	9C 7211
Sept.	75	9C 5651		Jan.	77	9C 7251
Oct.	75	9C 5809		Feb.	77	9C 7277
Nov.	75	9C 5901		March	77	9C 7441
Dec.	75	9C 6100 Est.		April	77	9C 7535
Jan.	76	9C 6202		May	77	9C 7614
Feb.	76	9C 6325		June	77	9C 7709
March	76	9C 6492		Sept.	77	9C 7763
April	76	9C 6570 Est.		Oct.	77	9C 7858 Last
May	76	9C 6632		Tractor		
June	76	9C 6700 Est.		Source: D. Gentner		

Agricultural tractor manufacture, Banner Lane, Coventry 1964 – 1993

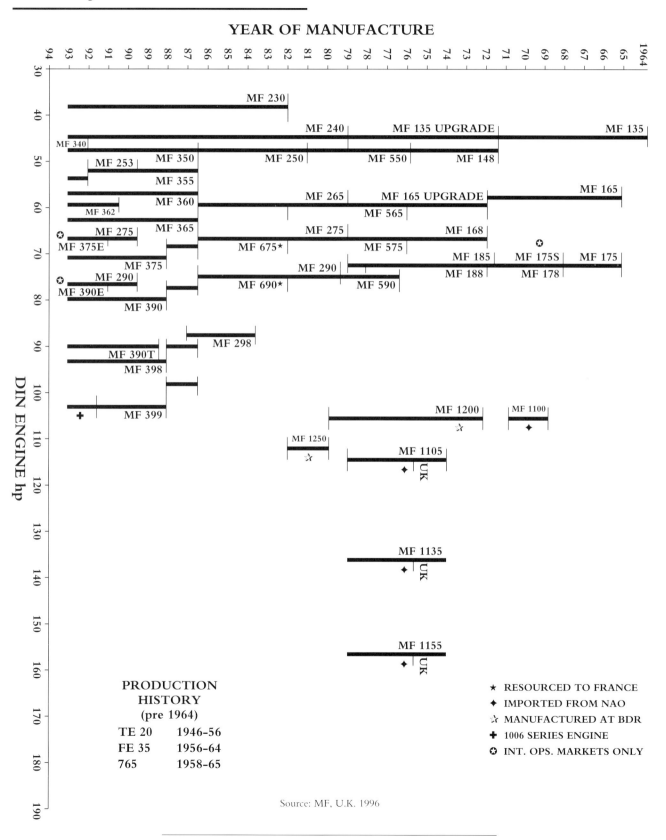

YEAR OF MANUFACTURE

DIN ENGINE hp

MF 230
MF 240 | MF 135 UPGRADE | MF 135
MF 340
MF 253 | MF 350 | MF 250 | MF 550 | MF 148
MF 355
MF 360 | MF 265 | MF 165 UPGRADE | MF 165
MF 362 | MF 565
MF 275 | MF 365 | MF 275 | MF 168
MF 375E | MF 675★ | MF 575 | MF 185 | MF 175S | MF 175
MF 375 | MF 290 | MF 188 | MF 178
MF 290 | MF 690★ | MF 590
MF 390E
MF 390
MF 298
MF 390T
MF 398
MF 399 | MF 1200 | MF 1100
MF 1250 | MF 1105 UK
MF 1135 UK
MF 1155 UK

PRODUCTION
HISTORY
(pre 1964)

TE 20	1946–56
FE 35	1956–64
765	1958–65

★ RESOURCED TO FRANCE
✦ IMPORTED FROM NAO
☆ MANUFACTURED AT BDR
✛ 1006 SERIES ENGINE
✪ INT. OPS. MARKETS ONLY

Source: MF, U.K. 1996

Agricultural tractor manufacture, Beauvais, France 1960 – 1993

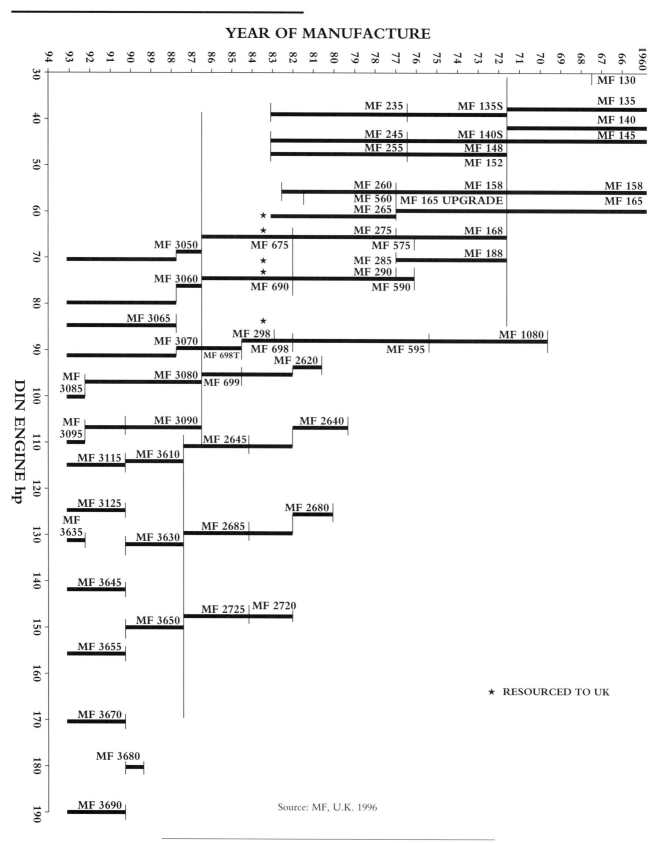

YEAR OF MANUFACTURE

DIN ENGINE hp

★ RESOURCED TO UK

Source: MF, U.K. 1996

Further Reading

Condie, Alan T., *Massey Ferguson 1958–82* (A.T. Condie Publications, 1995)
Cook, Peter, *Massey at the Brink* (Collins, 1981)
Denison Merril, *Harvest Triumphant* (The Falcon Press Ltd., 1949)
Farnworth, John, *Ferguson Implements and Accessories* (Farming Press, 1996)
Harry Ferguson and I (Massey Ferguson Tractors Ltd., 1993)
King, Alan C., Massey-Harris. An Advertising History (Independent Print Shop Co., 1988)
King, Alan C., *Massey-Harris Data Book No. 6* (Independent Print Shop Co. 1992)
Neufield, E.P., *A Global Corporation* (University of Toronto Press, 1969)
Wendall, C.H., *Massey Tractors* (Motorbooks International, 1992)
Williams, Michael, *Massey-Ferguson Tractors* (Farming Press, 1987)

ORGANISATIONS

The U.K. club, Friends of Ferguson Heritage Ltd. at PO Box 62, Banner Lane, Coventry, U.K. specialises in Ferguson, Massey-Harris and related makes. It publishes three *Ferguson Heritage* magazines per year.

Also in the U.K., the Ferguson Club specialises in Ferguson tractors and equipment and can be contacted via The Secretary, 21 Greytown Avenue, Upper Malone Road, Belfast, BT9 6UG, Northern Ireland, U.K.

The magazine *Wild Harvest Massey Collectors News* is published in the U.S.A bi-monthly, and can be contacted via The Editor, PO Box 529, Denver, Iowa, 50622, U.S.A.

Index

Numbers in bold indicate illustrations

A

Acquisitions
    AGCO – Deutz-Argentina, 1997, 254
    AGCO – Fendt, 1997, 254
    Case Corp. – FERMEC, 1996, 132
    Case Corp. – MF Industrials from FERMEC, 1992, 253
    FERMEC – Massey Ferguson Industrials, 1992, 132
    MF – Hanomag Co., 1974, 154
    M-H – Deyo-Macey Co., 1913, 213
    M-H-F – Midwestern Industries Inc., 1957, 141
AGCO Corporation, 253, 254
Aircraft parts, **172**
Ambulances, **173**
Anantharamkrishnan, Shri S., 250
Art Woodwork Co., 194
Autotronic MF control system, 243

B

Backhoe loaders
    MF 1996 range specifications, 161
    MF 860, **160**
    MF range 1965, **150–1**
Backhoes
    MF 1217 Quick–Attach, **201**
Badges
    cast iron machinery, **227**
    lapel, **230**
Bain Wagon Co., 42–3
    Boer War wagons, **169**
    First World War wagons, 170
    sleigh products, **187**
Baldwin loader, **9, 138**
Bale handlers, 109–111
    MF 21 thrower, **110**
    MF 22 thrower, **111**
    MF 512, **110**
    MF hay, **109**
    MF No. 6 thrower, **111**
Balers
    M-F 1970, 291
    MF 5 large square, **107**

MF 12, **107**
MF 35, **58**
MF 124 and **126, 107**
MF 130SB series, **256**
MF 146, **108**
MF 190, **108**
MF 560 giant round, **107**
MF 822 and 828, **107**
MF high and low density, **106**
MF round, specifications, 108
Balers – stationary, 33
Bank notes, **226**
Barn machinery, 1–8
Beach cleaner, **210**
Bean harvesting, 130
Bicycles, **180**
Binders, 54–8
    Harris Brantford No. 2, **54**
    M-H corn, **57**
    M-H No. 6, **56**
    M-H No.16, **56**
    M-H 701, 108
    M-H oxen pulled, **55–6**
    M-H pto drive, **58**
    M-H push type, **56**
    M-H Sunshine 6B, **57**
    M-H tractor drawn, **57**
    Massey Low Down, **54**
    Massey Toronto, **55**
    Patterson light steel, **54**
Blackstone & Co.
    elevators, **10–11**
    engines, **223**
    hay-making machinery, **52**
    potato diggers, **123**
    roller mill, **3**
    root cutter, **7**
Buck rakes
    M-H 723, **120**
Bulldozers
    MF 3366, **152**
Butter churns, **181**

C

Carroll, Tom, 65, 103
Cellular Manufacturing, **244**
Clocks, **227**

Columbia Bicycle Co., 180
Combines
    Ferguson, **77–84**
    'Harvest Brigade,' 176–8
    MF 32, **81**
    MF 35, **81**
    MF 35 pto drive, **79**
    MF 35 trailed, **79**
    MF 39 rice, **82**
    MF 72, **79**
    MF 205 and 222 corn header, **81**
    MF 206, **83**
    MF 300 and 321 corn header, **81**
    MF 410–510, **82**
    MF 515, **82**
    MF 585 Sunshine, **79**
    MF 760, **82**
    MF 892 rice, **79**
    MF 3342, **82**
    MF 8000 series, **84**
    MF maize, **88**
    MF No 1. Whole Crop, **102**
    MF Pickups, **83**
    MF production 1955-66, 276–7
    MF Quick-Attach tables, **125**
    MF rotary recleaner attachment, **83**
    MF specifications, 80
    M-F products 1970, 291
    M-H 9A–9B, **67–8**
    M-H 60 self-propelled, **74**
    M-H 80, **74**
    M-H 82, **74**
    M-H 90 specials, **75**
    M-H 92 hillside, **76**
    M-H 685, **76**
    M-H 722, 71
    M-H 726, **72–3**
    M-H 890, **74**
    M-H Clipper, **70–1**
    M-H Model 22, **71**
    M-H No.16 pto drive, **69**
    M-H No. 20, **69**
    M-H No. 21, **69**
    M-H No. 21A, **69**
    M-H No. 60 pto drive, **73**
    M-H production 1946–54, 268
    M-H self-propelled, **73**
    M-H specifications, 66, 78
    M-H Sunshine 585, **76**

M-H Sunshine No. 4 header, **76**
M-H Sunshine Ferguson 1948–55,
	Serial nos. data tables, 303–60
Sunshine M-H Power drive
	harvester, **71**
Wallis centrifugal, **67**
Communications equipment, 175
Compact tractors
	garden, lawn and riding mowers,
		200
	grass and power equipment series,
		198–9
	MF 7, 10 and 12, 196–7
	MF 20C Turf Special, **203**
	MF 35 Turf Special, 202–3
	MF 200 series, 198
	MF 205, **197**
	MF 1200 series, **201**
	MF Executive lawn, **196**
	MF Landscapers, **204**
	MF Lawn tractor range, 200
Compressors, 8
Construction machinery
	MF range, **150–1**
Cord and pulpwood saws, **208–9**
	MF 20 cordwood, **209**
	M-H No. 1A cordwood, **208**
	M-H No. 2 tilting frame, **207**
	M-H No. 3A pulpwood, **208–9**
	M-H No. 4 pole, **209**
	M-H No. 5 pole, **208**
	Sawyer and Massey portable, **209**
Corn pickers, **87–8**
Corn shellers, 40
Cotton harvesters, 127
Cranes, 9
	Baldwin loader, **9**
	Ferguson rear-mounted, **9**
	M-F 12-10 jib, **9**
Crawler dozers
	MF 300, **154**
	MF 600C, **152**
Crawler shovel
	MF 3366, **152**
Cream separators, **182**
Cultivators
	M-F 1970, 292

D

D. R. Clark Engine Co., 220
Datatronic monitoring, 245
Datavision display system, 251
Dealers' signs, **228–9**

Deering tractors, 57
Deyo-Macey Co., 213
Dickie Co.
	hay-making machinery, 52
Digger loaders
	MF 220, **145**
Diggers
	MF 710, **143**
Ditchers, 21
	Wills on TO tractor, **141**
Dozers
	MF 3366, **207**
Drill ends – cast iron, **226**
Dump skip, **41**
Dump-trailers – contractor
	MF 79, **168**
	MF range 1995, 167
Dynashift transmission, 246
Dynatorque, 247

E

Earth-moving equipment, 17–21
Elevators, 10–11
Engines
	Armstrong Siddley diesel, 103, 223
	Bamford, 11, 223
	Blackstone 'Fuelol,' **223**
	Briggs and Stratton, 223
	Continental range, **221–2**
	Cushman 'R', **218**
	Cushman vertical 'LK', 219
	Deyo-Macey, 213
	H. V. McKay Massey Harris Sundex,
		217–18
	H. V. McKay Sunshine, **217**
	Hercules, **222**
	Hornsby, 11, 223
	Johnston Harvester No. 2 Kerosene,
		217
	Lister, 11, 223
	MF 'Powerstations,' **223**
	M-H 3-20, **214**
	M-H 25, **220–1**
	M-H E35, **219**
	M-H Clark 'S' series, 220
	M-H Harvester Co., 217
	M-H NR Type 1, 213–14
	M-H OR, 213
	M-H Pump Jacks, **224**
	M-H Type 2, **215–16**
	M-H Type 3, 215
	M-H-F Weather King, 220–1
	New-Way, 223

Novo, 223
Olds range, **211–13**
Perkins, 247, 255
Petter, 11, 223
Ruston, 11, 223
Wisconsin, 103
Wisconsin petrol, 223
Ensilage cutters, **12–13**
Excavators
	MF 350 hydraulic, **153**
	MF 450 hydraulic, **153**
	MF mini range 1996, **158**

F

F. Perkins Ltd.
	production 1933-58, 273
Fayette Co., 165–6
Ferguson Ltd.
	baler, **104**, **105**
	beet lifter, **125**
	beet topper, **125**
	combine harvesters, 77
	compressor, **8**
	cranes, 9
	disc terracer, **21**
	dump skip R-JE-20, **41**
	earth-moving equipment, 18–19
	forage harvesters, 98
	French imports and production,
		288
	hammer mill, **5–6**
	hedge cutter, **8**
	hitch systems, 44–5
	industrial tractors, **137–40**
	irrigation pumps, 15
	Kale Cutrake, **128**
	muck loaders, 22
	N. American tractor engines, 336
	PA-EE-20 game flusher, **94**
	Paddy Disc Planker, 21
	subsoiler, **36**
	tractor production 1946-54, 269
	tractor serial nos., 308
	trailers, 23, 44
	transporters, 41
	winch, 49
FERMEC, 253–4
	acquisition of MF industrial division,
		132
	MF industrial equipment, 158–61
Footplates, 230
Forage blowers, 14
	M-F 1970, 292

Forage harvesters, 98–101
    Ferguson 'Tractor Mate', **98**
    MF 620 forage chopper, **101**
    MF Self-propelled, 100–101
    M-H, **99–100**
    M-H Forage Clipper, **98–9**
Ford Ferguson
    industrial tractor, **9**
    winch, **49**
Fordson
    V trenching tool, **21**
Forestry tractors, 205–7
    MF 165 'Kubik,' **205**
    MF 390/4, 206
    MF Skidders, 205–6
    MF Treever, **205–6**
Fork lifts
    MF 10, **15**
    MF 204, **148**, **207**
    MF 737, **15**
    MF 6500, **154**
    MF range 1984, **156**
    MF specifications 1966, **149**
Freezers, home, 184
Funk Manufacturing Co., 144

G

G. Stephenson & Sons
    hay presses, **34**
    mole drainer, **36**
    tipping cart, **43**
Game-flusher, **94**
Garden gates, **183**
Garden tillers, 195
Garden tractors. *See* Compact tractors
Global Positioning Satellite (GPS), **251**–2
Grassland aerator, **210**
Grinders, **1–3**
    MF 15, **6**
    M-H No. 1, **2**
    M-H No. 2, **2**
Gun equipment, 174

H

H. V. McKay
    First World War 'G S' wagons, 170
    M-H-F takeover, 194
    mowers, **91**
    Sunshine Harvester, **61–2**
H. V. McKay Massey-Harris Pty. Ltd.
    garden gates, **183**

Sunshine Auto Header, **65**
Sunshine factory war production, 175
Sunshine Sunfeed No. 1 grinding
    mill, **3**
Hanomag Co.
    acquisition and sale by MF, 154
Harris, A., Son & Co.
    binders, **54**
    Brantford mowers, **89**, **90**
    Brantford self-raking reaper, **52**
Harrows
    M-F 1970, 292
Harry Ferguson
    sales and production, 267
Harvesting equipment, 51–130
Hay loaders, **118**
Hay presses, **34**
Haypacker, **119**
Hedgecutters, **8**
Hesfords' winch, **49**
Hesston Ltd, **256**
Highway tractors, **161**–64

I

Irrigation equipment, 15
    bund formers, **20**

J

J. &. J. Taylor Ltd. safes, **186**
James Beresford & Son
    irrigation pump, **15**
Johnston Harvester Co., **52**
    stationary engines, **217**

K

Kale harvesting, **128**
Kemp Manure Spreader Co., **27**

L

Landini
    tractor model nos., 332–5
    tractor production 1945-66, 274
Landscape tractors. *See* Compact tractors
Loader shovels
    MF 1965 range, **150–1**
    MF 205, 148
    MF 356, 144, **146**, **207**

MF 470, 144, 146
MF 702, **144**
Loaders
    Davis equipment, 140–1
    MF 11 wheel, **154**
    MF 24 Powershuttle, **155–6**
    MF 32, **154**
    MF 55, **153**
    MF 515 XP skidsteer, **159**–60
    MF 702, **143**
    MF 711 B skid steel, **154**
    MF 1246 Quick–Attach, **201**
    MF tractor range 1996, 160
    MF Varity period range, 157
    Midwestern Pit Bull, **137**
    Shawnee, **142**

M

Maize shellers, 37
Manure spreaders
    M-F 1970, 292
Massey
    binders, 54–5
    mowers, 89–91
    reaper harvester, 52
Massey Ferguson Industrial Ltd.,
    253–4
Massey Ferguson Ltd.
    48 Haypacker, **119**
    540 Corn Harvester, **129**
    adoption of ISO 9002, 244
    backhoes serial nos., 313–4
    bale handlers, 109–111
    balers, 105–8
    Banner Lane manuf. record, 361
    bean lifter, 130
    Beauvais manuf. record, 362
    binder, 58
    bund former, 20
    Cellular organisation, 244
    combine harvesters, 88
    combine production, 1955-66, 276–7
    combines serial nos., 344–5
    Compact tractors serial nos., 316
    construction and forestry equipment
        serial nos., 314–16
    construction equipment, 150–53
    corn sheller, 40
    crop blower, 14
    disc ridgers, 20
    earth-moving equipment, 19–21
    FE35, 765, 702/203/205 serial nos.,
        347–8

FERMEC period industrial equipment, **158–61**

forage blowers, **14**

forage harvesters, 48, **101**

fork lift, **15**

forklifts, 313–4

French imports and production, 288–90

French tractor production, 325

French tractor serial nos., 345–6, 348, 350–1, 353

German tractor production, 326

grinder mixer, **6**

hay conditioners, **95–6**

Highway tractors, **161–4**

industrial equipment, **142–68**

industrial machine range 1977-80, 155

industrial tractor development, 140–51

industrial trailers, 165–**6**

Italian industrials identification, 343

Italian tractor production, 326

jib crane, **9**

loader serial nos., 313–4

loaders, **23–6**

machine/tractor suitability guide, 1976, 278–82

machine/tractor suitability guide, 1980, 283–85

maize combine, **88**

MF 48 planter, 126

mowers, 92, 94–7

muck spreaders, 29–30

N. American harvest equip. engines, 338

N. American industrials engines, 340–1

N. American tractor engines, 336–8

N. American tractor serial nos., 356–60

pallet tipper, **24**

peanut shellers, **121**

post drivers and post-hole borers, **32**

potato harvesters, **124**

Powershuttle transmission development, 155

present developments, 243–60

products list worldwide, 1970, 291–3

rake tedders, **117**

rakes, **115–6**, **117**

recent industrials identification, 341–3

self-unloading wagons, **48**

slurry tankers, **31**

small equipment serial nos., 311–13

snow equipment, **188–90**

soil scoops, **17–18**

soya bean harvesters, **124–5**

stripper-header combines, **85**

subsoiler and pipe-layer, **36**

sugar cane harvesters, **126–7**

swather, **60**–1, **116**

threshing machine, **40**

tippers, **46**

tractor 300/253/240 serial nos., 354

tractor model nos., 339–40

tractor production 1955-66, 270–2

tractor serial nos., 308–11, 354–5

tractor serial nos. 1982-90, 349–50

tractor/horsepower/implements compatability, 1989, 286–7

trailers, **44–7**

transporter, **41**

UK tractor production, 326–30

UK tractor serial no. prefixes, 331

UK tractor serial nos., 352

Varity period industrial equipment, 157

Whole Crop Harvesters, **102**

MF Worldwide product lists, 291–302

Massey-Harris

  angle dozer, **18**

  balers, **108**

  barn machinery, **1–8**

  bicycles, **180**

  binders, **56–8**

  branch sales, 1935-1945, 265

  Clipper peanut picker, **121**

  combine harvesters, 51, **67–76**, 78, **86**, **103**

  combine production, 1946-54, 268

  Combine serial nos., 321–4

  corn pickers, **87**

  drag scraper, **17**

  elevators, **11**

  employees 'war effort', 175

  ensilage cutters, **12–13**

  feed mill, **3**

  forage chopper, 101

  forage harvesters, **98–100**

  French imports and production, 288

  grinders, **1–2**

  hammer mills, **4–7**

  'Harvest Brigade' campaign, 176–8

  hay baler, **103–4**

  hay loaders, **118**

  Hay Maker, **92–3**

  hay presses and balers, **34**

  household and farmyard products, 180–7

hydraulic loaders, **23**

industrial tractor development, 131–6

machinery sales 1892-1949, 261–4

machinery sales, 1945-46, 266

maize sheller, **7**, **37**

manure spreaders, **27–8**

milking equipment, **22**

mole drainer, **36**

mowers, **91–3**

muck spreader, **22**

peat press, **49**

pick-up balers, **103–4**

plate mill, **3**

post U-frame engines, 316–17

post-hole borer, **32**

potato cutters and graders, **32–3**

potato diggers, **122–3**

rakes, **112–4**, **116**

Raussendorf straw press, **86**

reaper-thresher engines, 317

reaper-threshers, **63–68**

reapers, **53**

root pulper and slicer, **7**

'Rust' cotton pickers, **127**

sleigh, **27**

speed jack, **2**

straw cutter, **8**, **12**

straw trussers, **35**

stripper harvester, **62**

sugar cane harvester, **126**

swather, **59**

sweep rakes, 120

tedders, **112–3**

threshing machines, **39–40**

tractor and engine identification, 318–20

tractor production 1946-54, 269

tractor serial nos., 304–7

wagons, **42–3**

war products, **170–78**

winnower, **2**

Massey-Harris Blackstone

  elevators, **10–11**

  potato diggers, **123**

  rakes, **114**

  roller mill, **3**

Massey-Harris Dickie

  rakes, **115**

  swath turners, **115**

Massey-Harris, Sunshine Ferguson sales 1948-55, 274

Massey-Harris-Ferguson

  202 Work Bull, **36**

  pipelayer, **36**

Midwestern Industries Inc.
    acquisition by M-H-F, 132
    Davis loaders on MF tractors, **140–1**
    Pit Bull loader, **137**
Milk coolers, **185**
Milking machines, **22**
Mills, 1–7
    Ferguson hammer, **5–6**
    MF 45 combination hammer, **7**
    M-H 'Rowell Mastiff' hammer, 4–5
    M-H electromatic, **6**
    M-H No. 721A Hammer, **4**
    Massey-Harris Tornado feed, **3**
Mountville Manufacturing Co.
    potato graders, 32
Mower conditioners
    MF 37-7 hay, **95**
    MF 40 hay, **97**
    MF 81, **96**
    MF 164/6, **97**
    MF 165/7, **97**
    MF drum, **97**
    MF 'Haytender,' **97**
Mowers, 89–97. *See also* Compact tractors
    Harris Brantford No. 1, **89**
    Harris Brantford No. 3, **90**
    MF 30, 95
    MF 41, **96**
    MF 82 rotary, **96**
    MF mid-mounted, **94**
    MF No. 6 semi-mounted pto drive,
        95
    MF semi-mounted pto drive, **94**
    M-H 'Dyna balance,' **93**
    M-H 7060 pto drive, **93**
    M-H No. 14, **91**
    M-H No. 16, **91**
    M-H pto drive mounted, **92**
    M-H semi-mounted pto drive, **93**
    Massey Toronto, **91**
    Patterson 'Queen of the Meadow,'
        89
    Patterson rear cut, **89**
Muck loaders
    MF 800 series, **25–6**
    MF 890, **23**
    MF 1246, **26**
    M-H hydraulic, **23**
    NF 95, 24
    TAL Allied front-end, **24**
Muck spreaders
    MF No. 18, **29**
    MF 19, **29**
    MF 110, **29**
    MF 900 series, **30**

M-H 15, **29**
M-H 712, **29**
M-H No. 3, **27**
M-H No. 4, **27**
M-H No. 8, **28**
M-H No. 10 T, **22**
M-H No. 11, **28**
Munitions
    M-H products, **174**

O

Office furniture, 194
Oil palm harvesting, 130

P

Pallet tippers, **24**
Patterson & Co. Ltd.
    binder, **54**
    mowers, **89**
    Oxford five-rake reaper, **51**
Peanut Harvesters, **121**
Peat presses, **49**
Pens and penknives, **242**
Pick-up balers, **103–108**
    Ferguson 'Tractor Mate,' **105**
    Ferguson F-12, **104**
    MF No. 3 engine-driven, **105**
    MF 701, **109**
    MF No. 10, **105**
    M-H 701, **103**
    M-H hay, **104**
    M-H No. 1 hay, **103**
    M-H No. 1 'Slicer' specifications,
        104
    M-H No. 3, **103**
    M-H Sunshine self-tying, **103**
Pick-up press
    M-F 1970, **291**
Pipelayers, **36**
Playing cards, **242**
Ploughs
    M-F 1970, **292**
Post-hole borers and drivers, **32**
Potato equipment, **32–3, 122–4**
    MF 711 harvester, **124**
    M-H Blackstone No. 4, **123**
    M-H 'Junior,' **122**
    M-H 'King' specifications, 122
    M-H No. 1 digger, **123**
    M-H shaker digger, **122**
    Sunshine M-H digger, **122**

Power Shovels
    MF 702, **143**
Pumps, **185–6**

R

Rakes
    Ferguson forestry, 209
    M-F 1970, 291
    MF 19 mounted dump, **116**
    MF 35/36/38/40 finger wheel,
        117
    MF 36 semi-mounted, **115**
    MF 85 gyro swather, **116**
    MF 104 hydraulic V, **117**
    MF rake tedders, **117**
    M-H Blackstone forward action
        haymaker, 114
    M-H Blackstone horse rake, **114**
    M-H Blackstone self-acting, **114**
    M-H Blackstone side delivery, **114**
    M-H Dickie No. 716, **115**
    M-H Dickie side-delivery, **115**
    M-H Dickie swath turner, **115**
    M-H horse-drawn, **113**
    M-H No. 11 side, **113, 116**
    M-H No. 517 side-delivery, **114**
    M-H Sharp, **112**
    M-H Windrow turner, **115**
Raussendorf straw trussers, 35
Reaper-threshers
    M-H, 63–4, 66
    M-H No. 14, **68**
    M-H specifications, 68
Reapers, **52–3**
    Harris Brantford self-raking, **52**
    Massey, **52**
    M-H No. 2, **53**
    Patterson Oxford, **51**
Rice equipment
    combine harvesters, 65
    MF combine harvesters, **79, 82**
    M-H 90 combine harvester, **75**
    Paddy disc harrow, 21
Road making equipment, 16–17
    angle dozer terracer, **18**
    Atkinson gritter, **143**
    Ferguson earth mover, **19**
    Ferguson scoop, **18**
    Ferguson trip pump scraper, **19**
    MF 18 scarifier, **19**
    MF 338 drag scraper, **20**
    MF 830 blade, **19**
    MF soil scoop, **17–18**

M-H Columbus drag scraper, **17**
Sawyer and Massey grader, **16**
Sawyer and Massey road roller, **16**
Sawyer and Massey rock crusher, 16
Sawyer and Massey sprinkling tank, **16**
verge trimmer MF 16 trailed, **143**
Root cutters and pulpers, **7**

S

Sack trolleys, **186**, **192**
Safes, **186**
Sales literature, **231–5**
Saws
   M-F 1970, 292
Sawyer and Massey Co. Ltd.
   'Monitor' clover huller, **37**
   lumbar saws, 209
   road making equipment, **16**
   threshers, **38–9**
Sawyer-Massey Co. Ltd.
   gun modifications, 174
   sprinkling tank, **16**
   steam traction engine, 37
Scales, **186**
Seager Engine Works, 211
Seats, **236–7**
Simplicity Manufacturing Inc., 198
Sleighs, **27**, **187**
Slurry tankers, **31**
Snowmobiles, **189**
Snow blowers, **188**
Snow ploughs, **134**
Snow throwers, **190**
Soya bean harvesters, **124–5**
Spanners and tools, **238–9**
Stamps, 226
Steels Agricultural Machinery, 52
Stoves and heaters, **190–1**
Straw cutters, 8, **12**
Straw presses, **86**
Straw trussers, **35**
Subsoilers, **36**
Sugar beet equipment, **125**
Sugar cane harvesters, **126–7**
Sunar Ltd., 194
Sunshine Massey-Harris
   trailer bulk bin, **47**
Sunshine Waterloo Co.
   cooking utensils, 181
   office furniture, 194
Swathers, **59–61**
   MF30 pull-type, **60**
   MF35 pull-type, **60**

MF36 self-propelled, **60**
MF 220, **60–1**
M-H land-wheel drive, **59**
M-H No. 8 pto drive trailed, **59**
M-H self-propelled, **59**
Sweepers, 134
Sweet corn harvesting, **129**

T

TAFE Access Ltd.
   TAL Allied loader, **24**
   training school, 250
Tanks
   M-H M 44 howitzer, 171–2
   M-H M 5 and M 24, **171–2**
   M-H Stuart, **178**
Tedders, **112–3**
Telescopic handler
   MF 24, **155–6**
   MF 8937, **257**
Thermometers, **227**
Threshers, 37–40
   MF 139, **40**
   M-H Pacemaker tractor, **38**
   M-H steel threshers, **39–40**
   M-H 'White' No 4, 39
   Sawyer and Massey 'Daisy', **38**
   Sawyer and Massey 'Peerless', **38**
   Sawyer-Massey steam traction
     engine, 37
   Wallis, 37
Tobacco harvesting, **128**
Toolboxes, **239**
Towing tractors, **165**
Toys, **240–1**
Tractor loader
   MF 50C, **146**
Tractors. *See also* Compact tractors;
   Forestry tractors
   current accessory options, 258–9
   F. Perkins production, 273
   FE 35, 15
   Ferguson 35D, **94**
   Ferguson Brown industrial, **137**
   Ferguson production 1946-54, 269
   Ferguson TE and TO, 320
   Ferguson TE industrial, **138–9**
   Ferguson TE-20, **21**
   Ferguson TEF semi-industrial, **139**
   Ferguson TO and ditcher, **141**
   Ferguson TO industrial, **140**
   Ferguson TO type, **77**
   Ferguson TO-35, **15**

Ford Ferguson 'all purpose', **138**
Ford Ferguson 'Moto-Tug', **138**
Ford Ferguson industrial, 9
French imports and manuf. 1994,
   288–90
Harry Ferguson production and sales, 267
Landini 1945-66, 274
MF 20 industrial, **147**
MF 30 industrial, 147
MF 35, **23**, 32, **44**, **142**
MF 35 four-cylinder D, **106**
MF 35 Industrial equipment, 144
MF 44 tricycle, **109**
MF 50, **94**, **95**, **115**
MF 50 industrial, 147
MF 65, **79**, **105**, **127**
MF 65D, **115**
MF 65 gasoline, **95**
MF 65 Industrial equipment, 144
MF 65D, **115**
MF 165, **111**
MF 180, **24**
MF 200 industrial, **148**
MF 202 Work Bulls, **142**
MF 205 industrial, **144–5**
MF 240, **130**
MF 362 H highway, **163**
MF 390, **244**
MF 390 H highway, **163**
MF 660 industrial, **160**
MF 825, **23**, **94**, **106**
MF 1240, **26**
MF 2130 highway, **162**
MF 2135 highway, **161–2**
MF 2135 industrial, **148**
MF 3305 industrial, **148**
MF 4200 series, 255
MF 4270, **260**
MF Highway class, **161–4**
MF implement suitability guide,
   1989, 286–7
MF industrial range 1965, **150**
MF production 1955-66, 270–2
MF products 1970, 291
MF suitability guide, 1976, 278–85
MF towing range, 165
MF 'Visioporteur' range, 164
M-H 12-20, **57**, **68**
M-H 30, **99**
M-H 33, **99**, **116**
M-H 33 rowcrop, **104**
M-H 44, **99**, **100**, **113**, **120**
M-H 44D, **127**
M-H 44K, **103**
M-H 50, **18**, **29**, **93**, **100**

M-H 55K, **76**
M-H 80 industrial, 134
M-H 81, **71**
M-H 81 industrial, 134–**5**
M-H 101, **28**
M-H 102 Super, **70**
M-H 201, **99**
M-H 333, **73**
M-H 744D, **29**, **108**, **128**
M-H 745D, **93**
M-H Challenger, **68**, **92**
M-H Colt, **93**
M-H General Purpose 4WD, **134**
M-H 'I' industrial versions, 134–**5**
M-H Model 25, **68**
M-H Model 25 industrial, **133**
M-H Pacemaker, **70**
   threshing, **38**
M-H Pacer, **103**
M-H Pony, **22**, **93**
M-H production 1946-54, 269
M-H products in war, 175
M-H Sunshine Ferguson 1948-55, 274
M-H 'Work Bull,' 131
M-H-F FE 35 industrial, **142**
M-H-F Work Bulls, **135–7**
Pit Bull, **137**
rebuild schemes, 247–8
serial nos. data tables, 303–60
Wallis 12-20 industrial, **132**–3
Wallis 20-30, **13**, **67**
Trailers, 23
   Ferguson, **44**
   MF 22 high-level tipper, **46**
   MF 200 low loader, **45**
   MF 200 Monocoque, **46**
   MF 700 Monocoque, **46**
   MF 700 series, 47
   MF 717, **44**
   MF hydraulic tipping, **44**
   MF Model 700B, **46**
   M-H war production, 173
   Sunshine M-H 50, **47**
   Sunshine M-H 508, **47**
Trailers – industrial, 165–**6**
Training centres, **248–50**
Transporters, **41**
Trucks
   M-H war vehicles, **173**

V

Varity Corporation
   MF highway tractor production, 163

MF industrial equipment, 157
Verity Plow Co.
   sack trucks, **186**

W

Wagons, 42–8
   Bain 'New Ontario,' **43**
   Bain Niagara, **42**
   Bain two-horse, **42**
   Boer and World War 1, **169**–70
   H. V. McKay war products, 170
   MF self-unloading forage, **48**
   M-H 102, **45**
   M-H First World War models, 170
Wallis Tractors, **59**
   20-30 tractor, **13**
   combine harvesters, **67**
   industrial tractors, **132–3**
   serial nos., 303
   threshing machinery, **37**
Washers and detergents, **184**
Washing machines, **191**
Water carts
   H. V. McKay 'Furphy,' 170
Water pressure systems, **192**
Wheelbarrows, **192**
White Tractor Co.
   threshing machines, **39**
Whole Crop Harvesters, **102**
Winches, 49
Windmills, **193**
Winnower, **2**
Wood Bros.
   thresher self-feeder, **38**
Wringers, **191**

Y

Yield monitoring, **251–2**

Farming Press

We are publishers of a wide range of books, videos and audiocassettes on farming, farm machinery, animal health and the countryside. For more information or a free illustrated catalogue please contact:

Farming Press
Miller Freeman UK Ltd
2 Wharfedale Road
Ipswich
IP1 4LG
United Kingdom
Email farmingpress@dotfarming.com
Website http://www.dotfarming.com

The Massey Legacy Volume One
JOHN FARNWORTH

The companion to Volume Two includes a wide survey of agricultural tractors and also a chronology of company development and key people in it; company and product promotion; cultivation; planting and general field equipment; price lists and sales data.

Massey on Parade
VIDEO

A video recorded at the 150th anniversary celebrations of the Massey company at the Farm Museum, Ontario. Covers the key points in the development of M-H, including tractors and other equipment. A striking series of interviews give the flavour of the loyalty earned by this exceptional company.

Ferguson Implements and Accessories
JOHN FARNWORTH

Illustrates and describes the majority of the implements and accessories designed and built for the grey TE Ferguson tractor, and also gives some coverage to those made for the Ferguson-brown, Ford-Ferguson, the US-made TO Ferguson and some of the Ferguson 35 and 65 tractor era.

The Massey Ferguson Tractor Story
VIDEO

Michael Williams begins with early models such as the Wallis and General Purpose, and follows the story through to the Pacemaker and Pony. He also describes the development of the Ferguson System and the link with Ford.

Massey Ferguson Tractors
MICHAEL WILLIAMS

Michael William's readable text and 150 photographs are the ideal introduction to MF told with reasonable technical information, including production data.

The Two Thousand Mile Harvest
VIDEO

Broadcaster Dylan Winter follows ten of the world's largest combines – John Deeres – as they pursue the cereal harvest from Texas up to Alberta. The ultimate harvester's road movie!

Operation Harvest
VIDEO

This is the story of the farmer's war effort, told through archive and contemporary film. Characterful first-hand accounts create a unique and informative view of the countryside community in their finest hour. The video is brilliantly brought to life with the narration of ex-Dad's Army star Ian Lavendar.

Other Tractor and Machinery Books and Videos

Farming Press has a wide range of titles on farm mechanisation, from modern ploughing to an introduction to stationary engines. John Deere, Ford and its converters, Marshall, Roadless and many other companies are covered in detail.